RED

The Worldwide Dangers of Nuclear Power

Books by Judith Cook

Directors Theatre; Harrap, 1974
National Theatre; Harrap, 1976
Apprentices of Freedom; Quartet, 1979
Women in Shakespeare; Harrap, 1982
Portrait of a Poison – 245T (with Chris Kaufman); Pluto, 1982
Shakespeare's Players; Harrap, 1983
Close to the Earth; Routledge & Kegan Paul, 1984
The Waste Remains and Kills; Pluto, 1984 (fiction)
As I Walked Out to Lyonesse; Hodge, 1984
The Price of Freedom; New English Library, 1985
Who Killed Hilda Murrell?; New English Library, 1985
Red Alert; New English Library, 1986

RED ALERT

The Worldwide Dangers of Nuclear Power

Judith Cook

NEW ENGLISH LIBRARY

To Glenys

Copyright © 1986 by Judith Cook

First published in Great Britain in 1986 by
New English Library, Mill Road, Dunton Green, Sevenoaks, Kent.
Editorial office: 47 Bedford Square, London WC1B 3DP.

Typeset by Rowland Phototypesetting Ltd
Bury St Edmunds, Suffolk
Printed in Great Britain by
Biddles Ltd, Guildford and King's Lynn

British Library Cataloguing in Publication Data
Cook, Judith
  Red alert: the worldwide dangers of
  nuclear power.
  1. Nuclear industry
  I. Title
  338.4'762148   HD9698.A2

ISBN 0-450-39905-2

Nuclear logic

'*Common sense might lead one to believe that the comparatively high rate of leukaemia at Seascale is connected with British Nuclear Fuel's plant at Sellafield, but common sense is not science.*'

> Sir Douglas Black, Chairman of the inquiry set up to look at the incidence of leukaemia in West Cumbria, speaking at the annual conference of the British Association, Norwich, 1984

'*I have had to advise Congress that there is a forty-five per cent chance of another serious nuclear accident within the next twenty years.*'

> James Asseltine, Head of the US Nuclear Regulatory Commission, speaking on BBC TV on 27 May 1986

Contents

Acknowledgements

Because of the Freedom of Information Act, it is far easier to get information about the nuclear industry in the United States than it is in Britain. My thanks to the United States Information Service and the Union of Concerned Scientists. Finding out what goes on here is like digging for gold. Thanks, therefore, to Paddy Ashdown MP, his researcher Tony Meredith and Jim Large of Large Associates, as well as to a number of people who, for reasons that are fairly obvious, do not wish to be named.

I would like to acknowledge the help I have received from Yorkshire Television, Channel 4, Greenpeace, Friends of the Earth, Television South West and journalistic friends and colleagues. My very special thanks to my long-suffering husband, Martin Green, who thought it was all over after I had finished my book on Hilda Murrell, only to be immediately plunged into this. His practical and emotional support made it possible.

FOREWORD, by Paddy Ashdown M.P.

Some nuclear experts still attempt to dismiss public concern about nuclear dangers on the basis that only experts can properly evaluate the risks. The truth of the matter, as I see it, is that the public has recently been acquiring a pretty shrewd understanding of some of the key issues of the nuclear world. This book helps take the process further, not as a technical manual, but by outlining something of the history, the people and the political background in which it is all embedded.

We have seen a very considerable change in understanding since the days of the mid-1970s. And I believe that the full extent of change in world opinion following Chernobyl will take several years to become clear. At the moment of writing this, the nuclear industry appears to be on the defensive, for the first time in its history. As a remarkable example, Lord Marshall, Chairman of the CEGB and, until now, one of the most vigorous proponents of full-blooded commitment to nuclear power, has recently started to offer his views on the relative costs of immediate and phased close-down of all UK nuclear capacity.

It would be mistaken to imagine that the nuclear power debate is over. Perhaps it is fair, however, to hope that the old imbalance in the debate is now coming to an end.

I have often been seen as 'anti-nuclear'. In fact, my strongest feelings are not directed at nuclear technology, but at the secrecy and arrogance of some of the proponents of that technology. For far too long we have been given deceptions, half-truths, three-quarter-truths and, indeed, anything except the whole truth. Many of my own battles have been fought simply to obtain information from the UK nuclear industry. The picture of events, those of the 1950s equally with those of recent years, keeps changing month by month as more information is dragged out. This book looks into some waters that remain too murky for the public good.

The trustworthiness of the nuclear industry has grown to be

one of the key issues in the whole debate. Time and again, official spokesmen put forward their repeated assurances that there is no cause for concern. Time and again, the revelation of events proves them false. For myself, I have to say I am convinced we are not yet seeing the whole truth about the UK nuclear industry.

For instance, even now, after Chernobyl, the present Conservative government is still refusing to release any technical safety documents for independent study. The official studies of radiation exposures of members of the public from 'normal' operations of the old Magnox power stations are among the papers being kept secret.

Many parts of nuclear technology are deeply complicated. But we should always remember that, at root, the decisions about nuclear power are taken by non-scientists – Parliament contains very few trained scientists. We have to make up our minds in other ways. Common sense plays a large part, second only to judging the credibility of witnesses. I believe that questioning what we are told is a fundamental step in reaching good decisions.

There are undoubtedly some difficult decisions to be made in this country. The disposal or long-term storage of nuclear waste is something we have to face up to, and pay for, because the waste exists and will not go away. Shutting down nuclear power stations is likely to add very considerably to our waste problems, at enormous cost; unless we choose a cheap and nasty option, such as sea-dumping. Will the voters, instead, pay for a 'Rolls-Royce' solution? And, even then, where do we put it? Decisions on both nuclear power and nuclear waste are, quite frankly, too important to be left to scientists or 'experts'.

The questions posed by this book will help draw more people into the debate about nuclear power, and I am delighted to welcome it as a timely and valuable contribution.

August 1986

Introduction

The nuclear industry does not seem to be doing too well just at the moment – its image has become somewhat tarnished. This is in spite of a massive advertising campaign (much of it at taxpayers' expense) to persuade people that all is well, and also despite a well-publicised visit of the Prime Minister herself to British Nuclear Fuels Ltd's reprocessing plant at Sellafield in Cumbria in the autumn of 1985. Television watchers were privileged to see Mrs Thatcher, in a safety helmet, scurrying around the place assuring us of her total confidence in the industry.

Yet in spite of all the advertising and all the public relations exercises, people seem to be becoming more cynical rather than less, and the results of a Gallup Poll published on 1 October 1985 showed growing distrust. A majority of people had reservations about nuclear power in general, and when it came to nuclear waste and its disposal, the division was even more pronounced: only 5 per cent of those polled did not think the disposal of nuclear waste was much of a problem, but 85 per cent did; 86 per cent thought the public should be given more information on nuclear matters, with only 7 per cent disagreeing; 67 per cent did not think that British Nuclear Fuels Ltd was doing a good job keeping the public informed of its activities, while only 14 per cent did.

The reasons for these views are not hard to find. People, on the whole, are not stupid, yet they are all too often treated by the nuclear industry as if they were. What generally happens in this country if there is a nuclear accident – or 'incident' as the industry prefers to call it – is this:

Stage 1 Something happens.
Sometimes the statutory body in question tells us.
Sometimes it does not and we have to rely on a 'leak'.

Stage 2 The body concerned says it was only a very minor incident.
There was no release of radioactivity.

1

Nobody was affected.

The press and other interested parties then get to work and dig around a little and this leads to:

Stage 3   There was a release of radioactivity, but it was a very small amount. It did not get into the atmosphere. It was well within permitted limits.

Some workers might have been marginally affected.

There is no cause for concern.

At this point concerned MPs, bodies such as FoE and interested journalists begin exerting pressure. It is followed by:

Stage 4   There was a larger release of radioactivity than had originally been admitted and, yes, some did get into the atmosphere, but it is well within permitted safety limits.

Some workers were affected – indeed, one or two may have received a fairly large dose – but they have suffered no ill effects. Yet.

Stage 5   Information is almost impossible to obtain.

Anyone who doubts the truth of this scenario need only look at the sequence of events surrounding some recent nuclear 'incidents'.

• It took the Central Electricity Generating Board five days to admit that there had been an accident at the Hinkley B power station in Somerset in October 1985: then we were all told there had been no release of radioactivity. It took questions in Parliament from Paddy Ashdown MP to elicit that this was untrue.

• In January 1986, British Nuclear Fuels dumped uranium into the sea from its Sellafield plant. We were informed at first that 'it was only a few kilograms': it turned out to be nearly half a tonne.

• In February 1986, after what became known as the nuclear 'mist' incident at Sellafield, we were told that radio-activity had been contained within a building and that nobody had been affected. Then we were told that the mist had not been so contained, and that two men were affected at the lowest discernible level. Then we were told that fifteen men might have been affected. Eleven certainly were, and one of those had received the maximum permitted dose for a whole year 'but he had suffered no ill effects.' Yet.

Introduction

Those who question the nuclear industry sometimes end up dead like Karen Silkwood. At best, they are subjected to everything from ridicule to accusations of subversion. Journalists in particular can find themselves under many kinds of pressure – for example, a phone call threatening legal action.

The nuclear industry has been protected in every way – legal, financial and economic. It can get away with its statements on public health and safety because there is, as yet, no way of proving beyond a shadow of doubt that illnesses known to be associated with radiation have actually been the result of working or living near nuclear installations. In this it is very lucky because most of these illnesses – such as bone marrow cancer and leukaemia – can take a long time to develop. It has also a very powerful lobby indeed, with friends in high places, in part because of its close links with the military uses of plutonium.

The result is an industry that is complacent, arrogant and shrouded in secrecy. We are constantly told how foolproof nuclear technology is, how special care is taken to ensure that nothing can go wrong, yet a look at the reality behind those confident statements reveals a catalogue of faulty design, bad workmanship, careless management, cost-cutting, poor maintenance and sheer human error, which is worldwide. It is only after something goes wrong with sophisticated modern technology that we find out the truth. A non-nuclear example is the tragic end of the space shuttle *Challenger* in 1986. Beforehand, everybody was told how safe it was, how foolproof the system, how chances were never taken; afterwards it appeared that a combination of circumstances had made such an accident all too likely.

The nuclear industry lards its information with off-putting jargon, and it jumps hard on those who criticise. Yet it still has no answer to the question of what to do with the high-level nuclear waste that is the result of the nuclear power programme. (If the Romans had invented nuclear power, we would still, 2000 years later, have armed militia guarding their dumps of high-level waste.)

This book grew out of two others. The first was on official secrecy and the need in this country for an American-style Freedom of Information Act. This would help us to find out

3

more about nuclear power as well as a whole host of other things. The second book investigated the strange – and still unexplained – murder of the rose-grower Hilda Murrell who was to have read her paper on the hazards of nuclear waste at the Sizewell inquiry. *Red Alert* is an attempt to put before the general public some of the information that exists on the hazards of nuclear power, information that is available but widely scattered.

The Congressional Committee of Inquiry investigating what happened at the time of the accident at Three-Mile Island in the United States said afterwards, somewhat rue-fully, that they did not think much would be done about their report, for two reasons: one was that officialdom at every level suffered from what they called 'mindset' – a refusal to face new facts; the other was that the memory of the public is short and today's accident soon becomes yesterday's story. In Britain, we suffer from both afflictions.

This book had been completed and sent to press before the Soviet nuclear accident at Chernobyl. It therefore required additional material to be added. In the interests of both speed and clarity I decided to make the addition in the form of separate material at the end. Chernobyl made the major part of the book into a prophecy.

JUDITH COOK
NEWLYN, CORNWALL, 1986

Glossary

The nuclear industry is bedevilled with jargon and acronyms. It is also encumbered with organisations usually known only by their initials. The following is a brief glossary of these words and terms, and organisations mentioned in the text.

A word of warning. Becquerels, grays and sieverts were introduced about the time the bulk of this book was finished, so all the reports on which information in it is based still retain the old measurements. None of the new measures is very precise – for instance, a becquerel is variously described as a unit of activity of one disintegration per second, or one count of radioactivity per second. It is also a very small measurement, so small that it is colloquially known in the trade as a 'buggerall'. It is the unit now used for measuring radiation in milk and water.

A gray equals 100 rads and is the new measurement of absorption of radiation into the body. The sievert equals 100 rems and measures the effect of the dose on the body. The new measurements indicate the rate at which disintegrations are taking place and its biological significance. This type of measurement takes into account the way in which the radio-nuclides behave in the body, their biological half-life and their physical half-life and whether or not they tend to concentrate in particular organs. It can be seen, therefore, that it is not easy to work out an average dose of radiation.

AGR   Acronym for advanced gas-cooled reactor.

Alpha particle   Nucleus of the helium atom, consisting of two protons and two neutrons. Alpha particles are emitted from the nuclei of some radioactive substances in the process of decaying into other elements.

Atom   Smallest amount of an element which can exist independently and still retain the chemical properties of that element. It consists of a *nucleus* around which small particles, *electrons*, travel in orbit.

Becquerel   One unit of disintegration per second.

Beta particle   High-energy electron emitted by a radio-nuclide.

Blanket   Fuel elements surrounding the core in a fast-breeder reactor; these contain uranium-238, which is converted to plutonium by neutron bombardment.

Breeder   Reactor that produces more fissile material than it uses.

BWR   Acronym for boiling-water reactor.

Caesium-137   Fission product; a hazardous beta-emitter.

CANDU   Acronym for Canadian deuterium uranium (reactors).

Chain reaction   Self-perpetuating process whereby the fission of one nucleus releases neutrons which cause the fission of other nuclei and so on.

'China syndrome'   Theoretical consequence of a core melt-down, when the heavy molten mass of highly radioactive material actually goes straight through the vessel in which it had been contained and down through the earth's core. From the US, it would reappear in China.

Cladding   Metal sheath that seals in the reactor fuel.

Control rod   Rod of neutron-absorbing material inserted into a reactor core to soak up neutrons and shut off or reduce the rate of the nuclear reaction.

Coolant   Liquid, usually water or gas (carbon dioxide, helium, air), piped through a reactor core to remove heat generated in it.

Cooling pond   Deep tank of water into which spent fuel is discharged from a reactor. It then requires either shipment for reprocessing or storage.

Critical   Or 'going critical': the point in a chain reaction when neutrons are being captured and released at exactly the same rate.

Curie	Quantity of a radioactive isotope that disintegrates at the rate of 37,000 million disintegrations per second.
Daughter	Element caused by the transformation of one substance into another through decay.
Decay	Disintegration of radioactive elements over time, releasing radiation.
Depleted uranium	Uranium with less than the natural proportion (0.7%) of uranium-235; the latter is removed in the enrichment process and transferred to enriched uranium.
Dose	Amount of energy delivered to a unit mass of material by radiation travelling through it.
Dose rate	Time rate at which radiation delivers energy to a unit mass of a material through which it is passing.
Electron	Negatively charged particles that travel around the nucleus of an atom.
Enrichment	Process of increasing the concentration of the isotope uranium-235 beyond the 0.7% contained in natural uranium.
Fallout	Radioactive-fission products created by nuclear explosions which fall back to earth as a dust.
Fast breeder	Reactor that is fuelled with a mixture of plutonium and uranium oxide and has no moderator to slow down the neutrons. Known as an FBR.
Fissile	Isotope of an element whose nucleus will split upon being hit by a neutron in a spontaneous process when a critical mass is formed. Uranium-235 and plutonium are fissile.
Fission	Division of the atomic nucleus into two lighter fragments releasing energy.
Fuel	Arrangement of fissile material in a reactor. It can be natural uranium in some, slightly enriched in others, while some military reactors use highly enriched fuel. Others use plutonium. Enriched fuel contains plutonium-235.

7

Fuel cycle	Stages in the production of nuclear power from mining the uranium to disposal of the waste.
Fuel pin/rod	Single tube of cladding filled with pellets of fuel.
Fusion	Merging of two light nuclei to make a heavier one, releasing energy.
Gamma ray	High energy electromagnetic radiation emitted by the nucleus, of great penetrating power.
Gas centrifuge **Gas diffusion**	Uranium-enrichment processes.
Gray	Unit of exposure to radiation.
Half-life	Time taken for half the atoms in a radioactive substance to disintegrate into atoms of another element. The characteristic is constant for each particular substance.
High level	Very radioactive nuclear waste with a medium-to-long half-life.
HTR	Acronym for high-temperature reactor.
Iodine-131	Biologically hazardous fission product with a half-life of eight days. Attacks the thyroid gland.
Ion	Atom or molecule that has lost or gained one or more electrons and is thus positively or negatively charged.
Ionising radiation	Any form of radiation that knocks electrons from atoms, turning them into ions.
Irradiation time	Length of time that fuel spends in a reactor being bombarded by neutrons.
Isotopes	Atoms of the same chemical element but with a different atomic mass, i.e. having the same number of protons in the nucleus but different numbers of neutrons.
Kilowatt	1000 watts.
Krypton 85	Chemically inert gas that is a fission product released into the atmosphere by reprocessing plants.
Leukaemia	Cancer-like disease of the blood characterised by a proliferation of white cells. It can be caused by exposure to radiation, but it is not exclusively due to such exposure.

8

Glossary

Light water	Ordinary water used as a coolant and/or moderator.
Light-water reactor	Either a Pressured-Water Reactor or a Boiling-Water Reactor. Known as an LWR.
Loca	Acronym for loss of coolant accident.
Low level	Radioactive waste with a short half-life.
Magnox	Magnesium alloy used as fuel cladding in first-generation British gas-cooled reactors, called Magnox Reactors.
Manhattan Project	Codename for the World War II project that developed the first atomic bomb.
Maximum permissible level	Radiation dose defined as the upper limit to which people can be exposed.
Megawatt	1 million watts.
Meltdown	When the reactor core overheats, thus allowing part or all of the solid fuel in a reactor to reach the point and temperature at which the cladding (and possibly the fuel and the structure that supports it) would liquefy and collapse – the ultimate nuclear accident, which nearly happened at Three-Mile Island.
Moderator	Material used to slow down neutrons in a reactor to enable them to be captured and allow fission. Moderators include graphite, water and heavy water.
NaK	Sodium potassium alloy with a low melting point, used as a coolant in early fast-breeder reactors and as an emergency coolant in some others.
Neutron	Uncharged particle in the nucleus of the atom, which is released during fission.
Nucleus	Centre of the atom that contains all the protons (positively charged) and neutrons (uncharged). It comprises almost all of the mass of the atom.
Nuclide	Nucleus of an isotope.
Pile	Name used for the original nuclear reactors, where 'piles' of uranium were cooled by gas or water and moderated by graphite or water.
Plutonium	Heavy, totally synthetic metal made by neutron bombardment of uranium. It has

9

94 protons and the atomic nuclei are fissionable. Extremely toxic and highly chemically reactive, it has a half-life of 24,400 years.

Pressure vessel   Large container of welded steel or pre-stressed concrete which contains the reactor core, etc.

Pressuriser   Found in a Pressurised-Water Reactor (PWR): Electrically heated boiler in a cooling system, which boils water as necessary to maintain coolant pressure.

Proton   Positively charged particle that is a constituent of a nucleus.

PWR   Acronym for pressurised-water reactor.

Rad   Unit of the radiation that can be absorbed by tissue.

Radiation   Neutrons, alpha or beta particles or gamma rays, which radiate out from radioactive substances.

Radioactivity   Behaviour of a substance in which the nuclei are undergoing transformation and emitting radiation.

Radio-isotope   Radioactive isotope.

Radio-nuclide   Radioactive nuclide.

Radon   Alpha-emitting radioactive gas given off by radium.

Reactor   Arrangement to create and control a chain reaction.

Rem   Unit for measuring radiation doses, which takes into account the degree of harmful effects on biological tissue caused by each type of radiation – e.g. exposure to one roentgen of X-rays gives an absorbed dose of one rem. The term comes from 'roentgen equivalent: man'.

Reprocessing   Chemical separation of irradiated nuclear fuel into plutonium, uranium and other radioactive 'waste' components.

Roentgen   Unit for measuring a radiation dose, measured by the number of ions released in a gram of air by X-rays or gamma rays.

Runaway   Accidental, uncontrolled chain reaction.

Scram   Emergency shutdown of fission material in a reactor.

Shielding	Protective wall of material (concrete, lead, water) surrounding a source of radiation.
Sievert	New unit of measurement. Technical explanation–unit of radiation exposure, compensated to allow for extra biological damage. Simply, it means a unit which takes into account the effect of different kinds of radiation on human beings. It replaces the rem (Roentgen Equivalent: Man) although the term rem is still often used. 1 sievert equals 100 rem and sieverts are often described in millisieverts (i.e. thousandths of a sievert).
Spent fuel	Fuel that has undergone a chain reaction and is nearing the point where it can no longer do so because its fissile material has been transformed into other elements and has thus been removed from the reactor.
Strontium-90	Hazardous beta-emitter with a half-life of 28 years. It is accepted by plants, animals, people, etc. as an 'analog' of calcium – that is, it is so similar to calcium that it is absorbed in the same way. It attacks the bones and can cause bone cancer.
Tailings	Fine sand left over after extraction of uranium ore. It contains radium and emits radon gas.
THORP	Acronym for thermal oxide reprocessing plant.
Uranium	Heaviest natural element, a metal. Isotopes 233 and 235 are fissile, 238 fertile. It is an alpha-emitter.
Vitrification	Fusing of high-level waste into glass-like blocks.

Organisations

AEA (UKAEA)	United Kingdom Atomic Energy Authority
AEC (USAEC)	United States Atomic Energy Commission
BNFL	British Nuclear Fuels Ltd

CEGB	Central Electricity Generating Board
FoE	Friends of the Earth
IAEA	International Atomic Energy Authority
ICRP	International Commission on Radiological Protection
NIREX	Nuclear Industry Radioactive Waste Executive
NRC	Nuclear Regulatory Commission (responsible for licensing facilities in the US)
NRPB	National Radiological Protection Board (UK)
SSEB	South of Scotland Electricity Board

Chapter 1

The Alchemists

In 1610 the poet and playwright Ben Jonson wrote a play called *The Alchemist*. It has remained popular ever since. The main reason for this is that human nature does not change; there are always those who con and those who seem only too eager to be conned.

Briefly, the plot concerns two crooks, one of whom is servant to a wealthy man who has fled from London because of the plague. They use the man's house to set up an alchemist's 'consultancy'. One poses as an alchemist, the servant as his secretary-assistant-agent. Most of the requests with which they have to deal are pretty routine: potions for sexual virility, love philtres, horoscopes, formulae for total success in gambling, swordplay, business, etc.; today's equivalents tend to feature large in Roger Cook's Checkpoint programme on BBC's Radio 4.

Alchemy itself was a mixture of the beginnings of real discoveries in chemistry and science, hocus pocus, and 'magic'. The Alchemist has a vast array of impressive-looking equipment to show clients a serum or a stone (he offers both) which will transmute base metal into gold. In pursuit of that dream, his clients offer him more and more money. One is merely a rich man who wants to be even richer and he is given a rather basic idea of the supposed processes involved.

But the Alchemist has more of a problem with two Protestant ministers who want the gold for political reasons. They are too bright, they say, to be fobbed off with simple explanations of how it is done. When we meet them they have already paid out substantial sums though without achieving the required result.

At this point the Alchemist bursts into a torrent of supposedly technical jargon. Of course, as these two gentlemen are so extremely clever, perceptive and forward-looking they are bound to understand what he says: he does not need to make any concessions to them, does he? So he feeds them with a mishmash of dog-Latin, laced with apparently scientific fact. After all, it is surely an investment – 300 marks to make them six million?

All he needs is more money to buy

> 'Another load.
> And then we've finished. We must now increase
> Our fire to *ignis ardens*, we are past
> *Fimus equinus*, *balnei*, *cineris*
> And all those *lenter* heats . . .'

Fimus equinus was horse manure, *balnei*, a boiler and *cineris*, ashes. It all sounded rather better than 'We need money to buy more coal to get more heat than we can get in our boiler from horse manure.'

The clients dare not expose their own ignorance; after all, has not the Alchemist told them repeatedly how intelligent and clever they most obviously are? So, once again, they pay up after listening to him open-mouthed and in bemused silence.

And the outcome? Ah, well, eventually the whole lot blows up.

It would not be just to equate the nuclear power industry exactly with Ben Jonson's pair of chancers in *The Alchemist*. The industry has not proposed something which cannot one day be achieved at some price. But there *are* some underlying similarities. Like the alchemists, the industry has had reasons for pushing ahead with its civil nuclear power programme other than those always obviously stated. It has also promised something similar to the elusive stone which transmutes base metal into gold – a process which will produce unlimited energy. 'Electricity too cheap to meter' was the slogan of the pro-nuclear lobby during the 1950s.

In their desperate search for this miraculously cheap form of energy, the 'philosopher's stone' which would transmute a mineral into electric power, staggering sums of real money have been poured into the nuclear industry. Certainly it has been proved that it is possible to produce electricity from nuclear power stations – but at a cost. It is far more expensive than that produced by other means and it is infinitely more hazardous. However, those who question the assumptions of the nuclear-power lobby are written off at best as cranks and at worst as subversives requiring surveillance.

Members of governments of all shades, energy ministers such as Tony Benn and Peter Walker, civil servants, employees of public utilities, have sat, like Jonson's Puritans, open-mouthed and bemused, listening to the flood of jargon which has promised that the millennium is just around the corner.

Billions of pounds of taxpayers' money have been poured into the nuclear industry all over the world – give us more money and we'll get there. Never mind that each nuclear power station has cost millions of pounds more than was estimated, that they have all taken years longer to build, that at the end of all of it they have only produced a modest proportion of the electricity required by all countries, except France; all that is disregarded. Keep the money coming in and we'll get it right in the end.

But overshadowing the industry is the question of safety. For the nuclear industry there *is* no question. Nuclear power is perfectly safe, they say; nuclear installations are among the safest in the world, there is no proof, real proof, that radiation either within the workplace or near to nuclear power plants has ever caused one single death or one case of cancer. Disposing of nuclear waste is a little more tricky but any time now we should get that one sorted out.

In 1979, at Three-Mile Island in the USA, the magic equipment, like that of Jonson's Alchemist, nearly blew up. The nuclear reactor, with a bubble of hydrogen gas inside it some 1800 cubic feet in size, was within 30 minutes of a full meltdown. Nobody is completely sure why it did not actually blow up. But for the time being the nuclear industry was off the hook.

Next time we may not be so lucky.

This book is an attempt, in layman's language, to explain

some of the problems and hazards of nuclear power. It is very hard to make up your mind about the benefits or drawbacks of something if you are kept in ignorance of all the hazards and potential hazards.

We will be looking later at some of the politics behind the nuclear power programmes both here and abroad and at the sequence of events in Britain which has led to the building of the Magnox and Advanced Gas-Cooled nuclear reactors. It is a highly topical subject because of the government's proposal to build a new generation of nuclear power stations – the PWRs or pressurised water reactors – the first of these to be at Sizewell in Suffolk.

When we talk about 'splitting the atom' this is not strictly true. It is the nucleus of the atom which is split. If you can imagine taking a small piece of any mineral and continuing to cut it in half, you will finally reach a stage where, if you were to divide it any further, what you would be left with would no longer be that mineral. At this stage, while it still remains intact, what you have is an *atom*.

But if you keep on cutting away at it the next part you will remove is called the *electron*, and it is negatively charged. The remainder of the atom is positively charged. The part you have removed has become a negative ion and what are left are positive *ions*. Every time you remove another ion those that remain become more strongly positively charged. But if you finally succeed in cutting them all away, what you are left with is the nucleus of the atom itself. This contains only positive charges, immensely strengthened and held together by a tremendous power. It is the shattering of this nucleus and the release of the awesome power within it which produces a nuclear bomb. Carefully controlled, in what is known as a *controlled chain reaction*, it can produce nuclear power.

For simple diagrams, explaining far better than words can how the process of nuclear fission works in a nuclear reactor and how some different types of nuclear reactors work, we can do no better than reproduce the diagrams published by Friends of the Earth.

They show the three main types of commercial nuclear

A

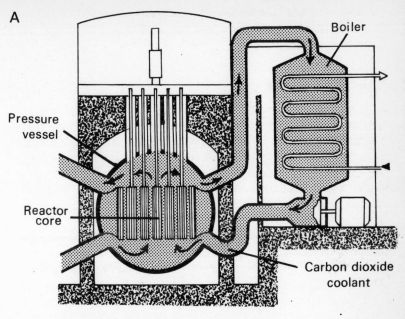

Boiler

Pressure
vessel

Reactor
core

Carbon dioxide
coolant

B

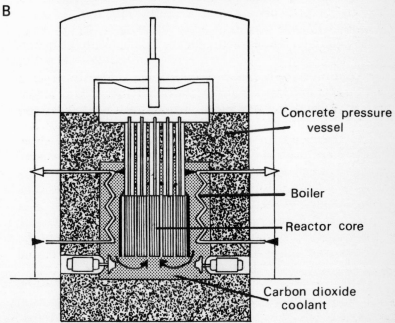

Concrete pressure
vessel

Boiler

Reactor core

Carbon dioxide
coolant

17

reactors. The Magnox Reactor (A), the Advanced Gas-Cooled Reactor (B) and the Pressurised Water Reactor (C), the type to be built at Sizewell.

Gas-cooled reactors

Unlike pressurised water reactors, gas-cooled reactors have a separate moderator and coolant. The reactor core consists of a large block of graphite, which is the moderator, containing a number of vertical tubes or 'channels', in which the fuel rods or pins sit, and through which the coolant normally flows. As in the PWR, the nuclear reaction is controlled by neutron absorbing rods which can be inserted into or withdrawn from the core.

In the *Magnox* reactor, whose name derives from the material used for fuel cladding, natural uranium fuel is used. Heat generated in the core is transferred to the carbon dioxide coolant which is circulated past boilers (steam generators). Heat transferred to the boilers by the coolant gas causes the water inside them to boil, and the steam created is fed to turbines driving the electrical generator. In early Magnox stations the core is housed in a large steel pressure vessel inside a concrete containment building with the boilers outside it. The later stations, which are larger, use a pre-stressed concrete pressure vessel, containing all the primary cooling components, including the boilers.

The Advanced Gas-Cooled Reactor (AGR) follows this development, having a more compact core and using enriched uranium fuel, clad in stainless steel. The whole primary circuit is again enclosed in a pre-stressed concrete pressure vessel. The AGR has a much higher efficiency, since the coolant reaches a temperature of 650°C, more than 300° higher than normal Magnox operating temperature.

The *High Temperature Reactor* (HTR) utilises a concrete pressure vessel of similar design, but the composition of the reactor core is very different from that of the AGR and Magnox reactors. Whilst AGR and Magnox fuel consists of many vertically oriented rods, HTR fuel is in the form of tiny spheres of highly enriched uranium (up to 93% in comparison with an AGR enrichment level of around 2%). These par-

C

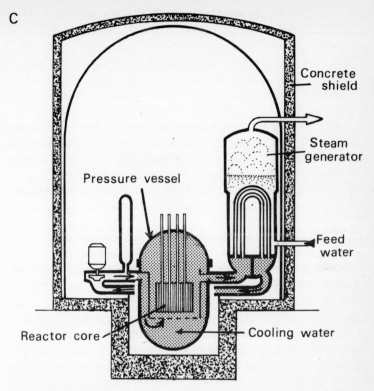

Concrete shield

Steam generator

Pressure vessel

Feed water

Reactor core

Cooling water

ticles are embedded in the graphite moderator, giving a more uniform distribution of fuel and moderator in the core, which itself is much more compact than in other gas-cooled reactors.

The Pressurised Water Reactor

Heat created in the core is transferred to the pressurised (primary) cooling water which circulates through U-shaped tubes in the steam generators. This causes feedwater at lower pressure, which is injected into the side of the steam generator, to boil. Steam taken from the top of the steam-generator drives turbines and is condensed to water and returned to the steam generator. The containment building surrounds the primary cooling circuit to retain radioactivity in an accident. Both PWR and BWR are variants of a general reactor type known as light water reactor (LWR), because they use ordinary water (light water) as both coolant and moderator. The term LWR is used to describe both PWR and BWR. A schematic drawing of a PWR is shown on p. 19. Like virtually all conventional stations the immediate power source for the electrical generators is steam under high pressure, which is evaporated from water in boilers and used to drive turbines. In a conventional plant heat is transmitted to the boilers directly (for instance, by burning coal or oil). In a PWR heat is transmitted to the boilers (or steam generators, as they are more commonly known) by thousands of small tubes. Water, which is heated by the assembly of nuclear fuel known as the reactor core, flows through these tubes and heats the boilers. The system of pipes leading from the reactor core to the steam generators and back again is known as the primary cooling circuit (since it cools the reactor core). Within the primary circuit the water temperature reaches about 300 degrees centigrade, and must be kept at high pressure (about 155 atmospheres) in order to avoid boiling.

The secondary circuit is that which leads from the steam generators to the turbines. Because the pressure in the secondary circuit is somewhat lower, roughly 70 atmospheres, water in the steam generators boils and is fed as steam to the turbines, after which it is condensed to water and returned to the steam generators. Both the primary and secondary circuits are sealed and physically separate, so that water does not pass between them.

The basic design of all PWRs is the same, but the number of steam generators used depends on the size of the plant. Submarine reactors are equipped with just one steam generator, which is used to drive a steam turbine connected directly to the propeller shaft. Large PWRs, such as that proposed for Sizewell, have four steam generators, each connected to the reactor core by a separate 'coolant loop', incorporating its own powerful pump. Water flows around each loop at a rate of 6 tonnes per second. The reactor core consists of an array of around seventy thousand fuel rods, each a vertical tube of zirconium alloy about half an inch in diameter and filled with uranium oxide. The uranium oxide fuel is slightly 'enriched' to increase the proportion of U-235 from the 0.7% in natural uranium to about 3.1%. The reactor core sits in a huge steel

20

pressure vessel forty feet high and fifteen feet in diameter, with walls ten inches thick. The pressuriser, the other main component of the primary circuit, is a large vessel connected to one of the coolant loops and situated above the other pipework. This contains the water surface and incorporates powerful heaters and sprays which are used to control the pressure of the coolant.

Disintegration of the U-235 atoms in the nuclear fuel creates heat as well as a number of neutrons – sub-atomic particles – with very high velocity. The neutrons will cause further disintegrations – thereby sustaining the reaction – but only if they are slowed down by a suitable 'moderator', a substance which reflects neutrons without absorbing them. Water has acceptable characteristics and functions as a moderator as well as the coolant in a PWR.

The reactor control rods, on the other hand, are made of a material which absorbs neutrons. The control rods can be inserted into and withdrawn from the core, in order to adjust the power level. In this way the reaction can be very carefully controlled to keep the density of neutrons at the correct level for the power being produced by the reactor. The reactor is shut down by fully inserting the control rods into the core. Under extreme conditions, as the result of a fault, the rods are allowed to drop freely into the core to terminate the reaction. This is known as a 'scram'.

It is obvious from the amount of power that can be released in a nuclear chain reaction that we have something which is quite different from any other method of producing electricity. People certainly die in coal mines mining the coal which can produce electricity, oil rigs can be swept away at sea as they drill the oil which can also be converted into electricity, but the damage done if a coal- or oil-fired power station were to be involved in a serious accident would be limited. Neither coal- nor gas-fired power stations pose long-term health risks to those employed at them or living near them, nor are there waste products left at the end of the process which we cannot handle.

We will consider in detail the possible health hazards of

radiation but it is probably useful here to quote, at length, the health hazards of the various radioactive elements involved in the nuclear power process. They were listed by Dr Helen Caldicott, President of the Physicians for Social Responsibility in the USA, in a paper, 'What Physicians Should Know About Nuclear Power', which she presented to doctors at University College, London in 1980.

She began by saying that the fuel cycle of nuclear power plants is complex, but not too difficult to understand.

It has many biological and medical implications which must be understood by physician and patient, as well as by the politicians who make most important decisions for society.

Mining   When uranium – the fuel for atomic reactors – is mined from the ground it emits the radioactive gas called radon. Often inhaled into the lungs of miners, after four days radon converts to lead-210 which remains radioactive for more than a hundred years. Because radiation in the body is carcinogenic, it has been discovered in the USA that up to 20 per cent of uranium miners die of lung cancer over a twenty-year period of mining.

Milling   After the uranium ore is mined, it is then milled and refined. Thousands of tons of waste ore (tailings) are discarded and left lying in huge heaps on the ground. The gas radon is continually emitted from the waste uranium in the tailings. The tailings generated to provide uranium for nuclear power in the USA over the next twenty-four years may produce, through the causative agent radon, forty-five cases of lung cancer in the world per year for tens of thousands of years.

Enrichment and fuel fabrication   The uranium is then enriched and fabricated into rods which are transported to the nuclear reactor and put into the reactor core. A typical 1000-megawatt reactor contains 526 bundles, each bundle consisting of twelve rods. The radioactive uranium produces heat by fission which is utilised to generate electricity. But during this process the uranium is converted to many radioactive by-products which are the ashes or wastes of nuclear power. Once a year one quarter of the rods are removed from the reactor core because their generating life has ceased. The rods are both thermally and radioactively very hot and must be stored on racks in cooling ponds containing water. They now contain a very large number of biologically dangerous radioactive materials, including strontium-90, iodine-131, caesium-137 and plutonium. Eventually these rods are transported to a reprocessing plant where they will be dissolved in nitric acid.

Reprocessing The plutonium is purified and removed from the solution in powder form as plutonium dioxide. It will then be used as either fuel for atomic bombs or fuel for 'fast-breeder reactors' (reactors which breed plutonium). It is at this point in the fuel cycle that the greatest dangers arise once the plutonium is separated.

Plutonium is an extremely potent cancer-producing agent appropriately named after Pluto, god of the dead and ruler of the underworld. It enters the body by inhalation of contaminated air and is deposited in the lungs. Because of its potent cancer-producing properties, the acceptable body dose has been set at less than one millionth of a gram. There is some evidence that this level has been set too high. Cancer will not appear until fifteen to twenty years after inhalation. By extrapolation, 1 lb of plutonium, universally disposed, would be adequate to kill every man, woman and child on earth.

Most of the plutonium manufactured in the fuel cycle will be in powdered form, and by the year 2020, the USA will have produced 30,000 tons of plutonium and there will be 100,000 shipments of material annually on American highways. Because plutonium is the basic material of atomic bombs it is more valuable than heroin on the black market and therefore vulnerable to theft by terrorists, racketeers, non-nuclear nations and deranged individuals.

Reactor grade plutonium makes inefficient but dirty bombs. It also has a curious physical property of igniting spontaneously when exposed to air, thereby producing tiny aerolised particles which are dispersed by wind currents and available for inhalation by humans and animals.

One could envisage disastrous consequences if a truck were to crash and discharge some of its deadly contents. Plutonium must be transported very carefully, packed in small quantities in separate containers because only ten lb is 'critical mass', which means that a spontaneous atomic explosion could occur if ten pounds or more were compacted together in a finite space.

The most awesome property of plutonium is its half-life of 24,000 years (half-life of a radioactive substance being the period of time for half of a given quantity to decay, and a similar period for half of the remaining radioactivity to decay, *ad infinitum*). Therefore radiation from man-made plutonium will exist on earth for at least half a million years. To illustrate the enormous medical problems arising from the physical properties of plutonium, if an individual dies of lung cancer engendered by plutonium, his body will return to dust but the plutonium lives on to produce cancer in another human being. Although it will be used as 'fuel' in breeder reactors, more plutonium will be produced than will be utilised. So there will be a continual net increase in plutonium manufactured. The nuclear industry has not yet decided what to do with all this plutonium; there are no safe methods of disposal and storage available at this point in time.

Waste storage   After the plutonium is extracted from the radioactive waste, biologically dangerous elements remain, which have no further use and are pure waste products. This remaining solution contains some plutonium, radioactive iodine, strontium-90, caesium and many other highly toxic radio-nuclides. Because it is extremely hot it must be stored in tanks which are cooled continuously for years. Every month numerous leaks of radioactive wastes are reported in the United States in quantities from several gallons to 200,000 gallons. When this dangerous fluid leaks it will inevitably contaminate the water system of the planet, and the various elements will be taken up by the food cycle. Radioactive iodine, strontium-90 and caesium are absorbed by roots of grass and vegetables and are further concentrated in the flesh and milk of animals when they eat the grass.

Iodine-131, strontium-90 and plutonium are concentrated in both human and animal milk. Caesium is concentrated in muscle (meat) and plutonium is also a thousand times more concentrated in fish compared to background water concentration. These substances are invisible, and because they are tasteless and odourless, it is impossible to know when one is eating or drinking or inhaling radioactive elements.

Biological properties of radioactive waste Genes are changed by radioactive particles. Cells and genes which are actively dividing (as in foetuses, babies and young children) are most susceptible to the effects of radiation. If a gene which controls the rate of cell division is altered by radiation, the cell may divide in an uncontrolled fashion to produce cancer and leukaemia. It may take from fifteen to twenty years before the cancer appears after the cell is exposed to radiation. If a gene in the sperm or egg is altered by a radioactive particle, either the young may be born with an inherited disease or the baby may appear normal but will transmit the damaged gene to future generations, to become manifest in later years.

Radioactive iodine is absorbed through the bowel wall and migrates in the blood to the thyroid gland, where it may produce thyroid cancer.

Strontium-90 is also absorbed through the bowel after being ingested in contaminated milk and is incorporated in bone because it chemically resembles calcium. This element causes osteogenic sarcoma – a highly malignant lethal bone tumour – and leukaemia. The blood cells formed in the bone marrow are subjected to the effects of radiation from strontium-90 in the adjacent bone.

Caesium-137 is deposited in muscles of the body where it can produce malignant changes.

25

Plutonium is one of the most carcinogenic substances known. It is not absorbed through the bowel wall, except in infants in the first four weeks of life when it is ingested in milk. (As previously described, infants are extremely sensitive to the toxic effects of radiation.) The route of entry of plutonium is by inhalation of contaminated air into the lungs. Small particles of plutonium are deposited deep in the respiratory passages, where they tend to remain for years. It is accepted that one millionth of one gram of plutonium is sufficient to produce lung cancer fifteen to twenty years after initial inhalation of the element. Plutonium is also absorbed from the lungs into the bloodstream where it is carried to the liver where, like strontium-90, it causes osteogenic sarcoma and leukaemia, and it is selectively taken up from the circulation by the testes and ovaries where, because of its incredible gene-changing properties, it may cause an increased incidence of deformed and diseased babies, both now and in future generations.

Plutonium also crosses the placenta, from the mother's blood into the blood of the foetus, where it may kill a cell responsible for the development of part of an organ (e.g. heart, brain, etc.), causing gross deformities to occur in the developing foetus.

Production of foetal deformities is different from the deformities caused by genetic mutation in the egg or sperm, because although the basic gene structure of the cell of the foetus is normal, an important cell in the developing foetus has been killed leading to a localised deformity (similar to the action of the drug thalidomide).

Massive quantities of radioactive wastes are being and will be produced in the future. The safe storage of waste is unsolved and even if there were a present-day solution, we could not predict a stable society or a world for half a million years. We could not guarantee incorruptible guards or moral politicians and we certainly cannot prevent earthquakes, cyclones or even wars. As waste is leaking now, so inevitably will it leak in the future. We could therefore predict epidemics of cancer and leukaemia in children and young adults, and an increased incidence of inherited disease (there are 2000 described inherited diseases). It is also inevitable that plutonium will be stolen and utilised for atomic weapons production; two tons of plutonium are presently [1980] unaccounted for in the USA.

It has been claimed that 80 or 90 per cent of all cancers may be caused by environmental pollutants. There was a 5 per cent increase in cancer in the USA in the first seven months of 1975 and a total 3 per cent rise in 1975.

Governments spend millions of dollars researching the causes of cancer, leukaemia and inherited disease, but simultaneously spend billions of dollars in an industry that will directly propagate these diseases. As a doctor, I appeal to my medical colleagues to investigate this enormous present and potential threat to our patients.

It is well to keep Dr Caldicott's guide in mind when looking into the performance of the nuclear industry. This is the industry in which 'impossible' accidents like that at Three-Mile Island happen, and where the word 'waste' means a substance we have, so far, found no way of dealing with adequately.

Chapter 2

'The Waste Remains and Kills . . .'

The word 'waste', when used of products or material, suggests substances that can be thrown away or otherwise disposed of. Dictionaries define it as 'superfluous', 'rejected', 'refuse', 'useless', 'worn-out material', etc. 'Waste' implies, most of all, something completely harmless that we have finished with. To use the word in the connection 'nuclear waste' is, however, something of a misnomer for we cannot just throw it away or dump it or forget about it because much of it will remain a hazard to human beings for years – in some cases for thousands of years, longer than any timescale we can imagine. When experts talk of keeping high-level radioactive wastes 'safe', they are talking about a timescale of stable conditions and care which, if we looked retrospectively, would take us back to the era of the dinosaurs.

There is argument even among experts as to what exact classification each type of nuclear waste should be given, but the most basic categories are high-, intermediate-, and low-level waste.

Low-level waste, of the disposable variety, consists mainly of material which has become contaminated by radioactivity. This includes items such as gloves and overalls used in medical work, plastics, papers, building materials and slightly contaminated laboratory equipment and is mainly dealt with at present by burial in shallow land trenches. It was dumped at sea by Britain until unions decided not to participate in this form of disposal. Low-level waste can also include discharge of gases and liquids from nuclear plants and we will look in detail, in the chapter on Windscale/Sellafield, at what has been considered 'safe' material and discharged in such a way.

Intermediate-level or short-lived waste is more hazardous

28

than low-level waste but it still has only a relatively short hazardous life, i.e. it does not contain a high level of plutonium. It consists of larger and more solid items than the previous category, such as 'glove boxes', equipment used in work with radioactive substances such as process cabinets, sludge from tanks, resins, and all kinds of odds and ends from nuclear power plants and laboratories. Some used to be dumped at sea but now it is stored mainly either near the nuclear power stations themselves or at Sellafield. It is this kind of waste for which the British government is currently looking for a home.

High-level waste is, of course, extremely dangerous and it is this waste which will give countless future generations a continuing problem. It mainly consists of the fuel taken from reactors themselves (the rods are taken back to Windscale/Sellafield for reprocessing) and any liquid waste left over from reprocessing fuel rods.

This kind of 'waste' is a continuous hazard from when it travels in its special flasks along our railway system to its arrival in Cumbria for reprocessing, and beyond. Nobody anywhere in the world has yet come up with a sound solution as to what to do with it. It generates large amounts of heat and has to be constantly cooled. The liquid wastes need to be solidified before they are finally disposed of, and although there is plenty of research going on here and elsewhere as to how this might be achieved no one so far has come up with a workable system.

Before looking at some of the real-life horror stories that have occurred with nuclear waste, let us look at what it is surmised *might* happen, given a certain set of circumstances. Since the end of 1983 the Central Electricity Generating Board has changed the design of the cubic steel flasks (each side eight feet long) in which the spent fuel rods are transported from the power stations for reprocessing at Sellafield. Here the word 'waste' is even more of a misnomer, for the rods are far more hazardous on their way back to Sellafield than they were when they were taken to the power stations in the first place, for the original plutonium has been broken down into a number of fuel elements.

A typical load might be:

29

Heat production: 3–10 watts
Radioactivity: 1,600 curies
Weight: 12 kg
Depleted uranium: 99 per cent by weight
Caesium-137: 0.0125 per cent by weight
Strontium-90: 0.006 per cent by weight
Ruthenium-106: 0.001 per cent by weight
Plutonium-239: 0.12 per cent by weight
Plutonium (total) 0.2 per cent by weight

According to the 1976 Royal Commission on Nuclear Energy (from whom these figures derive), one 30-millionth of a gram of ruthenium lodged in the lung is enough to produce terminal cancer. A typical consignment of waste contains six grammes.

The CEGB insists that accidents involving leakages from the flasks are so improbable as to be almost impossible. However, a spokesman did tell me, back in 1981, that in an extremely severe accident of major force, it is conceivable that flasks might leak and it is also conceivable that a flask might be breached by terrorist activity.

The latter is a somewhat chilling notion, for at that time there were a number of well-substantiated reports of flasks being left alone and unattended for hours at railway sidings. Early in 1980, a group of people at Stratford, East London, had carried out a dummy run and 'fired' an imitation bazooka at flasks standing in sidings there. They had reached their target merely by buying platform tickets: British Rail said it could not stop people carrying such an item from going on to the platform. In October of that year, friends and I were able to stroll around a flask in a siding near Ipswich in Suffolk – although since the publicity given to that incident there is now apparently an armed nuclear policeman with a guard dog keeping an eye on the flasks.

In May 1981, the *Birmingham Post* ran a piece about what might happen if a flask leaked somewhere near the centre of the city when travelling through Birmingham to Sellafield, as all of them do. The diagram on page 31 shows what the spread of radioactivity and its results would be.

This article prompted an immediate response from British

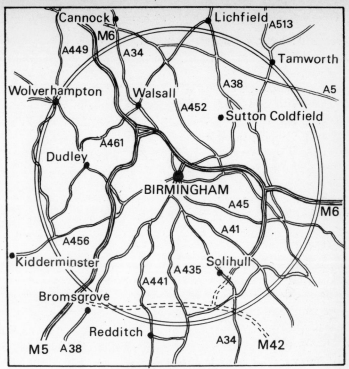

Ten-mile radius

One-mile radius

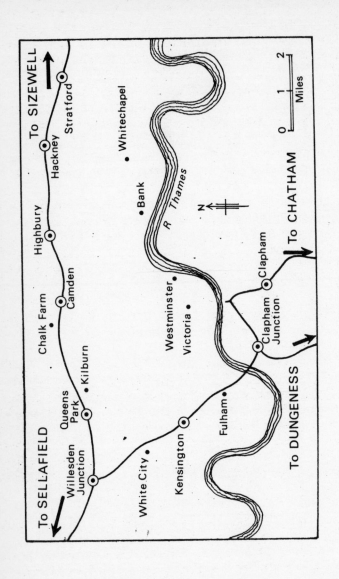

32

Nuclear Fuels to the effect that there could not be any accident in such a place. However, on 20 August 1981, a train carrying just such a flask was derailed in the very central marshalling yards used as an example in the diagram, when a shunting engine crashed into the wagon carrying the flask. A story circulating at the time (which remains unproven) is that coming along down the line behind the shunting engine was a train carrying rocket fuel on its way to the Polaris base in Scotland. We will never know the truth since British Rail has refused to release any of the findings of its own subsequent inquiry unless the Department of Transport orders it to do so – which of course the Department of Transport never has.

The possibility of an accident to a flask in a built-up area is not merely an academic point, nor are the marshalling yards at Birmingham the only potentially hazardous spot, for waste from the nuclear power stations in the south-east passes through London each week (see map on p. 32). One nuclear expert has explained what would happen if an accident to a flask of fuel from the Dungeness power station occurred on the Earl's Court section of the line along which the flask travels.

> . . . a west wind would force the evacuation of 80,000 people – including the Royal Family from Buckingham Palace – for 25 years and the loss of at least 20,000 households for times ranging from a few months to 125 years. Even at the average cost of council housing we are talking about at least £400 million worth of property [1981 property values]. We are also talking about creating a ghost town in the middle of the Royal Borough of Kensington and Chelsea.

He assumed a 10 per cent release of radioactivity. Should a 100 per cent release occur, the whole of London would have to be sealed off for a century. This calculation was arrived at by using the UK Atomic Energy Authority's own computer program, Tirion.

Three flasks travel through London each week, coming from the three Magnox reactors at Sizewell, Bradwell in

33

Essex and Dungeness A. The fuel from Sizewell and Bradwell travels in via Stratford (it was waste from Sizewell we found in the railway sidings near Ipswich station). Fuel from Dungeness comes in via Croydon, Streatham, Wandsworth Common, to Willesden Junction via Kensington, Olympia and Shepherd's Bush. Residents in Edgeley Road in Clapham have also seen flasks travelling down the line through Wandsworth Road station. Fuel from all the south-east reactors then goes from Willesden to Cumbria through Wembley Central, Harrow and Wealdstone, Watford Junction and from there on to Rugby, Coventry and Birmingham on its way north.

There have been a number of derailments of flasks in transit, in addition to the one in Birmingham, but we know very little about any of them. In January 1978 the then Energy Secretary Tony Benn was told by the CEGB there was no document listing safety-related incidents involving flasks containing spent nuclear fuel: such incidents would have been reportable by the operators had they occurred and no such incidents had been reported. Yet on 8 November 1979, Kenneth Clark, then Parliamentary Under-Secretary at the Department of Transport, stated in Parliament that since 1976 there had been eight instances of contamination above the permitted levels, involving spent-fuel flasks.

The CEGB regularly insist that emergency arrangements are in hand should there be a spillage from a flask, and that the police, fire brigade, British Rail staff and expert teams are always at the ready. Yet the union branch secretary at Battersea Fire Station (which would be called in to deal with a fire at Clapham Junction) told the authors of the book *Power Corrupts* (London, Pluto Press) in 1982 that he had never been told when flasks were passing through or what the drill was if there were to be an accident. On 11 January 1980, the CEGB admitted that no full-scale exercise had ever been carried out to practise what would be necessary, nor was one envisaged.

When I spoke to British Rail, the CEGB and the UKAEA after the Birmingham incident and asked what would have happened had there been a leak, I was told that the fire brigade would have been called in to deal with it, and the CEGB told me that 'experts' would be called in from Bradwell to measure the amount of radiation. It would take these experts more than three hours to get to the site of the accident even if they set off as soon as it took place.

On 5 April 1984, the *Daily Telegraph* carried a very brief report under the heading 'NUCLEAR TRAIN FIRE'. It appears that a train carrying a flask caught fire at Aldridge in the West Midlands – not far from the Birmingham marshalling yards. It was three hours before the firemen who had dealt with the relatively small blaze allowed the train to continue, after checking radiation levels. As with the Birmingham derailment, British Rail have refused to give any further details.

Having got your radioactive waste, of whatever level, from Point A to Point B, what then?

Residents in areas chosen to play host to intermediate- and low-level radioactive wastes are far from happy. Plans to find sites for the disposal of nuclear waste are in the hands of an organisation called NIREX (Nuclear Industry Radioactive Waste Executive), a commercial body established to dispose of these levels of radioactive wastes by land burial. It has never been an independent organisation, as is often suggested, for all its members are drawn from the nuclear industry – British Nuclear Fuels Ltd (BNFL), the Central Electricity Generating Board (CEGB), the South of Scotland Electricity Board (SSEB) and the United Kingdom Atomic Energy Authority (UKAEA).

During 1985/6, when the House of Commons Select Committee on the Environment was looking into the question of nuclear waste, the government announced that NIREX would become a limited company – United Kingdom Nirex Ltd – with the government holding a 'special share' and, with it, the power of veto. This still did not satisfy the Committee, who wanted NIREX to become far more open and accountable and to have members from outside the nuclear industry itself.

35

However, back in October 1983 NIREX announced that two sites had been selected for the possible disposal of nuclear waste. One was at the ICI chemical works in Billingham, Cleveland, the other in the London clay near Elstow in Bedfordshire. The announcement that Billingham and Elstow had been chosen to be the first hosts to material which might constitute a possible hazard for a considerable length of time aroused the fury of those destined to be the possible recipients, causing them to unite in a most unusual alliance of big-business, local Conservative MPs, and every kind of amenity and political body.

The outcry at Billingham eventually led ICI to refuse NIREX permission to look over the underground mine workings the latter had selected for storing the waste, and faced with intransigence from such a quarter, NIREX finally gave in: in 1985 it was announced that Billingham was no longer on the list of possible sites. This apparently left Elstow as the first choice. Elstow residents pointed out that they have never received any satisfactory explanation as to why their site was chosen in the first place, nor the criteria used for such a selection.

The CEGB already own the 450-acre site next to the St Pancras–Bedford railway line, about six miles south of Bedford. The waste would lie in trenches, the low-level waste at 6 to 8 metres below the surface, the intermediate waste in specially engineered trenches lined with concrete about 15 metres below the surface. Approximately 50 trenches occupying some 60 acres would be needed by the year 2000. 'Over its 50-year-life,' say Friends of the Earth in their excellent booklet on waste disposal, *The Gravedigger's Dilemma*, 'the site would require 250 trenches occupying 300 acres. After the trenches were filled with intermediate-level waste, they would be clay-filled and capped with reinforced concrete.' Nearly all the intermediate Elstow waste would come from nuclear reactors, mainly wastes from the cooling systems and sludge from the ponds used to store spent fuel. If chosen, Elstow (according to Friends of the Earth) would eventually receive 250,000 cubic metres of low-level waste – some 50,000 by the end of the century – and the trenches for this kind of waste would merely be filled with soil and not capped with concrete.

Early in 1985, the government announced that NIREX would be considering at least three other sites besides Elstow for waste storage. An announcement of which sites had been selected was expected in the late autumn of 1985, but it was delayed – possibly by the succession of incidents in the nuclear industry – and it was not until the end of February 1986 that the full list was given. As well as Elstow, the sites were Bradwell in Essex, Fulbeck in Lincolnshire and Killingholme in South Humberside.

The announcement had the local populations of all four areas up in arms. More than that, it appeared that all four local MPs – all Conservatives – had suddenly joined 'NIMBY'. NIMBY is the acronym invented in the United States for the reaction of those faced with this kind of problem: 'Not In My Back Yard'. The MPs told Parliament, with hands on heart, that they were fully in support of the government's nuclear programme and obviously waste had to be disposed of somewhere – but not in their constituencies.

Bradwell is in the constituency of the present government Chief Whip, John Wakeham, and in an unprecedented action for a man in this position, he issued a statement saying Bradwell was totally unsuitable for nuclear dumping. After a slow start, Douglas Hogg said nobody wanted it at Fulbeck either. Michael Brown, MP for Brigg and Cleethorpes, informed the House that if Killingholme was chosen he would resign his seat and fight a by-election on the issue.

At the time of writing, it is not known which site will be selected, but there are some political pointers. John Wakeham is the government Chief Whip, Fulbeck is in the Grantham constituency where the Prime Minister was born, and the resignation of Michael Brown would not only cause an unwanted by-election but one that would be fought on just about the last issue any government would wish to test the public mood on. It looks as if Elstow, therefore, will – as first thought – draw the short straw.

Fuel for the NIMBY MPs' argument has come in the House

of Commons Select Committee report, which is not at all happy about land disposal of nuclear waste in this fashion. The country's abysmal record of research into options must be improved, and in the meantime, says the Committee, trench burial seems quite unsuitable for intermediate-level wastes and barely suitable for short-lived low-level waste; if such waste is buried in this way, the trenches must be fully engineered on a complete containment basis.

However, when we look at the future for long-term high-level radioactive 'waste', the prospect is even bleaker. While there are often optimistic statements by the nuclear industry about imminent 'breakthroughs' in the technology needed to deal with the problem, the position has not changed since Denys Wilkinson, chairman of the Radioactive Waste Management Advisory Committee, published a paper on the subject, much of which was republished in the *Guardian* on 24 June 1982.

Basically, his premise was that if Britain closed down all its nuclear power plants tomorrow, it would still have to deal with the nuclear wastes of the last thirty years and that storage, rather than disposal, must not be accepted simply as a soft option. The waste already exists and this 'cannot be over-emphasised. The problem will not go away, we have to remove it ourselves.' He pointed out that a plant for solidifying high-level waste (a process known as vitrification) is already in operation in France at Marcoule, and there should be no delay in vitrifying the high-level wastes currently stored in liquid form in Britain. But that will only be the start of the problem. Even if far more thought is given and research is undertaken into how to store the solidified waste than is currently being done in this country, even if every kind of geological sounding and exploration has been carried out, it is the sheer timescale of the problem which is so hard to imagine. Wilkinson says:

> The alternative to permanent disposal is permanent storage, which implies surveillance into the remote future. It would seem unwise, if not absurd, to contemplate this. If long-term storage were to be transformable into permanent disposal by sealing off the store at some appropriate date

the store would have to have been constructed to have an integrity measured in thousands of years.

And even this is not the worst of it, for nobody has even begun to hazard a guess at what the future holds for the disposal of the most radioactive waste of all – that from nuclear power stations themselves and their reactors when they are finally decommissioned. The cost of such decommissioning, based on the clean-up operation at Three-Mile Island, would run into billions of pounds at 1986 prices. The best that has so far been suggested is that these stations and their reactors should be sealed off, guarded, and left standing, possibly for hundreds of years.

Meanwhile there have been numerous incidents concerning nuclear waste, one appalling accident, and one instance where a whole town has been stricken because of its proximity to a nuclear waste dump. There may well be instances of which we do not know, but here are some of the known ones.

Hanford Reservation, Washington State

High-level liquid nuclear waste – some 250,000 cubic metres of it – is stored in this facility in 151 tanks. It is waste recovered from the US nuclear weapons programme. Storage of the waste in the tanks was never considered a long-term solution as the average useful life of the tanks is only between 20 and 25 years. The idea was to use them as an interim storage facility until a safe, long-term storage method was discovered. There have, to date, been over a dozen leaks from the tanks, the worst one occurring between 20 April and 8 June 1973 when Tank 106T leaked 435,000 litres of high-level waste into the earth beneath it, while those operating the plant continued pouring waste into the leaking receptacle. According to Walter C. Patterson, an independent nuclear consultant, about 40,000 curies of caesium-137, 14,000 curies of strontium-90 and 4 curies of plutonium were released. While those called in to investigate the plant said they did not think the radioactivity would leach into the ground-water level, they decided against drilling into the ground to try and locate where the waste had gone in case it made matters worse.

However, trouble with the storage tanks was not the only problem at Hanford. It was decided to dispose of low-level nuclear waste in shallow trenches such as those currently being planned for as-yet-unfinalised areas in Britain. It had been assumed that low-level radiation from the waste would harmlessly disperse itself into the ground. This did not prove to be the case.

In 1973, the US Atomic Energy Commission investigated a leak at Z9, a low-level waste burial trench. Its report said:

> Due to the quantity of plutonium contained in the soil of Z9, it is possible to conceive of conditions which could result in a nuclear chain reaction. These conditions would be the re-arrangement of the contaminated soil, flooding of the enclosed trench following, say, a record snowfall and rapid melting, and failure to implement planned emergency actions (pumping off flood water from adjacent terrain and additional neutron-absorbing materials in the enclosed trench).

It was possible, said the AEC, that rapid heating of the water in the trench could turn it into steam and the steam produce a 'mud volcano'-type of explosion.

It cost $2 million to clean up the mess, and the risk was lowered in this case by Hanford's dry climate. However, some experts now believe that, during that period, Hanford came close to the type of accident which occurred at Chelyabinsk in the Soviet Union in 1957 (p. 43).

Studies of the cancer rate among workers at Hanford have led to more controversy along with accusations that official support for these studies was unaccountably withdrawn once it appeared that embarrassing conclusions might be drawn about the future health of the workers involved.

West Valley, New York State

In 1959 New York State decided it wanted a share in nuclear technology and set up an agency to attract the industry. In 1961, the agency bought land thirty miles from Buffalo in West Valley, a fertile dairy-farming area of great natural beauty. Shortly afterwards it began to negotiate with the Davison Chemical Company which wanted to set up a nuclear storage and reprocessing plant in the Valley. There were considerable rumblings from the local population as to the safety of the project, and it was decided that the waste-management aspect of the plant would be owned by the state agency but run by Davison, which now renamed itself Nuclear Fuel Services. The company had to put up $4 million as collateral, the interest on which was to cover the waste-management side of the enterprise – in perpetuity. The US Atomic Energy Commission would assist with details of the technology needed for military reprocessing, and it was agreed that spent fuel from Hanford would be sent to West Valley until the plant could get hold of enough civil nuclear waste to carry on without it.

Building began in 1963 and the plant started working in 1966. According to Walter Patterson, again economy and profit-making were the watchwords at West Valley. Corners were cut in the design of the plant, in the way it was run – workers had to enter radioactive areas as this was cheaper than operating them by remote-controlled equipment – and maintenance was skimped. The plant apparently leaked like a sieve.

It was an incredibly dirty plant from the radiation point of view. According to the subsequent US Atomic Energy Commission investigation, the average exposure of workers at the West Valley plant increased with each year it was in operation. In 1968 it was 2.74 rems, 1969 3.81 rems, 1970 6.76 rems and in 1971 7.15 rems. The maximum permitted safety level at that time was 5 rems. It is not known how high were the radiation exposures of the casual labour brought in to keep mopping up the worst of the leaks. Obviously, as all the experts point out, the figures given above are only averages – some people must have received substantially higher doses.

41

Another fact then emerged about the safety of West Valley and its nuclear waste storage facilities: it was built near an active earthquake fault. In spite of its keen desire to make a profit and cut costs, Nuclear Fuel Services lost money heavily. By 1972 the local population was calling for the plant to be closed down because of seepage into adjoining waterways. Overwhelmed by the rising tide of protest, knowledge of the earthquake fault becoming public and mounting costs, Nuclear Fuel Services first closed down its plant, ostensibly for 'expansion' and then declared bankruptcy.

However, that still leaves the inhabitants of West Valley with an appalling problem: some 600,000 gallons of high level radioactive waste in two underground tanks with a life expectancy of about thirty years. The waste has a hazard life measured in thousands of years. According to the US Department of Energy Report published in June 1982, if a tank at West Valley springs a leak the waste will be discharged into two neighbouring creeks and into Lake Erie, just upstream from the water intake of 1 million people in the Buffalo metropolitan area. A further 11 million people downstream, both in the US and Canada, will have seriously polluted drinking water. Currently the US government is experimenting with trying to solidify the waste which, the residents say, must then be removed and stored elsewhere.

Two other American commercial sites have been closed down by their state legislatures because of the safety factor. The Kentucky Department of Human Resources discovered in 1972 that the Maxey Flats low-level waste storage facility appeared to be leaking as increased quantities of radioactivity were found in water samples taken from around the area. However, the Department did not consider the levels sufficiently high to constitute a health hazard, but public disquiet grew until eventually, in 1976, the state legislature imposed a tax of 10 per cent per pound excise duty on the waste received at the site for disposal, which made the whole operation so prohibitively expensive that it had to close down.

A further site at Sheffield, Illinois, was closed in 1979 due to public pressure, the state attorney general refusing to agree to a continuation of its licence on the grounds that there were too many doubts about its safety.

Accident at Chelyabinsk

Most of the information we have on nuclear incidents and accidents and their repercussions comes from the United States, still the most open society in the world (even if we accept that some of that American information takes a good deal of effort to obtain). We do not expect similar information to come from the Soviet Union. Even so, we hardly expect our own and the American Establishment to do the Russians' cover-up work for them, but this appears to be what happened when the story first broke of the world's most serious accident to date concerning nuclear waste.

Like most Soviet dissidents, Dr Zhores Medvedev received a hero's welcome in the West – until, that is, he quite casually let slip that there had been an accident connected with nuclear waste in the Soviet Union. He said, quite simply, that in 1957 there had been a major catastrophe due to the explosion of nuclear waste near Kyshtym and Chelyabinsk in the Urals. He had assumed everyone in the West knew about it and was totally unprepared for the reaction his statement caused. On 4 November 1976, Dr Medvedev wrote a piece for the *New Scientist* called 'Two Decades of Dissidence' in which he mentioned the Chelyabinsk accident.

The reaction was immediate. As he was later to write in a contribution to a small booklet on the hazards of nuclear power,

I was unaware at that time that this nuclear disaster was absolutely unknown to Western experts and my *New Scientist* article created an unexpected sensation. Reports about this 20-year-old nuclear disaster appeared in almost all the major newspapers. At the same time, some Western nuclear experts, including the chairman of the UK Atomic Energy Authority, Sir John Hill, tried to dismiss my story as 'science fiction', 'rubbish', or 'a figment of my imagination'.

43

Such an accident, said Sir John Hill, was 'impossible'.

Why should there have been such a strong reaction? The reason is not hard to find. Both the United States and Britain were coming under increasing fire from environmental bodies and the public over the hazards of nuclear waste storage, and the British government in particular was having a hard time over Windscale/Sellafield and its many problems. The ultimate horror which was never talked about – that nuclear waste itself might explode – could not be countenanced.

At this stage the Central Intelligence Agency (CIA) coyly admitted that it knew of an 'incident' in that area at that time but it stated that the accident was due to a nuclear reactor which went out of control and threw out radioactivity. Its report said that the reactor was 'only distantly related to present nuclear power plants and the accident's relevance to the safety of civilian nuclear power today is probably minor'.

Dr Medvedev then found himself at the end of a torrent of abuse from those who had previously welcomed such a prominent dissident with enthusiasm. Not only his scientific ability but his character were called into question.

Yet Medvedev stuck to his story, which well he might since it appears to be quite true and, as he pointed out, a month after his piece appeared in the *New Scientist* he received confirmation from another quarter – Professor Lev Tumerman, former head of the biophysics laboratory at the Institute of Molecular Biology in Moscow, who had emigrated to Israel in 1972. In 1960, Tumerman had himself visited the area between the two Ural cities of Chelyabinsk and Sverdlovsk, at the heart of the Soviet nuclear programme, both civil and military.

Tumerman found a wasteland, with hundreds of square miles so heavily contaminated by radioactive waste that the area was forbidden territory: 'All the villages and small towns had been destroyed so as to make the dangerous zone uninhabitable and to prevent the evacuated people from returning.' This confirmation did not, however, satisfy Sir John Hill who still continued to say it could not have happened.

On 24 January 1977, the CIA came up with a real winner. It had received, it said, an 'unevaluated report' to the effect that the Soviet government had constructed a special city in the Urals which would be blown up to see what would happen in a real-life nuclear attack; a 20-megaton device had been dropped from a plane and this had caused the disaster. Actually, at the time of the Chelyabinsk accident Russia, like the United States, was still testing atomic weapons in the atmosphere, and it was possible for the CIA to use one of the Soviet tests to explain away the 'incident' in the Urals. However, as Dr Medvedev pointed out, this version did not satisfy informed opinion.

Then Granada Television found two more Russian dissidents living in Israel who also knew of the event and in November 1977 they gave their evidence in a programme on the subject. They had been living in the area when they heard rumours, they said, of a disaster at Chelyabinsk and 'that there had been a terrible nuclear explosion, an accident caused by the storage of radioactive waste from a nuclear plant'.

Doctors who were friends of the dissidents had told them similar stories. One of the dissidents said that he had visited a hospital in Sverdlovsk to have a wart removed and a doctor informed him that the entire hospital was crammed with the victims of the catastrophe. All the hospitals throughout the region – enormous teaching hospitals with hundreds of beds – were full, he was told, not only in Sverdlovsk but also in Chelyabinsk. The doctor told him that all the victims were suffering from radiation sickness. The number of casualties was estimated in thousands, most of whom died.

Then a nurse, also living in Israel, added her testimony in a letter to the *Jerusalem Post*. She said that as late as 1967, while there were no signs of destruction in the area in which she was working (Kyshtym), everything brought into the market place, or even fruit and mushrooms picked in the wild, had to be monitored for radiation, and people carried little radiometers with them. She had become pregnant while working in the area and was told to have an abortion because the continuing high levels of radiation might cause the child to be born deformed.

To go back to the evidence of Professor Tumerman, he

gave a chilling description of what it was like in the region in 1960.

> On both sides of the road as far as one could see the land was 'dead'. No villages, no towns, only chimneys of destroyed houses, no cultivated fields or pastures, no herds, no people . . . nothing. Later I was told that this was the site of the famous Kyshtym catastrophe in which hundreds of people had been killed or disabled.

He spoke of road blocks on roads leading towards the area, of warning notices, of being told to drive fast through contaminated areas without stopping or opening a door or window as the level of contamination was so high. He stressed the fact that it was known to many scientists in the Soviet Union that the accident was due to 'mismanaged' nuclear waste.

Dr Medvedev said that two study centres were afterwards set up near to the site of the accident, and that there were a number of scientific papers in Soviet technical journals about the effects of radioactive contamination. At first, all such papers and information had been classified, but by 1965/66 the accident was beginning to be public knowledge and such information became available.

Dr Medvedev told of experiments carried out in the forest and meadow areas between 1968 and 1970 – eleven to thirteen years after the accident. A report given to the Praesidium of the Soviet Academy of Sciences in 1970 described areas

> which had been contaminated by high doses of radioactive substances . . . In these circumstances some species died out, some continued to suffer for a long time, their populations reduced in size, and some evolved towards a higher resistance.

Some of the information is so chilling that it sounds almost like science fiction. Lakes, too, became heavily contaminated and one, although it had a 'high turnover' of water, was found to contain large quantities of both strontium-90 and caesium-137.

The lakes in the Urals region usually have very thick bottom silt deposits. The total amount of strontium-90 in the bottom silt of two lakes which Rovinsky studied was at least ten times higher than in the water, once equilibrium was reached. However, these were non-running-water type lakes. The third lake studied . . . had an intensive turnover of its water supply – the strontium-90 concentration could vary up or down by more than 400 per cent in one month. These conditions meant that the bottom silt and water plants became the main accumulators of radioactive materials – a process which had started many years before the experiments.

It was calculated that the total amount of strontium-90 and caesium-137 in the water plants, plankton and silt was about 1000 times higher than that in the water. 'This means,' said Medvedev, 'that the total minimum amount of strontium-90 and caesium-137 in the whole lake must be about *50 million curies* . . .'

Medvedev stuck to his statement that the accident was due to nuclear waste exploding. He said that different kinds of nuclear accidents release different kinds of radioactive particles into the environment. If nuclear waste from a reactor is scattered from a storage area

the result will be quite specific. The numerous short-lived radioactive isotopes with very intensive gamma and beta radiation will have already disappeared during the storage period. Only long-lived isotopes, which constitute about 5 to 6 per cent of the initial radioactivity, remain dangerous after the first two or three months. Radioactive strontium-90 and caesium-137 are the most important of these and both have half-lives of about 30 years.

He went on to say that caesium-137 is an isotope with gamma radiation and is more dangerous for external irradiation but it is less cumulative and disappears more rapidly both from animals and from soil, than strontium-90. Strontium-90, however, closely resembles calcium and can substitute for it both in bones and soil. Since calcium forms part of the permanent body structure, strontium-90 can be fixed in bones for years, and may remain for hundreds of years in the soil, which is why it is considered one of the most danger-ous products of the nuclear industry. It was the presence in large amounts of these two isotopes that convinced Medvedev that there had been an explosion of nuclear waste.

Gradually, by the use of the US Freedom of Information Act, more information came to light in the United States to back up Medvedev's claim, and few now doubt that there was, indeed, an accident of this kind in Russia. What is more, it transpired that a report on the Urals disaster had actually been given by Soviet scientists and had been presented in Vienna in 1971 to a meeting of the International Atomic Energy Agency. Sir John Hill's remarkable reaction was open to question right from the beginning, as he must have been aware of the conclusions of the USAEC regarding the waste at Hanford and the possibility of a chain reaction – if he was not, then one wonders why not.

Details, of the Chelyabinsk disaster are, of course, still scarce. Russian radiation victims have been given no oppor-tunity to exchange experiences with others who have suffered similarly, especially in Japan. A US study based on known data estimates that most of the industrial city of Kasli was contaminated, along with fourteen lakes and 625 square miles of countryside. There are still enormous 'graveyards of the earth' – huge dumps of contaminated topsoil. About 60,000 people had to be permanently evacuated, thirty towns were flattened to the ground, and there were an unknown number of casualties both from the initial radiation and subsequent radiation sickness. What caused it?

If the Russians know, they have not said. One theory is that a by-product of the nuclear waste-reprocessing cycle, ammonium nitrate, exploded taking the waste with it. Another is that suggested for the accident which nearly occurred at Hanford. Whatever the reason, the 'impossible' accident happened.

.ss

Living with death

Canonsburg, twenty miles south west of Pittsburgh, Pennsylvania, used to be famous for one thing: it was the birthplace of singer Perry Como. Now it is notorious for being one of the most radioactive hotspots on earth.

During the latter half of World War II a factory owned by Rare Vitro Metals was in operation in Canonsburg, in the town centre near the banks of a small creek. It processed uranium for the Manhattan Project – the research, development and manufacture of the United States' atomic bombs. Nobody knew exactly what it was they were working on (the workers were paid 60 cents an hour in the uranium processing plant) as it was both top secret work and a virtually unknown project. Just how dangerous those in charge of the Manhattan Project realised it was, we do not know. Even without the explosion of the bombs on Hiroshima and Nagasaki there was plenty of evidence to support the case that dealing with radioactive material in general and uranium in particular was extremely hazardous.

Eventually the Manhattan Project no longer needed the processing plant in Canonsburg, and in 1960 the factory closed down. The nuclear industry had become the concern of the US Atomic Energy Commission, and it was the Commission which, in 1965, decided to bury some 4500 tons of uranium-contaminated material right beside the town. According to the US Union of Concerned Scientists, that waste is at least a hundred times more radioactive than the AEC's own minimum regulations permitted, and they must have known that at the time.

The waste was bulldozed into a swamp where for years radioactive sludge had been poured. The whole lot was then covered over with earth and rubble, on top of which was poured 'red dog', porous waste from steel mills. The land was finally flattened out and part of it became a recreational facility – in fact the local playing field on which there was a baseball pitch. As the years passed, so light industry came to Canonsburg and opened up on other parts of the site. It appears that nobody told them what lay underneath the ground.

49

Then, in 1963, Robert Gallagher, a health physicist who specialised in radiation safety, was asked to survey part of the area for industrialists who wanted to build factories on it. 'It was a blistering cold day,' he told the *Observer* in an interview on 10 March 1985. 'I was really surprised by the readings I got. A person would have got a dose of radiation in ten hours that was more than the acceptable exposure for an entire year. And that was based on my average readings – some were much higher.' He told his clients that the ground was heavily irradiated and unfit for industrial use except at vast cost, but his findings were never made known.

Years later when the government was considering cleaning up the site, I heard the Department of Energy announce the release of a report on Canonsburg. I studied an advance copy and went to a meeting. I was absolutely astounded to find there was no reference to the years when the government had sanctioned the covering up of the piles I had surveyed in 1963. I asked why there was no mention of this in the report. The official said he had no answer to that and walked off the stage in a huff. I could not believe they were writing Russian-style history. What they buried there and the way they buried it was utterly inexcusable. There was too much known about radioactivity.

'Red dog' is very porous and not suitable for sealing radioactive material. The area is in a flood plain and contamination would be washed by flood waters into the environment. Contamination could also dry into dust and be blown into the environment. I felt that in the best interests of my profession and of the public as a whole, some information should be made public.

But what of the unfortunate inhabitants of Canonsburg? They had been hit by an inexplicable 'plague' of cancers.

The *Observer* journalist spoke to many people who had lost relatives or who were suffering from cancer themselves. Young Mark Humble used to play baseball on the radioactive field which is now guarded with chainlink fence and carries warning notices. Mark joined the Navy in 1979 at the age of seventeen, specialising in electronics. In June 1983, his mother was told he had an incurable malignant tumour. It started in his stomach, but eventually his whole body was affected, his chest cavity collapsed and he became riddled with it. 'I asked him once,' said his mother, 'if he thought playing down there on the ballfield where they found the radiation had anything to do with it. He said, "Well, Mom, who's going to stick up for you? Because the government isn't going to come forward and admit it."' He died on 9 November 1984 at the age of 22. He was the eleventh member of his 385-member class at high school known to have contracted the disease. Two other boys are also dead, one of lung cancer and another, who developed bone cancer at the age of fourteen, of lung cancer two years later. Independent scientists say such a percentage is 'astounding'.

Another of Mark's classmates, Lori Ewig, visited him while he was dying in hospital. Then, when she was nineteen, she too was discovered to have cancer and had to have one of her ovaries and a Fallopian tube removed, followed by chemotherapy. She is now twenty-three and subject to three-monthly check-ups.

Nuns who taught at the local Catholic school, downwind of the dump, also noticed increasing health problems. Nuns do tend, on the whole, to live longer than the average population, and members of this particular order had an average lifespan of about 90 years. Now it is 60. Five nuns, with an average age of fifty, died of cancer; five more, with an average age of sixty-six, of heart attacks; and another died of a cerebral haemorrhage. Nine more contracted cancer and another fourteen cysts and benign tumours. In 1983 the nuns closed down their school as they felt the children should no longer be exposed to the dangers from the waste. Now the Mother Superior, Sister Bernadine, has developed skin cancer.

Nobody, it seems, has taken an overall head-count of the cancer cases, but Janis Dunn, a housewife, was so concerned at the number of illnesses among her family and friends that she did a small survey of her own. She lived in a street of houses built in 1957, right next to the dump. There was much that was odd about the street anyway, she told the *Observer*. Trees grew in a strange way and leaves were brown instead of green; paint wouldn't stay on door or window frames, and after rain, puddles turned vivid scarlet and purple one day, yellow and green the next. This latter delighted the children who would then play in them.

Janis Dunn's mother-in-law had died of cancer, a sister-in-law had a breast removed because of it. She herself had had a tumour removed from her womb and had lumps on her legs and throat, a lung condition and broken blood vessels. Both her husband and brother-in-law had to have tumours removed. In 1980 she began knocking on doors; she found 67 cases of cancer behind 45 of them. In one street with 59 people, she found 20 cancers. 'Every house on the three streets nearest to the site had at least one case of cancer or a cancer-related death. The national leukaemia rate is three or four in 100,000. I found four cases in one street of only ten houses.'

She also found respiratory problems, heart disease, menstrual troubles, and tumours in the reproductive organs of young girls. There were blood conditions and strange allergies as well, and as she told the *Observer*, she became frightened by the sort of things that were starting to be revealed about the waste buried on the Canonsburg site. 'I was so scared,' said Mrs Dunn. 'I just didn't know what kind of a can of worms I'd opened.'

At one house in Payne Place, almost next to the dump itself, Kenny Davis, a 62-year-old former steelworker, produced all the family death certificates for her to see. About fourteen husbands and wives had died of cancer.

Mr Davis's wife then had breast cancer. In the summer of 1984, his sister died of cancer just before her 66th birthday. Their mother, father and grandmother had all died of cancer in the same house. So had four uncles, two aunts and two of their spouses. A sister had grown up in the house and moved next door, married and died in 1978 of cancer at the age of 58. Mr Davis's neighbours had lost their daughter. Another of his sisters, who had also lived next door, died of cancer early in the 1970s, to be shortly followed by her husband from lung cancer. The street was full of it, Mr Davis told Mrs Dunn; even the minister at the church had died of it. There were many more.

Following his brush with the Department of Energy, Robert Gallagher decided to go public. He called the local paper, the *Pittsburgh Press*, and told them what he had found out and where to start looking. America, of course, has its 1976 Freedom of Information Act and using this the journalists on the paper set to work, forcing the government to produce official files on the Canonsburg dump. The files showed a massive cover-up, not just of radioactive waste but of the truth. It appeared that back in 1965 the Pennsylvania Department of Health had approved the burial of a massive pile of uranium ore on the dump, ore so rich it needed a federal licence for its possession, use and control.

The *Pittsburgh Press* found that 37 residents of Mr Davis's street, Payne Place, spanning three generations, had died of cancer. They found another three current sufferers. In the next street they found 13 cancer-related deaths in ten houses. The reporter, David Templeton, said that 'nearly every resident believes radiation is the killer'.

Federal and state government agencies still insisted that the amount of radiation was 'safe', although independent scientists pointed out that there is now considerable controversy as to what constitutes a safe dose, some thinking that any dose, however low, can cause significant harm. It transpired that from 1977 low-flying aircraft were making radiological surveys, and that in 1979 government tests on soil samples had revealed huge amounts of radioactive contamination. At this stage, however, government experts were still telling Canonsburg residents that there was nothing to worry about, that the risk one ran from the sort of radiation one would be exposed to by driving through the area would be the same as the risk from 'smoking a cigarette'.

According to the US government's own figures, the site contained naturally occurring radiation – uranium and radium – at the rate of 1 to 2 picocuries (the standard measurement of radioactive material) per gram of soil. Soil samples from the Canonsburg dump showed concentrations of radium-226 (one of the waste products which appears when uranium decays) ranging from 21,800 picocuries per gram, as well as concentrations of uranium proper as high as 51,000 picocuries per gram. Radon gas might occur naturally in the area at a rate of 0.3 picocuries per litre of air, but radon gas from the dump showed an average of 106.5 picocuries per litre. Some of the readings were 757 times the natural background level.

Nor was it just the dump that caused anxiety. For years, people had used rubble from the site as hardcore for garage floors and porches. Scientists have found a further 130 radioactive hotspots all over the town, including bedroom walls, tool sheds, bathrooms and children's sandpits. Mrs Pattie DeLost simply walked out of her house for good after her front steps and porch were found to be heavily contaminated and she was told not to use her front door. She had sat for hours on that porch, and her son had played in a sandpit in the garden, another hotspot.

Finally, the authorities had to act. But what could they do with nuclear waste which would be a potential hazard for hundreds of years? One idea was to dig up the waste and then bury it in a more isolated place some twenty miles away, but the residents of the town nearest to the proposed new burial site were so incensed they threatened to arm themselves with shotguns and close off all the roads. So it was decided to dig it up, and dump and bury it on the same site but on higher ground under a proper clay cap which, it is hoped, will last between 200 and 1000 years.

But this has not allayed the fears of most of the residents. Some people in the town just don't want to know. They consider the cancers to be an Act of God, or they have business interests that adverse publicity would affect. Others are still happy to believe the government knows best, and if the government said there was no real problem then there wasn't one, and the cancers must be due to some other cause. Yet these same people have watched men wearing fully protective clothing and breathing apparatus at work on the site measuring radiation. Not surprisingly, property values have slumped and many people want to be evacuated and set up elsewhere at government expense. So far some 33 individuals have received out-of-court settlements and there are a number of court actions over health problems pending.

Having admitted so much, it might be thought that the federal and/or state government would go all the way and hold a full investigation into the health hazards of Canonsburg. But so sensitive is this issue of nuclear waste storage that it seems unlikely, at the time of writing, that such an enquiry will ever take place.

In 1982, the Pennsylvania State Health Department did promise an investigation into the amount of radioactivity and whether it had caused all the cancers, but the inquiry has never taken place. It is now well known, after all, that various isotopes home in on bones, lungs and the thyroid gland. Thirty million dollars has been allocated by the federal government for the Canonsburg clean-up but nothing has been put aside to compensate those who have suffered as a result of living near the dump.

The official view is, apparently, that neither examination of local death certificates nor a survey undertaken by a university graduate on lung cancers alone, merits a follow-up.

In 1985, when the Australian Royal Commission was meeting in London to examine the evidence of British victims of the 1950s bomb tests in Australia, one of the witnesses was Professor Edward Radford, former chairman of the US National Academy of Sciences' Committee on the Biological Effects of Ionising Radiation. He stated publicly that the people of Canonsburg who had been exposed to what had been thought to be only low doses of radiation had suffered severe health damage. Research carried out at Pittsburgh University in 1982 had shown a significant number of radiation-induced thyroid abnormalities. He found this surprising as he had been told that the Canonsburg residents had only been exposed to radiation two or three times the natural background level. He presented a paper on the subject to the International Congress on Radiological Research in 1983. He thinks funding should be made available immediately for a comprehensive health study on the inhabitants of Canonsburg, if only for moral reasons.

In August 1984, residents of Canonsburg called in Dr Rosalie Bertell, the international radiation expert, adviser to the US Nuclear Regulatory Commission and author of *No Immediate Danger: Prognosis for a Radioactive Earth*. She said the unwillingness to carry out a proper health investigation was criminal.

The people need to know how badly they are damaged, how much radiation is in their bodies. It is criminal if this information is kept back. They must have the opportunity to be tested to see how much damage has been done. It is tragic that it happened at all.

She agreed to co-ordinate a special testing programme, to be carried out by a scientist at the Argonne Laboratory in the USA, but before it could get under way the laboratory's funding was cut and the scientist was sacked.

The man in charge of the clean-up operation, David Bull of the US Department of Energy, insists there is no evidence that low-level radiation damages health. He has assured citizens that the new dump with its clay cap, fence and warning signs will be regularly checked and will be safe for a thousand years. But if the federal and state governments did not think there was a real hazard to people's health, why the clean-up operation?

Dr John Gofman, a former leading scientist at one of the US government's nuclear laboratories and now a professor at the University of California, told the *Observer*:

There is an excellent reason for the residents of this area to be seriously concerned about harm to themselves and to their children from exposure which has been thrust upon them as a result of the escape of radiation from this plant site.

This potential harm in the form of cancer and leukaemia is *not* a hypothetical thing. The evidence is overwhelming that it occurs and any person should indeed be concerned about receiving any unnecessary radiation . . . They and their children are receiving additional injury from ongoing radiation and hence experiencing an added risk of future cancers with each passing month.

The US government position is nothing short of scandalous. To say we don't need to worry is probably one of the most gigantic frauds in history. Why not do a health study? There's nothing like not having data, then there's no evidence. Why in the world is somebody not looking at this for the good of everyone, whatever the results?

There are half a million tons of radioactive debris still in the dump at Canonsburg. The town is known locally as Radiation City. It is only the first of some twenty-four similar sites in the US storing waste made as a result of producing uranium for military and civil programmes since the 1940s.

It is in its disposal of nuclear waste that the nuclear industry is at its most vulnerable. There is no sure way of storing it safely in the ground, as we have seen. Sea disposal, even if all the nations of the world were agreed and all those employed by the government at the docks or on ships were willing to carry it out, also poses many problems. Sea dumping was Britain's prime favourite for 'waste management' until the unions, Greenpeace and world opinion stopped it – possibly only temporarily – in 1983.

Between 1949 and 1979 the gross weight of radioactive waste dumped by Britain was 67,337 metric tonnes, of which about 70 per cent was concrete-and-steel packaging. We were the main sea-dumping nation, accounting for over 90 per cent of the radioactive pollution of the ocean from dumping. One nuclear waste sea-dump was said to be 500 miles from Land's End and 2½ miles deep, but in September 1983 a US nuclear submarine hit a nuclear waste dump only 175 miles south-west of Land's End and was so contaminated that even after five months at sea the paint on its hull had to be scraped off and sealed in bags. If this story is true, this amount of radioactivity could hardly have come from the kind of low-level waste we are told was dumped by Britain, and if it was where the submarine found it, then either there are more sites off Land's End than have hitherto been known, or it was dumped in the wrong place, or it has moved. None of these possibilities is very comforting.

That was British waste dumped from civil nuclear programmes. The Ministry of Defence has also used sea dumping for waste from nuclear weapons manufacture and from nuclear submarine reactors. It has on occasion attempted to dispose of high-level waste in this way, and also to avoid properly sealing off intermediate-level waste.

There are good moral reasons for not dumping at sea, not

least because many nations that have no nuclear programmes
and do not wish to have them can have their seas polluted by
those who do, with all the inherent risks.

On 2 January 1981, George Earl IV, who had been a
lieutenant-commander in the US Navy during World War II,
spoke out after 33 years of silence. He actually called a press
conference at his own home. He told how, when he was
stationed at Mustin Field, near Philadelphia, after the war, he
flew three secret missions on 16, 20 and 22 October 1947. He
had to fly half-a-dozen large metal canisters full of radioactive
waste, each weighing between 2 and 3 tons, to a site 100 miles
east of Atlantic City, New Jersey, and then drop them in the
sea. He was told to fly low so that they would not break
open. These trips were never entered in the flight log of the
plane.

Some time later leaking canisters of radioactive waste
were washed ashore on the coast near San Francisco,
and Earl contacted both the Navy and the US Nuclear
Regulatory Commission suggesting they also look into
dumping in the Pacific back in 1947. He never received a
reply.

Twenty-five years after his secret flights, it was discovered
that there had been continual dumping from both barges and
aircraft off the US coasts, the biggest dumps lying within a few
hours by boat of New York, Newark, Boston, Los Angeles
and San Francisco in prime coastal fishing areas and along
major holiday coasts. More information on the covert dumping was obtained: if a canister failed to sink, it would be
punctured with bullets; if the weather was rough, canisters
had been thrown overboard anywhere in San Francisco Bay.
By dint of using the Freedom of Information Act, it was
discovered that the Atomic Energy Commission had consistently lied about the possible hazards; a study carried out by
Pneumo-Dynamics in 1961 showed that 36 per cent of the
nuclear waste drums were damaged and four out of nine
concrete blocks completely destroyed. The official AEC
statement said that 94 per cent of the 162 canisters tested had
remained intact.

Nearly 50,000 canisters of radioactive waste were dumped
near the Farallon Islands, 23 miles from San Francisco,

according to Dr Rosalie Bertell, and a report released by the US Environmental Protection Agency in 1980 showed that sediment in the ocean there was 2000 times more radioactive than would be the normal for background radiation. Levels near New Jersey were found to be 260,000 times higher, and plutonium was found in edible fish.

The US Navy also deliberately sank a nuclear submarine, *Sea Wolf*, still containing its entire nuclear reactor with about 33,000 curies of radioactive material, off the Delaware-Maryland shore. However, there is also a theory that this was, in fact, the result of a reactor accident.

Nobody knows the true location of the sea dumps of radioactive waste, only that there are now a considerable number.

So if ground storage is hazardous, sea dumping dangerous, what remains? The main thrust is, as we have said, to vitrify the waste, but then what? Above-ground storage is mooted as a possibility but this would need to be guarded virtually for ever. Shooting it all into space is another suggestion. Until this problem is solved, nuclear power stations will have to remain in existence even when decommissioned, possibly surrounded by other nuclear waste.

The nuclear-waste problem won't go away. With every year that passes while there is a continuing nuclear programme, civil or military, the waste will continue to accumulate. Whatever you do with the waste, whether you bury it, drown it, or store it, the long-life radio isotopes remain for this very long timescale. *It won't go away.* It is also a monstrously expensive business and an expense which is rarely brought into the calculations showing how cheap and efficient nuclear power stations are compared with oil- and coal-fired ones.

The conclusion reached by the 1976 Royal Commission on Environmental Pollution, under Lord Flowers, in par. 338 of its Report is still valid:

. . . there should be no commitment to a large programme of nuclear fission power until it has been demonstrated beyond all reasonable doubt that a method exists to ensure the safe containment of long-lived, highly radioactive waste for the indefinite future.

Nothing has changed since 1976.

Chapter 3

The Impossible Accident

Researching details of accidents is easiest of all in the USA. This is, quite simply, because in 1976 the US Congress passed the Freedom of Information Act. This has not automatically meant that everything nuclear is now automatically open to the public or that nobody tries to cover anything up, but it does mean that it is possible to get hold of a great deal of information.

It is not just US citizens who benefit. When I wrote to the United States Information Service at their embassy in London, asking if I could see details of Congressional hearings on nuclear accidents and reports of the Atomic Energy Commission, I had a reply within a week asking merely that I give them a call a few days in advance so that they could sort out the relevant papers for me. This information included all kinds of highly embarrassing material connected with the accident at Three-Mile Island.

The other remarkable source is *The Nugget File* published by the Union of Concerned Scientists. When the Freedom of Information Act was passed this organisation immediately applied for details of safety problems within the civil nuclear power industry. Some material was immediately made available but not all of it. As the introduction to *The Nugget File* says:

> While reviewing a set of documents written by a senior NRC official, Dr Stephen H. Hanauer, which were reluctantly turned over to us, we happened across a 'buckslip' initialled by Hanauer. A buckslip is a standard transmittal form used by the bureaucracy to route memoranda and documents from one office in the federal labyrinth to another. This particular buckslip transmitted a document

61

from 'SHH' to 'EPE'. The document being transmitted was not attached to the copy of the buckslip we received but the buckslip itself contained a handwritten message: 'This one is too good to pass up'. And in the corner of the form there was the notation 'Nugget File dtd. 8/15/72'. We immediately telephoned Dr Hanauer and questioned him about this file which had never been mentioned in public by the AEC or NRC. Hanauer confirmed our guess: the Nugget File was a special internal file, maintained personally by Dr Hanauer for the last ten years, on serious accidents and safety deficiencies in US nuclear power plants. As one of the most senior officials in the US nuclear power programme, Dr Hanauer was routinely and promptly advised on safety problems that were detected in operating nuclear plants.

The Union of Concerned Scientists immediately asked for the whole file to be made public. The response of the Nuclear Regulatory Commission was to make public a list of just the titles and dates of the documents on file and nothing more. This, says the Union, would have meant an enormous and time-consuming search through ten years of files. Finally they managed to prevail on Joseph Felton of the NRC staff, who had always been helpful over processing Freedom of Information Act requests, to have the whole 'Nugget File' copied and placed in the NRC Public Document Room. 'Finally, the 12-inch-thick stack of nuclear safety documents squirrelled away by Dr Hanauer became available for public perusal.' Since then the Nugget File has continually been updated.

What it shows starkly, as the Union of Concerned Scientists emphasises, is that the so-called high safety standards of the nuclear power industry are blemished by 'simple and widespread carelessness'. For want of fuses, key nuclear safety equipment is rendered inoperative. Electrical relays fail because they have been painted over or welded together or disconnected. Safety valves are destroyed because switches on their motors have not been properly adjusted. A 3000-gallon radioactive-waste tank in one plant was found to be connected to the plant's drinking-water system . . .

There are routine failures of emergency power systems,

'bizarre' equipment failures are a common occurrence, and operator errors are endemic throughout the industry. Simple maintenance operations disrupt normal safety practices, as when valves that affect the water level in a reactor were accidentally shut off during the repair of a leaky tap in a laboratory. Sensitive pieces of safety equipment malfunction because 'they are frozen or burned or flooded or dirty or corroded or bumped or dropped or overpressurised or un-hinged or miscalibrated or miswired or guaranteed not to work because of bad initial design.'

It is obviously impossible to give details here of all the accidents in the Nugget File, but it is worth looking at a selection of them before going into more detail about the more serious American mishaps, ending with Three-Mile Island. Fortunately there is a wealth of material about this latter accident, from the Congressional hearings which took place afterwards, to a mountain of reports, both official and unofficial and an entire book.

What becomes obvious when you read the Nugget File is that all those accidents we are told cannot happen *do* happen and all those checks and safeguards which are supposed to stop operator error do *not* stop it – people being only human and therefore fallible. There is no reason to imagine from what we know of our own nuclear industry that the American experience is in any way unique.

San Clemente, California

On 9 September 1968, the AEC contacted Southern California Edison Company to discuss several matters of concern. It transpired that problems experienced at the San Onofre nuclear generating station should have been prevented through the early detection of signals pointing to potential trouble during pre-operational testing. In some cases, control instruments had become so useless that nobody any longer paid any attention to warning signals, signals which later proved to have indicated that there really was trouble in the system. The staff did not have sufficient ability to analyse anomalies in the neutron flux levels. Several reports on unusual plant behaviour appeared 'incomplete and exhibited poor analysis logic'. In some cases they had been withheld. It appeared that when he was most needed, the shift supervisor was rarely to be found in the control room. 'It is apparent,' said the report, 'that a safety system component had been inoperable for a period of *up to twenty months.*'

Haddam Neck, Connecticut

At the Connecticut Yankee plant in October 1968, all three diesel generators failed during a heat-removal operation. Two of them 'tripped' for reasons 'as yet unexplained' and the third overloaded, then failed too. The AEC expressed concern over this as the incident, it said, added weight to

> our recent statements in favour of independence within emergency power systems. If one dismisses as being incredible the possibility of two independent, random failures causing the initial trips, the only reasonable explanation is that the trips resulted from a single common cause. The point is that a truly independent system would have lost only one generator and not all three.

The incident, the AEC continued, also brought out the fallacy of a 'mechanistic approach in support of non-independent systems'. A mechanistic approach, according to Robert D. Pollard who edited the Nugget File for publication, involves analysing the system to detect all possible faults in design. When all the 'experts' agree that all possible faults have been eliminated, it is argued that a non-independent system is acceptable. 'Obviously,' said the AEC, 'there was at least one other potential fault which could involve all three generators and it did, and summarily negated our original conclusion that all faults had been considered.'

Radioactivity in the drinking-water

There is a report from April 1969 concerning an unidentified nuclear power station. Samples of water taken from a laboratory sink showed radioactivity levels above the normal background level. Further checking found radioactivity in a drinking fountain. Investigation led to the discovery of a hose connected from a well-water tap to a 3000-gallon radio-active-waste tank! The AEC's comment must have been the winner in the understatement-of-the-year competition: 'The coupling of a contaminated system with a potable water system is considered poor practice in general . . .'

Rocky Flats, Colorado

On 11 May 1969, a major fire occurred at the Rocky Flats plant operated by the AEC. The plant produces plutonium parts for nuclear weapons and is located about 21 miles north-west of Denver. The plutonium was handled inside glove-boxes which provided a means for working safely with plutonium while separating the operator from such hazardous material. The conveyor belts connecting the glove-boxes travelled down long, enclosed tunnels lined with plastic windows. In some cases, shielding both inside and outside the glove-boxes had, it transpired, been made from a laminate itself made from wood chips.

The exact cause of the fire is still not known, but whatever it was, it seems that plutonium in the form of small chips can spontaneously ignite. It appears to have done so and caused a storage cabinet, which was also constructed mostly of the woodchip laminate, to char and give off flammable gases which could have been ignited by the burning plutonium. Although prompt action was taken, the dense smoke, crowded conditions and presence of large quantities of combustible shielding material made the fire very difficult to fight. Water was not used at first for fear of it starting off a chain reaction leading to a meltdown. The firefighters first tried CO_2, and when this did not work, finally turned to water. It took four hours to bring the fire under control, with sporadic outbursts continuing all night.

The damage to the building was extensive and it was also heavily contaminated with plutonium. The AEC's final estimate of the financial loss because of the damage plus the cost of decontaminating the building was *$45 million*. This sum did not include the cost of trying to recover the still highly dangerous plutonium. Afterwards the AEC decided it ought to do further research on the burning of plutonium and of shielding materials and on the effect of water on burning plutonium.

Design error in an unidentified reactor

Checks on instrument wiring on a reactor in June 1969 revealed that an inherent design error existed. A single malfunction in the power supply could render six automatic shutdown circuits inoperable.

Humboldt Bay, California

An operational error resulted in a 'fire ball' when a large switch was opened at the Humboldt Bay nuclear plant. Because of improper backup, the main generator tripped out almost at once, closing down the nuclear reactor. This resulted in a whole series of mishaps leading to the automatic opening of relief valves in the primary system steamline and a consequent initial 400,000 lb/hour steam blowdown. Approximately five minutes later, the nuclear engineer ordered all the valves to be closed because he feared that the core would be uncovered.

An estimated 3500 gallons of water were lost from the reactor during the escape of steam, including 250 gallons from the core spray system which contains chromates and chlorides, and 1000 gallons of raw water from the core flooding system were introduced into the reactor vessel. It is thought that the water level fell to within six inches above the top of the core. The working limit is nine feet. The accident investigation report is full of comments to the effect that the various things that had gone wrong had been considered to be unlikely to happen, and that the entire set of circumstances which had occurred was considered to be a possibility 'so extremely low that detailed procedures to guide operations personnel had not been formulated'.

Savannah Nuclear Station, Galveston, Texas

This report was submitted in October 1970. When the primary coolant system for the reactor was being heated up, using reactor power, it was noted that the pressuriser spray isolation valve was in a closed position. (Water is sprayed into the pressuriser to limit the pressure increase in the reactor's cooling system.) Inspection showed that the valve's air-operator diaphragm had ruptured. This was duly repaired and the reactor was made critical again. The same thing happened again. It later appeared that the manual giving details on how to install the diaphragm was not very clear and *the diaphragm had been installed upside down*.

This gives a taste of the Nugget File which is crammed full of incidents involving faulty wiring, valves, generating equipment and so on, some due to poor design, others to poor implementation of those designs or to sheer cost-cutting or carelessness. For instance, in June 1973 the Maine Yankee Atomic Power Company requested AEC approval of a design change for its safety circuits. The outputs from all four instruments that were used to measure the power of the reactor and to provide input signals to the plant protection systems were connected together to provide an average power-level signal for a non-safety control system. The licensee wanted to do away with the interconnection between the four circuits. Yet experience at the plant had shown that failure of one instrument used to measure reactor power could lead to failure of all four instruments. Dr Hanauer sent a copy of this report to the Control Systems Branch of the AEC, saying that this was the supposedly 'good' separation of control and safety 'we were talking about', adding that 'some day we will all wake up'.

Operator error has included a technician disconnecting the horn used to signal the need for evacuation in order to service it, then forgetting to put it back together again and going away on holiday. During a shutdown period at another reactor, the decay heat-removal system failed to supply cooling water to the core for two hours because a technician performing a routine maintenance operation closed down the pump suction valve for a period while the system was in operation, causing the pump to become vapour bound. There was a specially prepared maintenance procedure expressly forbidding this valve to be closed without the consent of the control room supervisor but the technician had ignored it.

A low-power research reactor was operated for an hour with a radiation shielding plug left out. When the reactor reached full power, the supervisor asked the health physicist to make a radiation survey. He did not bother to do so straight away. About an hour later the supervisor noticed that the shielding plug had not been installed, although the reactor start-up checklist included the note: 'all shield plugs in place and locked'. After the mishap, the supervisor admitted that he had not checked to see if this had been done before signing the checklist.

Possibly the ultimate in operator bungling so far was at Brown's Ferry, Alabama, in March 1975, when two electricians sealing air leaks in a cable-spreading room right under the reactor control room of the nuclear power station, accidentally set light to the foam rubber they were inserting. This occurred because they were using an extremely sophisticated device to check for draughts – a naked candle-flame . . . After some delay the fire alarm was given but even then the control room staff carried on as usual for a vital sixteen minutes before taking any notice of it. By this time the fire had disabled many of the emergency systems including the emergency core-cooling system. A makeshift pump had to be rigged up to avoid the over-heating which could lead to a meltdown. The fire raged on for six hours before it was finally brought under control.

Waterford, Connecticut

One of the events often used by pro-nuclear apologists when thinking of something unlikely, to dumbfound critics, is that of a plane crash at a nuclear plant. If anyone brings this up, they are told the chances are virtually impossible. On 25 August 1972 a light plane crashed on the Millstone power station complex, the pilot having lost his way in a heavy fog. Fortunately the plane hit the transmission line and not the actual reactor core. However, it resulted in the disabling of the 27,600 volt electrical line which also meant it knocked out the transformer used to shut down the plant safely. The transformer remained out of order for eight hours. The crash also caused the loss of any outside telephone communication for over three hours.

The Idaho Falls accident

The United States' first major nuclear accident was an extremely macabre affair. It took place in one of the seventeen experimental nuclear reactors at the Atomic Energy Commission's military nuclear testing ground at Idaho Falls. On 3 January 1961 three young servicemen – John Byrnes, Richard McKinley and Richard Legg – were on duty at Stationary Low-power Reactor No. 1 (SL-1), a 3-megawatt prototype. It had been shut down for some time as work needed to be done on the instruments, and the control drive rods were, therefore, disconnected. The process which had to be carried out was a simple one which had been undertaken many times. The central control rod had to be lifted up 10 centimetres and then coupled to the remote driving mechanism.

Nobody knows what went wrong as nobody lived to tell the tale. Whatever it was, it was over in four seconds. It later transpired that the central control rod had been pulled right out of the core. The reasons given for this, or rather the surmises, vary from sheer ignorance to some kind of fooling around. An official AEC report suggested that the rod might have stuck and that two of the men then tried to lever it up manually; as they tugged at it, it suddenly freed itself and shot up not 10 centimetres but nearly 50.

With the withdrawal of the control rod the reactor core immediately went supercritical, overheating and boiling the fuel. There was an explosion of steam which blasted a solid slug of water right up through the pile cap. Legg and McKinley were killed outright, McKinley being impaled on the ceiling structure on a rod blown out of the control plug. Byrnes was knocked down by an enormous flash of radiation.

The automatic alarms went off and emergency rescue squads hurried to the scene, but before they reached anywhere near the site of the accident, their dose meters went right off the scale, showing 500 roentgens per hour – a lethal

69

dose. The level inside the reactor building was even higher, at 800 roentgens. In spite of this two members of the rescue team went inside and hauled out Byrnes, but it was far too late. He died in the ambulance on the way to hospital.

The bodies of Legg and McKinley had to be dismembered because some parts of them were intensely radioactive, and remote-control handling gear had to be used for this gruesome task. All three bodies were so radioactive that twenty days passed before it was considered safe to handle them for burial. In the case of Legg and McKinley, the most radioactive portions were buried in lead-lined canisters in lead-lined vaults. What portions remained, along with the unfortunate Byrnes, were buried in lead-lined coffins in the Arlington Military Cemetery, Washington. Fourteen other men, members of the rescue teams, received radiation doses of five roentgens or more during the rescue attempt. It was months before the level of radiation in the building fell sufficiently to permit anyone in to try and find out what had happened.

Postscript

On 17 May 1986, BBC 2 broadcast an American film *A New Way to Die*, which attempted to reconstruct what had happened during this accident and in which some of those involved were interviewed. It appeared that, contrary to reports at the time, there was some release of radioactivity into the atmosphere. Also that 791 people involved in the clean-up and rescue attempt received 'significant' doses of radioactivity even at a time when safety thresholds were higher than they are now. Some of these have now developed cancers of different kinds but the US Atomic Energy Commission are so far refusing to follow up and find all those involved.

As noted, the body impaled on the ceiling was very difficult to remove. When rescuers got it outside it was giving off 1500 roentgens of radiation an hour . . . The head, one arm and both legs had to be buried as high-level nuclear waste in a special box; only the trunk and one arm received normal burial and then it was wrapped in lead and put in a lead-lined coffin. Pathologists doing the autopsies on the bodies wore radiation suits with lead aprons and worked not with surgical instruments but with ordinary tools at the end of poles.

In the process of bringing out the bodies not only did the people doing it become contaminated but so did every vehicle, box or piece of equipment they touched. The ground around the plant and the public highway outside it were made radioactive, and those trying to clean it up became very frustrated as the more they tried to clean up the ground, the more the radiation spread.

It took eighteen months to clean up the reactor building and at first men had to work wearing protective suits for four hours at a time, during which period they actually went into the radioactive zone for only eight minutes. It took several relays of men just to loosen a simple nut and bolt.

It also transpired that some of those in charge had falsified the records of radiation doses to make them appear lower than they were. Finally, in discussing how the accident happened the idea was put forward that it was known that one of the men involved was suffering from severe emotional problems, had had a row with his wife, had had up to 'two fits of depression a week' and might well have removed the control rod as a bizarre suicide act.

The Detroit accident

There had been opposition from the local population right from the start to the proposal to build a nuclear power station on the shores of Lake Erie. Three million people lived within a 30-mile radius. It was an extremely ambitious project and it was supposed to be a showpiece. It proved a tough fight to get permission to build the reactor. The big unions in the United States are not noted for their radical tendencies but in this case the powerful United Auto Workers union led the principal trade union protest against the new reactor which was to be called the Fermi I, after the nuclear physicist Enrico Fermi. However, in spite of a hard-fought court case to prevent the construction of the plant, on 12 June 1961 Supreme Court Justice Brennan rendered the court's majority verdict in favour of granting the Edison Detroit Co. permission to go ahead. Justices Douglas and Black, however, not only registered their dissent but did so in extremely critical terms.

Things went wrong after the reactor went critical for the first time in 1963. It appeared to divide its time between being shut down altogether or working at only a fraction of its potential. The problems included the fuel swelling and distorting ('creeping' as it is called) because of intense radiation flux in the core, sodium corrosion in the core, problems with the handling of the fuel gear and trouble with the steam generators. After nearly three years the reactor had produced only a trickle of electricity, and that at vast expense.

However, by the beginning of October 1966 it was announced that now all was well and that any residual problems had been finally ironed out. On 4 October the operators gingerly started up the reactor again. The control rods were carefully lifted out of the core and the reactor simmered away on low power overnight. That part had gone off fine, so on 5 October it was decided to bring the reactor up to full power.

Then there was a valve malfunction. It took all morning to put that right, but after lunch the power level was brought up to 20 megawatts. Then a pump gave trouble and that had to be dealt with. Just before 3 p.m. the operator in charge noticed that a monitor was sending danger signals from the core and he switched over from automatic to manual control. The signals ceased and it was thought the signal had been caused by faulty instruments. The raising of power recommenced. Five minutes later, the danger signal showed again, and other instruments appeared to show that the rods had been withdrawn more than was normal and that there were unusually high temperatures in two parts of the core. Before anything else could be done, the radiation alarms went off and at 3.20 p.m., six scram rods were inserted to try and shut down the reactor. Operators tried desperately to find out where the radiation was coming from. Samples of the sodium coolant and the argon cover gas were found to be full of highly radioactive fissile products. The meaning was all too clear – part of the reactor core had actually melted. However, the operators had no idea how much of the core had melted, and whether or not it would slump into an even more critical mass, the fuel explode and Edison Detroit have first-hand experience of the 'China syndrome'.

No one was sure what to do next. Any attempt to enter the reactor with the remote-handling equipment might disturb the core still further. It was decided to do nothing hasty.

Later it was found that two pieces of metal had worked loose at the bottom of the reactor and had partially clogged the flow of the core coolant; the core assembly had overheated and a tiny part of it had melted, releasing radioactive gases. During the protracted row over whether the reactor should be built or not, a number of safety measures had been suggested, and at the very last minute it was decided to fit a safety device designed to disperse the molten core into sections in the event of a meltdown. This device consisted of six metal sheets in the form of a pyramid, placed beneath the core. Two of these had lifted and broken off under the pressure of the liquid sodium, jamming themselves across the bottom of the fuel elements and choking them off from their supply of coolant. The result was immediate overheating.

The operators should have shut down the plant at the first sign of trouble. In the subsequent enquiry it appeared that they were misled because the power of the reactor seemed to be dropping. The reason for this was that, as the fuel melted, it brought about a decrease in reactivity; the controller then misread the situation and raised the power level of the reactor to compensate for the fall. However, even when he detected that the fuel rods were in an abnormally high position he did nothing. He had still been running the reactor eleven minutes after the radiation alarms had sounded by which time parts of the core had started to melt. Only then did he finally close it down.

Walter Patterson quotes nuclear engineer Richard E. Webb on the Fermi I accident:

Had the reactor not been scrammed, or if the scram system had failed to function, a runaway-power situation could conceivably have ensued . . . to produce core meltdown and compaction. This in turn could have produced a severe nuclear excursion and explosion.

An excursion to China, perhaps?

However, even the serious nature of the accident did not stop the gung-ho approach of the operators who, four days later, held a 69th-birthday party in a conference room only one hundred feet away from the reactor core. It was for their boss, Walter Cisler, one of the most committed of nuclear enthusiasts. The Fermi I reactor was his prize project. During the preceding four days the party had been of a different kind, however. When the extent of the accident finally sank in, police and emergency services were alerted to prepare for an emergency mass evacuation of some *two million* people from the city of Detroit and its environs. Fairly large numbers of people were involved in these plans and stick by their story that such an alert was given. There is no official record of such an alert, though, and it is generally accepted that there was an official instruction to remove all traces of it from the records.

Six months passed before the extent of the damage could be ascertained and a full year before the cause of the accident was discovered. For months after it had happened, the operators were frightened that any attempt to discover either the extent of the damage or its cause would produce a nuclear reaction which would lead to a major explosion. It was assessed that such an explosion would be the equivalent of 1000 tons of TNT, which would certainly breach the reactor containment, releasing enough radioactivity to pollute an enormous area. One study carried out at the University of Michigan in which all known data were fed into a computer, suggested that at least 115,000 people would have been killed.

The Fermi I reactor stopped short of a complete meltdown, but this appears to have been largely a matter of luck. As Walter Patterson says:

One possibility was sardonically labelled 'the China syndrome'. The molten mass of highly reactive fuel, generating its own fierce heat and far beyond any hope of cooling or control, might sear its way through all containments and into the rock below the foundations of the reactor, melting, burning and exploding as it went, bound for China. The concomitant outpouring of radioactivity, assuming the

74

accident had opened a pathway to the surroundings, would make the locality a no-man's-land indefinitely.

It did not happen, however. Not quite.

Three-Mile Island: The night they nearly lost Pennsylvania

It is necessary to dwell at some length on this, the most notorious, American accident. Not only is it the best documented and investigated, it is also crucially relevant to our own nuclear programme – the pressurised-water reactor to be built at Sizewell is of virtually the same design. At the same time all the American nuclear utilities have abandoned the use of pressurised-water reactors following the Three-Mile Island accident. The information that follows is taken from a number of sources – from the Congressional hearings on the subject and the investigation, a series of articles in the *New Scientist*, and, most useful of all, from *Three-Mile Island – Thirty Minutes to Meltdown* by Daniel F. Ford. The book is still obtainable in the USA (it is published by Viking Press) but out of print in Britain. Daniel Ford is the former Executive Director of the Union of Concerned Scientists.

On 16 March 1979 (note the date), a Hollywood thriller opened at one of the main cinemas in New York. It was called *The China Syndrome* and it was an immediate box-office hit. It starred Jack Lemmon as the manager of a nuclear power station with a pressurised-water reactor, and Jane Fonda as the intrepid reporter from a local television station who uncovers the cover-up that follows an accident which almost led to a meltdown. The film was realistic: it showed instruments that were faulty or whose readings were disbelieved, components that had never been properly checked. It also showed the massive cover-up by everyone concerned, from the owners of the utility through to the state government and on to the federal government. Even the media complied with it, especially the local TV station whose reporter, Jane Fonda, had happened to be visiting the plant at the time, on a public relations trip. The meltdown having been narrowly avoided, Jack Lemmon was gunned down as he tried to tell a TV audience what had really happened and the film ended with our gallant girl hack trying to tell his story for him.

It went down well with those who saw it. The nuclear industry, which had seen previews, immediately rushed out statements to the effect that what had been portrayed could not happen. It was only a fairy story.

Just twelve days later on 28 March it did.

Three-Mile Island covers around 400 flat acres about 900 feet from the east bank of the Susquehanna River, ten miles south-east of the sizeable city of Harrisburg, the state capital of Pennsylvania. The west bank of the river is just over a mile away. Although lip service is paid to nuclear plants being built away from centres of population, when the Atomic Energy Commission gave the go-ahead for the Three-Mile Island plant there were some 621,000 people living within twenty miles of the site.

The island had been owned since the early part of the century by the General Public Utilities Company. The application to build a pressurised-water reactor nuclear power station there was filed on 1 May 1967. The station was to be operated by the Metropolitan Edison Company. A second unit was to be operated by the same company at Oyster Creek, New Jersey, but this ran into a lot of problems and it was decided, therefore, to build both PWRs on Three-Mile Island.

The AEC rushed the applications through, held only brief public hearings, and issued the permit for Unit 1 on 18 May 1968 and for Unit 2 on 4 November 1969. The AEC safety evaluator said he had been given 'reasonable assurances' that the plant would operate 'without undue risk to the health and safety of the public'. There was no real basis for such confidence as the AEC based its faith on the 'self-regulation' of companies rather than on thorough and independent checks and investigations. Unit 1 was completed in 1974 and was granted an operating licence by the AEC. Unit 2 was granted a licence by the Nuclear Regulatory Commission (NRC) which had, by that time, taken over the issuing of licences from the AEC. It was later revealed by the Union of Concerned Scientists that the private AEC files of Dr

Hanauer (he of the Nugget File) had expressed concern over possible safety factors at the plant as far back as 1969.

Unlike many other sites, Three-Mile Island did not provoke much hostile reaction. This was in part due to a massive, but non-aggressive and highly sophisticated, promotion campaign mounted by the Metropolitan Edison Company. It stressed not only the cast-iron safety of the plant but also all the new jobs that would come with its construction and the resultant benefits to the local economy. Like the media in *The China Syndrome* the local press accepted without question everything they were told about the new PWR. ON THREE-MILE ISLAND A NUCLEAR REACTOR IS NOTHING TO GET STEAMED UP ABOUT ran a headline in the Harrisburg *Evening News* of 14 January 1969. The author of the piece said that one of the main ingredients to be used at the plant was common-or-garden boric acid, just what you use in an eyewash.

The main problem during the construction phase was the frightening rising costs – always a spectre which haunts the nuclear industry. Unit 1 was supposed to have cost $110 million but this had risen to $400 million by the time it was completed in 1974. Unit 2, supposed to cost $130 million, finally cost a staggering $700 million. It was, in part, these high costs which led to cost-cutting during the operation of the power station. One way to cut costs is to keep the reactor running and on stream almost continually, as shutting it down leaves the plant idle and vastly increases the cost of electricity. So the idea is to shut down the plant as little as possible and then only for refuelling. This also encourages those running such a plant to delay any repairs as long as possible, preferably until the next time it needs refuelling or, if the AEC or NRC permits, for even longer than that if repairs would delay getting the reactor back on-stream again. No plant operator would want a reactor out of service for any appreciable length of time while, for instance, comprehensive safety checks were made or new safety systems installed.

According to Daniel Ford, Metropolitan Edison had persuaded the federal safety officials that adequate checks could be carried out just as well while the reactor was operating, even though this is the equivalent of saying that it is possible to perform major equipment checks or carry out maintenance on an aircraft in flight. One of the many major risks this attitude poses is the possible failure to return equipment to service or to restore the plant to its normal condition after tasks are completed – for example, a failure to reopen valves that have been closed or to restore power that has been shut off. Also, trying to carry out maintenance work while the reactor was running might, in itself, cause a serious accident. Another way of getting around adequate safety and maintenance checks was by classifying the equipment concerned as 'non safety-related components'. Metropolitan Edison did all this and more.

As early as October 1977, a faulty piece of equipment had been discovered. Water entering the reactor from the main feedwater system had to pass through special tanks known as 'polishers'. They filtered the water for impurities through special filters made up of thousands of tiny resin beads. There were eight polishers, only seven actually being needed while the reactor was running. Every twenty-eight days, the beads had to be changed for new clean ones, and sludge had to be cleaned out of the bottom of the polisher tank. These were routine measures. It was later found that the polishers were exempt from federal safety rules, that plant officials did not even have accurate engineering drawings for the Unit 2 polisher system, that those they did have showed valves in the wrong places, improperly identified components and had air-line positions and interconnections incorrectly displayed. Also missing were other types of useful drawings which, according to Daniel Ford, showed how the polishers related to other plant systems and equipment. It was also to transpire that there were long gaps between cleaning out the sludge from the tanks and replacing the beads, and that on numerous occasions when this was done, there had been serious problems. No attempt was made to really overcome them, yet it had been known for seventeen months before the accident that a blockage in the system could cause an accident.

On 19 October 1977, a maintenance engineer cleaning out the resin beads from Polisher 2 found a water leak, and this was followed by the unexpected closure of a set of valves in the system, cutting off the main feedwater system completely. Fortunately, the Unit 2 reactor was not working at the time.

An internal memo later noted that if it had been running 'the unit would have been placed in a severe transient [that is, abnormal] condition.' The memo recommended nine safety measures to ensure it did not happen again. All were rejected out of hand in a memo from R. J. Toole, the director of the start-up operations, who wrote 'no further action required' on a memo in reply.

On 12 May 1978 the valves again slammed shut and cut off the water supply system. Again the operators were highly fortunate, for the reactor was not running. Again the plant operator decided to do nothing although this time the shift supervisor, William Zewe, wrote a memo on 15 May saying 'it's time to really do something about this problem before a very serious accident occurs.' He suggested a means whereby a fast-acting automatic by-pass system could be installed which would keep the water running in the event that the valves closed again. Nothing was done.

So Unit 2 had been operating with a known and documented history of equipment faults for two years, a situation known to a management which had deliberately ignored the faults. Daniel Ford draws attention, in his book, to a similar accident noted in the Nugget File, at the Zion Nuclear Power Station in Zion, Illinois, on 12 July 1977. Dr Hanauer, in an internal NRC memorandum, said the accident showed 'obvious gross management deficiency' made worse by an 'unsafe' Westinghouse design for the plant's pressurised-water reactor. That accident was caused by technicians who, checking some of the safety-system circuits while preparing to restart the reactor after a brief shutdown, fed thirty-one 'dummy' instrument signals to the control room, which made it look as though the reactor had an adequate water supply when, in fact, it was actually losing water through a drainpipe. The plant safety systems designed to rectify such a fault did not work as they too had received false instrument signals. In fact, all the safety equipment designed to control an accident of this kind simultaneously failed to work. Forty minutes after thousands of gallons of coolant water had rained from the reactor, the plant operators finally realised something had gone wrong and halted it in time. Dr Hanauer warned that it could happen again, and urged a review of all pressurised-water reactors, Westinghouse and others.

As well as faulty equipment, the staff at Three-Mile Island, as at other nuclear plants, left much to be desired. No one on duty when the accident occurred was a qualified nuclear engineer or even a college graduate. Nobody had ever been trained in what to do in the event of a complicated nuclear accident. It was not necessary under the NRC regulations. Operators were taught merely how to carry out routine procedures. Nor had the plant supervisors any training for complex mishaps. Those on duty at the time of the accident included two ex-naval engineers who had experience with naval nuclear reactors, and William Zewe, the same shift supervisor who had called for a by-pass system less than 11 months earlier. There were also a number of maintenance men carrying out routine tasks, who were not required to have any special licences or qualifications nor to attend any training programmes.

Later, the head of the Presidential Commission into the Three-Mile Island accident, John G. Kemeny, was to say: 'Given what we have found out about the Nuclear Regulatory Commission, the utilities and the training of operators, we feel that even though this whole accident could have been prevented, an accident like that at Three-Mile Island was eventually inevitable.' When a set of mishaps similar to the two previous ones occurred on 28 March 1979, Metropolitan Edison were not so lucky: Unit 2 was operating virtually flat out, at 97 per cent capacity.

First, a small pipe leading from one of the eight polishers became clogged. The polishers were themselves being cleaned, the sludge removed and new resin beads put in. Just before 4 a.m., the Unit 2 shift foreman checked how the work on the blocked water-pipe was going. Suddenly – just as in the prophetic *China Syndrome* – he heard a loud, thundering noise 'like a couple of freight trains'. Over the loudspeaker came the words *Turbine trip, reactor trip*. The maintenance men had accidentally blocked the flow of water to the main feedwater system, forcing the turbine and reactor to shut down. The trip took place at thirty-seven seconds after 4 a.m.

Immediately, emergency procedures (supposed to be

failsafe) were activated. The devices were linked to the electronic alert system and were supposed to trigger off remedial action in the event of abnormal circumstances or signs of trouble, including any interruption of the main feedwater system. In addition there were three emergency pumps designed to start up in the event of a malfunction. But it all just kept on going wrong.

The nuclear reactor holding the uranium fuel reacted immediately to the shutdown of the feedwater system. The pressure of the coolant water inside it increased rapidly since it was still being heated by the uranium. A surge of pressure blew open a relief valve, one that should have closed after a few seconds. It stuck open. Coolant water began to rush out of the reactor at the rate of 220 gallons a minute.

This had happened because someone had shut off two valves that carried water from the emergency pumps into the cooling system. As a result, the three emergency pumps did not work. Possibly, it was thought later, the valves had not been reopened after a testing procedure carried out a few days earlier.

This resulted in the supposedly 'incredible' multiple safety-system failure that the nuclear industry had said was virtually impossible. There were, however, three more pumps connected to a special emergency reservoir capable of resupplying the reactor with a thousand gallons of water a minute, more than was needed to replace the present drainage. Two minutes after the accident, the pumps were automatically turned on, but the reactor operators in the control room who were monitoring all the instruments shut them off four minutes after the accident began. They quite simply did not believe what they saw on the monitor screens and deliberately over-rode the plant's own safety back-up equipment. They then compounded their error by opening a pipe to remove even more water from the reactor, doubling the amount of coolant lost.

The operators, trying to cope with an emergency for which they were quite untrained, had taken the instrument readings to mean the reactor had *too much* water, not too little. They did not know that a valve was stuck open. It was to remain open for two hours and twenty minutes, until the supervisor of the morning shift arrived for work and guessed what had happened. There were no gauges to tell operators how much water there was in the reactor; they just had to guess at it by monitoring the amount in another tank linked to the reactor's cooling system. Since their instruments told them that the other tank was full, they assumed the reactor was full as well.

Five minutes after the failure of the main feedwater system the reactor, no longer cooled down by water, began to destroy itself, torn apart by its own enormous energy. The water which remained inside turned to steam, which gradually expanded and knocked out the reactor's control rods thus finally preventing any possible cooling. There then followed a sequence of instrument, equipment and computer failures. 'It seemed to go on and on, surprise after surprise', said radiation protection supervisor Thomas Mulleavy afterwards.

At 7.24 a.m., station manager Gary Miller declared a 'General Emergency', the first ever at an American nuclear plant. For sixteen hours the uranium fuel remained inadequately cooled. The fuel rods overheated, swelled and then ruptured. About a third of the core was reduced to rubble, and large amounts of radioactivity were released from the fuel rods and escaped through the open valve into the building housing the reactor. This became lethally radioactive. Thousands of gallons of radioactive water were also accidentally pumped from the reactor building into a less-than-secure neighbouring building.

Throughout the day, officials told the public that there was no need for alarm, not the slightest threat from radiation. Every effort was expended to make it seem as if nothing much had happened – everything was under control. A statement to Congress by Joseph Hendry, the chairman of the Nuclear Regulatory Commission, on 29 May typified all this. He said that all that had happened was that there were some 'minor' cracks in about 1 per cent of the reactor's fuel rods; there was no serious 'ongoing problem'. The high radiation levels shown in the reactor building were merely an 'oddball instrument error'.

Two days after the start of the accident, on 30 March, those involved finally understood the horrendous magnitude of the disaster. It became clear that a large number of fuel rods were damaged. The NRC officials said they were 'dumbfounded' at the number of equipment failures, and concluded that the damage to the rods might make it hard to control the reactor.

Next came the news that radioactive gases had been released from Unit 2 and were being carried swiftly downwind to the neighbouring towns. Also it was concluded that a large, growing and potentially explosive 'hydrogen bubble' had formed inside the reactor, giving cause for real concern that there might be a large blow-out of radioactive material over a wide area.

It is reliably estimated by experts that the reactor itself came within thirty minutes of a full meltdown.

Before the full extent of the crises was finally – and publicly – admitted there had been large releases of Xenon-133 gas into the atmosphere. Readings above the plant showed radioactivity as high as 1200 millirem. Forty thousand gallons of low-level waste water had also been jettisoned into the Susquehanna River. Contingency plans were drawn up to start evacuating the area.

Nobody knew what to do about the hydrogen bubble, estimated at a size of about 1800 cubic feet. By Friday the amount of hydrogen in the bubble was estimated at 4 per cent. It was thought that when it reached ten per cent it would blow up, with the possibility of a complete meltdown following. 'The bubble is a complete surprise,' said Dr Levine, Director of the Thermal Reactor Safety Division of the Brookhaven National Laboratory. Three-Mile Island was just full of surprises.

By Monday, however, the bubble was beginning to decrease in size and the staff and owners of Three-Mile Island felt overwhelming relief. On the same day, the Union of Concerned Scientists released papers showing that the owners had been aware of the recurrent malfunctions in their plant and that workers had encountered similar problems at a similar reactor in Sacramento seven months earlier. Nothing should have come as a surprise.

The owners and operators of Three-Mile Island were in luck. Gradually the hydrogen bubble reduced in size and the danger of a full-scale meltdown receded. Five days after the start of the emergency it was declared to be over.

Afterwards it was said that Three-Mile Island was largely a media scare, a story hyped up and made more than it was by an overly melodramatic press. However, the Presidential Commission into the accident repudiated this, with one or two exceptions. One member of the Commission, Professor Carolyn Lewis of Columbia University, who lectures in media studies, said:

> There have been charges that in its coverage of the Three-Mile Island accident, the media was sensational. We found in our research and analysis of major national and local news coverage that the charge is basically unfounded. We found, in fact, that it reported more reassuring statements than alarming statements in its coverage. And we found that, where the press was reporting alarming statements, it was merely reflecting the alarm of its sources.

How the press got on to it at all again echoes *The China Syndrome*. The story was actually broken by the Harrisburg pop music station WKBO. A young reporter monitoring traffic information heard calls going out for a massive mobilisation of police and firefighters. He told the station's news editor who rang the Three-Mile Island plant to find out what was happening, and he was inadvertently put through to the control room where he was told nobody could talk to him as they had a big problem. He then rang the head office of Metropolitan Edison and was told that there was a full-scale general emergency. When he asked what that meant, he was told it was just a 'red tape' kind of thing which was required by the NRC under certain circumstances.

Two days after the start of the accident, urgent conferences had reached right up to President Carter in the White House. The federal government's evacuation plans were complete, down to the provision of food and shelter for the tens of thousands of evacuees. They also tried to find a drug manufacturer who could supply a massive amount of potassium iodate, which is known to help prevent thyroid cancer from the highly dangerous iodine-131 which attacks the thyroid gland. Local pharmacists could not cope with the number of requests, and arrangements were made to get the

Mallinckrodt Chemical Corporation to manufacture an emergency supply. All employees were called in, and they worked day and night over the weekend producing the drug. Then they ran out of bottles. Finally, the US Air Force flew in the deliveries of the drug to Harrisburg but the Three-Mile Island jinx was still at work: many of the bottles were found to leak, to be unlabelled, or unprovided with droppers; some were just plain dirty, not having been washed, and had polluted the drug inside. The state government are supposed to keep adequate stocks of potassium iodate in the event of a nuclear accident. The state governor, Dick Thornby, ordered the closure of all schools and advised pregnant women and all children within a five-mile radius to leave the area immediately. Plans were put in hand to evacuate no fewer than 165,000 people living within a 10-mile radius. Some 140,000 of them did not wait: they just took to the roads and fled of their own accord, clogging the highways in their wild desire to escape.

Nobody came out well from it. The final report of the Presidential investigating team ripped apart the power utilities, the Nuclear Regulatory Commission and everyone else for 'being unable to provide an acceptable level of safety in nuclear power.'

We heard the word 'mind-set' over and over again in our hearings [said Chairman Kemeny] and this tells us something about the attitudes that led to the accident. The first is that the Nuclear Regulatory Commission and the portion of the industry that we examined seemed to be hypnotised by their equipment. Indeed we found that, overall, their equipment was very good, although some could be improved. But we are convinced that if the equipment had been the only problem, we wouldn't be sitting here today.

The Presidential Commission made four key recommendations: (1) there should be periodic renewal of operating licences, a process to be conducted once every four or five years and subject to public hearings; (2) all future nuclear power stations should be sited away from large population centres; (3) the emergency response procedures must be improved to allay the fear and confusion that followed the early days of the Three-Mile Island accident; and (4) there should be a revamping of the display panels in control rooms so that the operators respond more efficiently to emergencies. At one point in the TMI accident over 100 alarms were ringing simultaneously, adding to the general confusion.

To date none of these recommendations appears to have been acted upon.

The aftermath of the accident seems to show that few people have learned anything from it. In April 1979, it was estimated that the containment building was 'bathing in a radiation level of up to 30,000 rems', a level far above the 500-rem lethal dose. Efforts to clean up the plant caused a series of leaks and spills resulting in considerable anxiety among the local population.

In March 1980, the team sent to inspect the cleaning-up operation reported more problems to the Nuclear Regulatory Commission. It appeared that the monitoring instruments inside the damaged Unit 2 reactor building were going out of action one after the other. It was thus becoming increasingly difficult to know what was happening. The area was still far too dangerous for anyone to go into it. By this time, the NRC were becoming very worried about the slow pace of the cleaning-up operation, fearing that the longer it went on, the more the plant would deteriorate. There were still huge amounts of radioactive krypton-85 gas floating around the reactor core, and this might be accidentally released.

Before any effort could be made to get rid of the gas, the experts involved were told that they had to complete an environmental impact survey, a long process which requires forecasts of any possible short- or long-term hazards. When the clean-up team reported this to the NRC, one of the commissioners blew a fuse and said: 'You can't sit around here and calculate environmental impact while we have a disaster waiting to happen in central Pennsylvania.' He went on to say that somehow they should have got inside the containment building months before.

The NRC wanted to release the radioactive gas into the atmosphere over a period of a few months, saying that the quantities would be so tiny at any one time that there would be no risk. The wrangles over this went on for a considerable time, hampered by the fact that just before the end of his term of office, President Carter sacked the chairman of the NRC.

So matters were allowed to continue as they were. In March 1982, members of the House of Representatives visited the TMI site to see what was happening. It appeared, said Harold Jackson in a report in the *Guardian* on 29 March 1982, that the alarm bells set off by the accident were still tolling for both the owners of the plant, General Public Utilities, and its operators, Metropolitan Edison, and indeed for the whole US nuclear industry. At that point the estimated cost of cleaning up Three-Mile Island was a thousand million dollars. Most of the 500,000 gallons of radioactive water from the containment building had been swilled out, but funds had begun to run low. The building was still grossly contaminated, and nobody knew what to do about the reactor core or what would be found inside.

Also there were now considerable problems with Unit 1, which had remained shut down since the accident in Unit 2. The NRC gave permission in 1982 to restart it but was overruled after a court case. Then it was found that Unit 1's steam generator was badly corroded and would take at least a year to repair. It turned out that this problem affects all pressurised-water reactors and results from a hitherto unsuspected chemical reaction between the radioactive core-cooling water and the steel piping carrying it. Of the 72 reactors in the US, 49 are PWRs and face this problem.

Then an undergraduate at Cornell University, John Stephens, came up with an even more alarming finding about this chemical corrosion. He discovered that one of the elements added to strengthen the steel piping turns into highly radioactive niobum-194 which emits powerful gamma rays and has a half-life of 20,300 years. According to Harold Jackson this means that when a power station has to be dismantled at the end of its useful life, 'there is a far greater problem about radioactive waste than had been thought.' There have been some fairly frightening calculations of the cost of dismantling, based on a waste-storage period of 30 years. For the average plant, it works out at about one hundred million dollars at 1978 prices and the waste storage accounts for two-thirds of that. 'What,' asks Jackson, 'is the price likely to be if the residue has to be kept safe 700 times longer?'

By July 1983, the picture at Three-Mile Island looked, if anything, even gloomier. The first television inspection of the rods found there had been greater danger than had even been thought. A meltdown had been very narrowly avoided indeed. The head of the inspection group, William Hamilton, said the inspection revealed that the uranium oxide fuel itself had melted. For this to happen the temperature must have reached at least 1250°F, 32 per cent higher than had previously been assumed. It had virtually reached the point at which the highly radioactive molten mass could have destroyed its container and anything else in its path. At the peak of the accident, it is estimated that the temperature was 3900°F, enough to melt the protective metal cladding on the fuel rods. The report estimated that 90 per cent of them had ruptures – against the 1 per cent so confidently predicted by the NRC at the time of the accident.

In addition, it was found that 226 minutes from the start of the accident a large section of the core had slumped downwards, and the fuel elements were badly damaged. Three-Mile Island had come within an ace of a fully blown 'China syndrome'.

Writs were flying all over the place. In January 1983 an out-of-court settlement of $37 million was paid by Bechtel, the manufacturers of the TMI equipment and the PWR. Metropolitan Edison said direct damage was estimated at at least a thousand million dollars and said it had already spent three hundred million on the clean-up. Another three thousand million dollars had been lost as the plant could not generate electricity. Metropolitan Edison was trying to prove that the manufacturers of the equipment were negligent: they were counter-suing saying that the plant had been incorrectly operated. The utility was also trying to sue the Nuclear Regulatory Commission for four thousand million dollars, claiming it had never warned them of safety hazards . . . At the time of writing, most of these suits are still unresolved.

On 14 April 1983, the plant was again the centre of a controversy. Two engineers swore affidavits to the effect that the clean-up operation designed to try and remove the damaged uranium fuel from the reactor was careless and sloppy. 'The present mentality on the island emphasises short cuts, expedience and disdain for professional safety standards,' said Edwin Gishel, engineering director for site operations, in an affidavit to his employer. Richard Parks, an engineer with the Bechtel Corporation, which built the plant and was therefore a prime contractor for the clean-up, said 'the operation is disorganised and, at times, irresponsible. There is a serious lack of co-ordination between Bechtel, the General Public Utilities, the sub-contractor and the federal agencies involved here.' For his pains, Bechtel sacked Parks.

To date, matters have only marginally improved. Unit 2 still poses a hazard. And what of the hazards to health?

There are none, say almost all concerned. Dozens of scientists have been wheeled out to say that there is no cause for concern; nobody has, nor will, suffer as a result of the Three-Mile Island accident – a tall order since cancers take anything from fifteen to twenty years to show up. But not everyone agrees.

In an interview in the *New Scientist* on 24 April 1980, Dr Ernest Sternglass, Professor of Radiation Physics at the University of Pittsburgh School of Medicine, disagreed with the experts. He claims the fallout released during the Three-Mile Island accident will turn out to produce the largest death toll ever to result from an industrial accident. He says the fallout was equivalent to that from a major nuclear test in the atmosphere. He discounts the readings on the monitoring badges of those involved, which showed 80 millirems, saying that because that was the average this meant susceptible organs, such as the foetal thyroid gland, might have absorbed anything from 10 to 100 times that dose.

He began to study the perinatal death rate in Pennsylvania and nearby states as given in the US *Monthly Vital Statistics*. He found beyond a shadow of doubt that there had been a dramatic increase in the number of infant deaths after the accident in areas within the path of the wind carrying the plume of radioactivity. In Pennsylvania, for example, the infant mortality rate rose by an unprecedented 92 per cent in the summer after the accident, the time when the perinatal death rate is usually at its lowest. By September the situation had returned to normal. During those four months there had been 240 baby deaths above the average, altering Pennsylvania's position from one of the lowest in the US perinatal death league to the highest east of the Mississippi. Sternglass .assigned one cause of this to the radioactive iodine-131 released during the first two days of the accident. Even minute quantities of this will damage the foetal thyroid.

Dismissing criticism that he cannot prove beyond all shadow of doubt the cause of the deaths, he pointed out that the causal factor behind cholera outbreaks remained unproven for years, as did that between cigarettes and lung cancer. He says he found clinical proof of the mechanism which caused the deaths 'right here in Three-Mile Island'. An independent study carried out against the wishes of the state government in Pennsylvania showed that infants in the area have a four-fold increase in hypothyroidism (i.e. abnormally low thyroid function). This corroborates the idea that babies were dying not because of major radiation exposure but because even a slight retardation of the thyroid function inhibits growth so that babies born full term are not really ready for life. He visited the Magee Women's Hospital in Pittsburgh and hospitals in Harrisburgh and went through every single paediatric record and found 'that they all died not of infections or gross congenital defects; they died specifically of prematurity and respiratory disease at birth, or both, which is exactly what I predicted.' Although his ideas are dismissed by pro-nuclear scientists, even an Atomic Energy Commission scrutiny, apart from picking up some minor errors, could not fault his research.

This was not the end of the story. On 2 October 1985, the undamaged Unit 1 at Three-Mile Island was started up again in the teeth of almost universal protest. Litigation had been carried on to the bitter end, but the private owners of the plant had been assisted by the appointment to the US Supreme Court, during the intervening years, of judges by the pro-nuclear Reagan administration. Protestors included not only most local residents, the Union of Concerned Scientists and anti-nuclear lobbyists but also the Republican governor and senators of the state of Pennsylvania. However, the reopening of Three-Mile Island was crucial to the credibility of the nuclear industry.

The owners of the plant have assured everybody that, this time, it will be all right. There had been big modifications, a change of management. There was no cause for alarm.

The sceptics remain unconvinced. In April of that year the Nuclear Regulatory Commission made an unannounced visit to another nuclear power station, this time the Davis-Besse plant in Oak Harbor, Ohio. When they visited one crucial part of the plant, they found an unlicensed operator fast asleep. Two months later, on 9 June 1985, a series of events began in the room where they had discovered the sleeper. Both the main pump controlling the reactor's cooling system and then the back-up pump failed. Against all the NRC rules, both drew their power from the same source. After that, events closely followed the Three-Mile Island incident. The loss of pumping capacity and coolant resulted in the failure of fourteen other pieces of equipment and two steam generators virtually boiled dry. Chaos and panic reigned again just as at Three-Mile Island. In the resultant pandemonium the engineers controlling the plant pushed the wrong set of buttons at least once and only managed to rectify their mistake by rushing out of the control room and getting the auxiliary pump restarted, according to Harold Jackson in the *Guardian* on 4 October 1985.

It had all the features of the Three-Mile Island disaster. It took twelve minutes before the auxiliary pump could be started again; the Three-Mile Island reactor had taken just eighteen to get out of control. On 2 October 1985, Mr James Asseltine of the NRC told a Congressional hearing that there was still no rule requiring a plant to install pumps powered by different power supplies. The accident at Davis-Besse – which was eventually attributed to 'lack of attention to detail' – was the eighth major incident in that complex in 1985 alone.

Congressman Edward Mankey, chairman of the House sub-committee studying the accident, said the whole episode raised serious questions of 'whether the Nuclear Regulatory Commission is guilty of malpractices', and asked why the NRC had dragged its feet on ensuring that all nuclear power stations had alternative power supplies during the six years since Three-Mile Island. In fact, it was ten years – 1975 – since the Commission had recommended that all pressurised-water reactors should have alternative power supplies.

In an effort to restore public confidence in the nuclear industry in general and PWRs in particular, various tests have been carried out to find out what might happen in given sets of circumstances. On 9 July 1985, the US Department of Energy test centre in Idaho decided to try and repeat what happened at Three-Mile Island on a small scale. It shut off the water supply to a small experimental reactor to study the result. Within thirty minutes they had to stop the experiment: the core had partially melted. No conclusions have so far been reached about the experiment because what is left of the core and the reactor is far too radioactive for anybody to go near it. It is, metaphorically, just down the road from Pennsylvania.

Three-Mile Island was supposed to be an 'incredible' event according to experts – the accident which could not happen. Presumably the series of mishaps at Davis-Besse are considered incredible too, but they happened all the same. Unit 2 at Three-Mile Island came within thirty minutes of a melt-down only three months after it became fully commercially operational. By relying on nuclear power, as Daniel Ford points out in his book, the USA now achieves 200 reactor years about every three years. The obvious implication is that if more and more nuclear power stations are built, then the chances of a serious accident somewhere are reduced to odds of about one every three years.

Shortly before Three-Mile Island's Unit 1 started up again, a spokesman for the Presidential Commission that looked into the accident expressed concern over the short memories of the American public and thought this was the reason why so little pressure had been brought to bear to increase safety measures. 'People worried about the Americans held hostage in Iran,' he said, 'but they have overlooked the fact that they, too, are hostages to the nuclear plants operating around the country. No one would question whether there will be another accident. It is merely a matter of when.'

Gore, Oklahoma

On 4 January 1986 an accident occurred at the Kerr-McGee company's nuclear-fuel processing plant in Gore, Oklahoma, which was later described by US commentators as the worst nuclear accident in the United States since Three-Mile Island.

Something of the history of Kerr-McGee will be told in Chapter 10, for the company became notorious following the mystery death of Karen Silkwood who was on her way to meet a reporter with proof of lax safety precautions at the Kerr-McGee plant at Crescent in Oklahoma. The Gore plant, like that at Crescent, had a long history of mishaps of various kinds, and had received considerable publicity for bending a variety of regulations over a period of ten years. There had been a number of leaks of radioactive material.

On 4 January a tank packed with 14 tonnes of uranium ruptured. A plume of white smoke shot into the air above the factory as the hot gas inside the tank reacted with the cold air outside. Brisk winds of about 30 mph helped disperse the radioactive plume over a wide area.

One 25-year-old man, James Harrison, died almost immediately from toxic chemical exposure. He had hydrofluoric acid burns (the acid used in that particular process), to the face, lungs and upper body. Some one hundred other people – some workers at the plant, the rest local residents – had to be rushed to hospital for treatment, many with breathing difficulties. Officials of the Nuclear Regulatory Commission – who had already been criticised for their attitude to Kerr-McGee in not being sufficiently stringent about insisting on better safety standards – immediately played down any danger saying it was 'more of a chemical problem than a radiation problem'.

A little later, a Kerr-McGee spokesman said the leak had sent radioactive gases into the air but there was no danger. However, the local authorities took the precaution of closing off all the roads in the area.

On 11 January the NRC announced that the workers at Kerr-McGee had not recognised the dangers of overfilling the flask and then overheating the chemical storage tank, which burst, the contents then breaking down into uranyl-fluoride and hydrofluoric acid. It was also revealed that Kerr-McGee had failed to draw up any new evacuation plans for chemical or nuclear accidents since 1972, when a previous accident had injured an employee. There were no public sirens or emergency drills for local residents, either. The 14-tonne tank had no alarms or safety valves and when questioned afterwards local people said they had very little idea of what the plant actually produced. The inquiry continues.

Chapter 4

Britain Without a Nugget File

Unhappily Britain has no Nugget File. What we have to rely on is what has been gleaned, leaked (in the sense of a leak of information) or, more rarely, published about the British nuclear power programme's mishaps before 1976. After 1976, following a serious unreported accident at the British Nuclear Fuels plant at Windscale in Cumbria, the then Energy Secretary Tony Benn ordered that all such incidents/accidents had to be reported to the government and to the public. We will look in detail at Windscale in the following chapter: there have been so many mishaps, incidents, accidents at Windscale – 300 from 1950 to 1985 – that it must have a chapter to itself. What follows is a brief look at some of the problems which have hit the rest of the nuclear industry.

The first thing that is obvious is the total certainty that pervades all the publicity material issued by the various bodies connected with the nuclear industry, whether they are discussing reliability, economics or possible hazards. There is never any suggestion that they might be wrong.

We do not yet have all that many nuclear power stations, but there is hardly one which has not been hit by faults or which has not spent considerable periods of time out of service.

It is unbelievable to imagine that, if our coal- and oil-fired stations had broken down so often, been taken out of commission so frequently and had possibly come so near to hazardous accidents, we would not have been assured over and over again that the risk and expense involved was just not worth it. Not so with the British nuclear power industry. Other criteria appear to apply.

The first major wave of reactors were the 'Magnox' reactors and these are at Sizewell A in Suffolk, Bradwell in Essex,

95

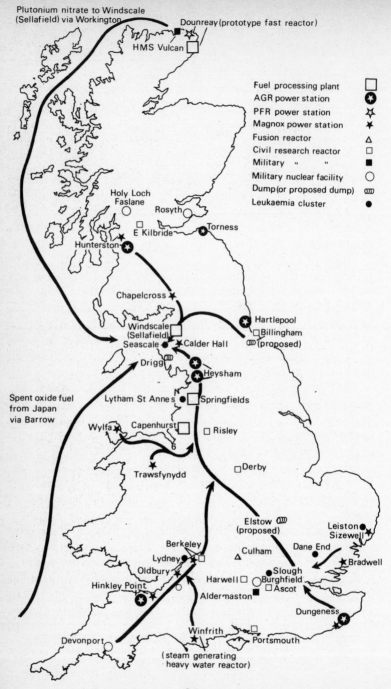

Plutonium nitrate to Windscale
(Sellafield) via Workington

Dounreay (prototype fast reactor)

HMS Vulcan

Fuel processing plant ▫
AGR power station ✪
PFR power station ✫
Magnox power station ★
Fusion reactor △
Civil research reactor ▫
Military   "   " ■
Military nuclear facility ○
Dump (or proposed dump) ⬭
Leukaemia cluster ●

Holy Loch
Faslane

Rosyth

E Kilbride

Torness

Hunterston

Chapelcross

Windscale
(Sellafield)
Seascale

Hartlepool

Billingham

(proposed)

Calder Hall

Drigg

Heysham

Spent oxide fuel
from Japan
via Barrow

Lytham St Annes

Springfields

Wylfa

Capenhurst

Risley

6

Derby

Trawsfynydd

Elstow
(proposed)

Leiston
Sizewell

Culham

Dane End

Bradwell

Berkeley

Lydney

Oldbury

Slough

Harwell

Burghfield

Ascot

Hinkley Point

Aldermaston

Dungeness

Winfrith

Portsmouth

Devonport

(steam generating
heavy water reactor)

96

Dungeness A in Kent, Winfrith in Dorset, Oldbury-on-Severn near Bristol, Berkeley in Gloucestershire, Trawsfynydd in North Wales, Wylfa on Anglesey, Calder Hall (part of the Windscale complex) in Cumbria, Hinkley Point A in Somerset, Chapel Cross and Hunterston A in Strathclyde. The next era produced the advanced gas-cooled reactors, at Torness near Loch Ness, Hartlepool in Cleveland, Dungeness B, Hinkley Point B, Heysham in Lancashire, and Hunterston B. There is also a prototype fast-breeder reactor at Dounreay in the far north of Scotland. There are, of course, other nuclear complexes, mainly concerned with weaponry.

Let us look at just some of the mishaps which have plagued Britain's nuclear power programme. What has happened in the USA is certainly not unique – it is just better documented.

The Magnox reactors

All the Magnox stations have spent time out of service and this has proved extremely costly. They have all been bugged by cracks and corrosion, the cracks appearing, in most cases, in welds in their cooling systems. The load factor of all of them – that is, the amount of energy they can produce – has had to be continually downrated.

Wylfa on Anglesey was the last of the Magnox stations to be built and it was confidently announced that all its problems would have been ironed out. It started up in 1971 and almost immediately ran into trouble with its boilers. In 1977, it had to be shut down for six months while a large team of workers carried out repairs inside the reactor pressure vessel itself.

Bradwell's two Magnox reactors were out of commission for over a year from February 1980 when cracks were found in the welding in the gas-cooling circuits. The cracks were hard to find (and had probably been there since the station started up 18 years previously) and were costly and difficult to put right. During the same period the two reactors at Dungeness A had to be closed down for the same reason, and in 1982 it was estimated that the cost of having these two nuclear power stations closed down at the same time came to something around £1 million a week in alternative power supplies.

However, it was only in November 1982 that it was admitted that there had been a shutdown of part of Sizewell A, which since June 1981 had cost the CEGB £16,500 a day. At that stage it was estimated that the reactor would be returned to full use by the summer of 1983 and the total bill for replacement power sources would be around £11.5 million. There was, said the CEGB, no health hazard. When one of the reactors was taken out of commission for its annual overhaul in June 1981, a suspect weld was found in a duct which is part of the gas-pressure circuit taking the heat-carrying carbon dioxide gas from the reactor to one of the four boilers, a similar fault to those found at Bradwell and Dungeness. The fault was found in a place which was particularly hard to get at, and it was difficult to inspect even with the latest examination equipment, so it had been decided to put the reactor back after its overhaul and seal off one of the four circuits to the boilers.

Cracks were also found at Hinkley Point A, and in some places these were over three metres long. Trawsfynydd was shut down because of a massive leak of water into the reactor vessel, possibly through a leak in a heat-exchanger unit. Outside the plant, both grass and cows' milk were found to have been contaminated. By the early 1980s most of the Magnox reactors either had been or were still out of commission.

As well as cracks, Dungeness A had other problems. A leak of radioactivity showed a weakness in the concrete roof beam supports in the building housing the gas/water heat exchangers. These structural defects could have led to an accident and were possibly caused by defective cement which was similar to that which led to the collapse of a roof over an indoor swimming pool in Camden, in London. The roof beams had moved by about half an inch possibly, said the CEGB, because the station had been shut down during a cold winter and the concrete could not cope with temperature differences. The problems with the concrete and temperature changes have led to fears over the safety of the concrete 'rafts' on which the reactors stand.

On *TV Eye*, on 12 June 1986, there was a report about fears of corrosion in the Magnox reactors, which is caused by the gas in the cooling systems. From 1969 to 1971, the Magnox reactor at Berkeley was on reduced power ('derated') so that the resultant rust could be cleaned up, but the corrosion has continued, more slowly, since then. There is concern about the welds in the feed pipes and the bolts and straps holding together the core. In addition, there are calls in Italy to close down the Magnox reactor at Latina (one of only two Magnox reactors exported from Britain) because of the possible dangers of this corrosion. At Hinkley Point, it was reported that two standpipes have been damaged by corrosion (they have been narrowed). Reactors at both Berkeley and Hinkley Point are due to be closed down in November for inspection and repair. In addition, at Berkeley the cooling-system pipes are exposed to the open air – i.e. there is no secondary containment.

The AGR programme

Then came the AGR programme. If there have been problems with the Magnox reactors they are nothing to those that occurred both during the building of the AGRs and afterwards.

In November 1979, a report presented by the Nuclear Installations Inspectorate to a meeting of experts in Madrid (but not published in Britain at the time) showed that the same kinds of problems had plagued the British nuclear industry as had affected the Americans: basic errors of design, human error, and general carelessness.

At the new AGR power station at Heysham in Lancashire, dangerously weak concrete had been used in the construction of the reactor vessel and this could have caused a complete failure of the system – another 'incredible' accident like Three-Mile Island. It was only after an NII inspector happened to notice that one section of the concrete was a lighter colour than the rest that it was carefully inspected: twenty cubic yards of defective concrete were found. Some was replaced and the rest was considered safe.

On 22 July 1983, one of the Heysham reactors had to be closed down after producing electricity for only 13 days. The start-up date (9 July) was just six years late.

In 1984, it was admitted that one of the Heysham reactors had been shut down again, this time for ten weeks, because of an operating mistake which was to cost the CEGB millions of pounds. On 4 June two of the 324 fuel channels in one of the reactors became too hot. The CEGB shut down the reactor and found that the affected fuel channels were obstructed by special plates which are used during the pre-fuel testing procedure and which should have been removed before the fuel was loaded. The NII ordered an investigation and the station was out of commission for months. The estimated initial cost of the Heysham station was £712.6 million. Its eventual cost was £1424.5 million.

Contractors working on the building of the nuclear power station at Heysham were found, by the NII, to have left a 'terrible assortment' of rubbish, such as broken welding rods, plastic sheeting, spare steel plate and general bits and pieces inside the reactor core at the end of each day's work. It took the threat from the NII of not granting an operating licence to make the workmen clear up after themselves.

By the time the Hartlepool station came on-stream and began providing electricity for the national grid in August 1983, it had cost £520 million (five times the estimated cost) and was nine years behind schedule. Almost immediately it had to be switched off again after developing a plumbing fault – a leak in a control panel in the turbine hall. 'You get these little leaks come along from time to time,' said a CEGB spokesman, 'but there is no suggestion that it is anything to do with the building delays.' The reactor had taken so long to build that there had been sheer relief in the industry when it finally started generating electricity. Work had stopped as far back as 1970 when the NII did not like the look of the concrete shells which were to contain the boilers; they had had to be re-designed.

The faults detailed to the Madrid conference in 1979 have continued to be found – faulty welds, corrosion, wrongly built vital shut-down pipe systems, gas-input pipes buried un-noticed in corrosive water, skimping and carelessness on quality control tests.

In December 1985, the CEGB announced that both re-actors, at Heysham and Hartlepool, would have to be taken out of service to try and overcome a variety of difficulties. It is expected that the cost will be in the region of £100 million which will have to be found by postponing other work. Neither station, admitted the CEGB, had ever provided more than a token supply of electricity to the national grid. The decision would mean that the CEGB would require more coal than had been foreseen, although because of the cost of rectifying Hartlepool and Heysham, work on coal-fired stations might also have to be delayed, thus shortening their operational life.

Incidents and breakdowns have been of varied importance but the following are some of them. At the time of writing, though, it is still proving almost impossible to get straight answers out of the nuclear industry or the CEGB and, as will be noted, on some occasions all that has emerged is misinformation.

Dungeness

One of the early Magnox nuclear power stations had already been built at Dungeness when the then government decided it should be the first site in a new and extended nuclear programme, and in 1965 the CEGB asked for tenders for Dungeness B. After some haggling over what type of reactor was required, it was decided to go for an advanced gas-cooled reactor (AGR). A number of consortia tendered and when the CEGB chose Atomic Power Constructions surprise was expressed, as it had been far from satisfied with the work carried out on another nuclear power station, at Trawsfynydd. However, the CEGB made much of APC having made 'bold advances' in its nuclear technology and that 'the technology on which the offers were based were found to be fundamentally sound.'

The cost, the CEGB estimated back in 1965, would be £87.5 million. By 1982 – when the power station was still not operating – estimated costs had risen to £587 million before nuclear fuel costs were taken into account.

In 1982, the *Daily Telegraph* ran a piece headed 'FAULTS

101

DISCOVERED IN LONG-DELAYED A-POWER PLANT' which said that equipment had had to be replaced or modified due to faults in construction. Rigorous tests had shown deficiencies in many components including pipes, control-system valves, and a variety of instruments. Tests also showed up design problems which meant extra insulation had to be added to the pipes linking the boiler with the nuclear reactor. It was described as a catalogue of design troubles.

This was an understatement. In 1969, welding of the steel liner for the pressure vessel of the reactor caused distortions which then made it impossible to install the boilers at all! So part of the liners had to be cut out and refitted. By this time it had been discovered that some reactors of this type were having problems caused by vibration from the onrush of high-pressure coolant gas, so the boilers themselves had to be completely redesigned.

Then it was discovered that the contractors had, in the words of the NII, 'failed to authenticate the manufacture of particular vital pieces of CO_2 [gas] pipeline'. That is, they had just not been properly checked. Walter Patterson rightly describes the situation in 1969 as a 'mounting technical, managerial and financial shambles'.

Finally – in 1982 – Dungeness B came on-stream. A spokesman for the CEGB is quoted in the *Daily Telegraph* as saying that part of the problems had been 'due to prototype design troubles. We are now satisfied that the equipment is entirely up to standard and there are no safety risks.' It is interesting to compare his statement with that put out by the CEGB when they commissioned Atomic Power Constructions to build the plant. This said that APC, as we mentioned, had made 'bold advances' and those bold advances were on the original advanced gas-cooled reactor prototype. Twenty-two years later they were blaming their problems on the fact that it was still a prototype design.

The *Daily Telegraph* called Dungeness B the 'worst ever advert for the nuclear and construction industries.'

But what of Dungeness A, the reliable Magnox station plodding along while Dungeness B had so many problems? In March 1979 it was found necessary to repair cracks up to one metre long in the welding of a gas bellows for the primary cooling circuit close to the core of the reactor. During a routine biennial inspection, the CEGB had cleared the reactor as safe, and it was only because the NII disagreed that a more thorough inspection was carried out and more cracks were discovered. The reactor had to be shut down for four days at an estimated cost of £4 million.

By January 1980, engineers were telling *Nature* magazine that they despaired of Dungeness ever working properly. Just before Christmas 1985, the CEGB proudly announced that Dungeness B should be operating at full capacity by the end of the year – 14 years later than expected.

Hinkley Point

During the autumn of 1985 there was a series of accidents at Hinkley B nuclear power station, one of which has been described by an expert in the nuclear industry as the worst at a British nuclear plant since the 1957 Windscale fire.

As at Dungeness and Hunterston, Hinkley Point has a Magnox A reactor and an AGR B reactor. In fact, Hunterston and Hinkley are twins: both came on-stream in February 1976 – and were off again within an hour because of faults.

Maintenance problems concerning Hinkley B had been noted as early as 1973 when it was still being built. Arthur Hawkins, then chairman of the CEGB, when giving evidence to a House of Commons Select Committee said (speaking of advanced gas-cooled reactors), 'they have once-through boilers in a very difficult situation where, for instance, it is difficult to control the water levels – you are facing two almost impossible reconciliations. You get corrosion outside in one condition and corrosion inside in the other.' Getting to the core was an appalling task. 'Have you crawled through Hinkley Point? I have. It is so difficult to maintain that the problem is keeping it in service for the fuel design life.' He went on to say that the CEGB would not be ordering any more reactors of a similar design.

Nine days before Hinkley B started to produce electricity, there was an ominous rattling noise from within the reactor. It was deduced that a large valve inside it was vibrating violently as it tried to stem the inrush of hot gases – a problem which had been foreseen during the continuing problems affecting Dungeness B, still not completed. But which of the 308 valves was it? 'The enormity of the problem only dawned slowly,' an engineer was to say later. Over a period of several months more and more valves were withdrawn. The damage to the reactor core itself turned out to be substantial. The tough stainless steel was scored, bent and battered and in some places torn away altogether.

In June 1977, a major cooling water pipe at Hinkley B, carrying water to the heat exchanger, broke. Station staff needed to rig up a fire hose to keep the temperature of the concrete shielding below danger level. The pipe carried water in the secondary coolant system yet water had to be channelled into that circuit in order to carry away heat from the primary coolant system. Because of a poor design feature the same broken pipe was then connected to the emergency back-up cooling system . . . It took staff several hours to get the fire hose rigged up and working properly. Afterwards, experts estimated that after no more than six hours of having a secondary cooling circuit out of action, the core would have become contaminated with volatile fission products and it would then have suffered severe damage.

On 25 October 1985 there was a serious accident at Hinkley B. In spite of the 1976 ruling which stated that the Energy Minister must be informed and then the information made public through the Nuclear Installations Inspectorate, no such announcement was made to the public until the local television station, TSW, broke the news on its 6 o'clock bulletin on 29 October. There was a brief report in some newspapers on the morning of 30 October. The CEGB flatly denied both to TSW and to me that there had been any release of radioactivity. The accident had happened at an embarrassing time for the CEGB, who were having secret talks with representatives of the relevant local authorities about building a PWR at Hinkley if the go-ahead should be given for Sizewell B.

There are discrepancies between what some sources say happened and what the CEGB says happened. One reliable source stated that there was a fracture in the boiler main feed pipe; the CEGB was to tell Paddy Ashdown MP, in a letter dated 29 November 1985, that it was a hole less than 1 inch in diameter in a single boiler tube. From whichever pipe, about 6 tonnes of water flooded into the reactor, and this was released into the Bristol Channel, radioactivity and all. An expert told Paddy Ashdown and me that if the accident was what informed sources said it was, there must have been a release of radioactivity into the atmosphere despite the denials of the CEGB. Following questions in the House of Commons, Paddy Ashdown was told on 15 November by the Secretary of State for Energy that there *had* been a release of radioactivity although it was within permitted safety limits.

Further publicity from the CEGB appeared which implied that this was the first incident of any kind at an advanced gas-cooled reactor since they came into commission. As we have seen, this is not only untrue of AGRs in general but of Hinkley B in particular. Following this first in a series of accidents in 1985, Hinkley B was out of commission for twelve days.

On 20 November there was a second accident or incident. Another pipe, this time carrying carbon dioxide coolant, broke and 28 tons of carbon dioxide leaked away. The safety valve which should have shut off the supply of carbon dioxide froze as the cold gas escaped, and was stuck open. This time the CEGB released news of the accident within 48 hours. Their spokesperson said that the gas was not irradiated and there was no cause for alarm.

Paddy Ashdown had arranged to visit Hinkley Point on 2 December 1985 to discuss a number of safety issues and to be given a special presentation. In the event, there was a presentation of another kind on November 29 – probably the most serious nuclear accident in Britain since October 1957.

This time the leak was in the cooling system of Hinkley B. It took four hours to plug the hole, during which time 23 tons of carbon dioxide gas had been released into the atmosphere, eight of which were unfiltered. Staff had to be evacuated and all 500 employees were also given potassium iodate tablets to take as a preventive measure against contamination by iodine-131.

The gas, which had a temperature of 300°C, escaped at high speed and more gas had to be vented into the atmosphere to reduce the pressure. The reactor had been shut down for maintenance work two days earlier and was running below normal heat when the accident happened. An expert source suggests that the reason the reactor was running below normal heat was because some of the fuel rods were being removed and then replaced by others. The gas would have come through the hole in the pipe at a pressure of 380 lb per square inch, on its way passing close to the core of the reactor and picking up radioactive debris including carbon-14. Once again the whole event has been shrouded in secrecy. This time the station was shut down until 12 December. The CEGB estimates the cost of each day of shutdown as £150,000 a day (G. H. Hadley, Secretary of the CEGB in letter to Paddy Ashdown of 31 January 1986), but organisations such as Friends of the Earth consider this to be an underestimate and suggest the sum is nearer £250,000 a day.

On 2 December 1985 Paddy Ashdown did visit Hinkley for his 'presentation'. The main reason for his visit was concern about the problems over the long-term safety reviews of the ageing Magnox reactors. Staff shortages and cutbacks have meant that most of these reviews are now running well behind schedule and those for Hinkley A and for Trawsfynydd in Wales may not be completed for another five to seven years. Paddy Ashdown is concerned that, even if the reviews had taken place on time, they would still be inadequate as no physical inspections are made to check the reactors' crucial safety feature: the strength of the steel pressure vessel. Paper exercises and computer models are used instead. As if to underline his point, Hinkley A broke down the following week . . .

'You need a jemmy to prise information out of the CEGB,' Paddy Ashdown told TSW viewers just before he visited Hinkley. He is still prising. A typical reaction of government to requests for information came on 12 December 1985 in a written reply to a priority question from Mr Ashdown asking the Minister of Agriculture to publish a report of the radioactive contamination following the site incident at Hinkley Point on 29 November. The reply was: 'No increase in radioactivity has been detected off site following the incident. I do not, therefore, intend to publish a report.'

The Hinkley saga is, however, far from concluded. On 12 February 1986, a remarkable story broke in the press. It appeared the CEGB want to build four more nuclear power stations at Hinkley Point and had so informed the local liaison committee. The plans involve building two stations on a new site and two more *on top* of the present ones. The CEGB want to acquire a further 175 acres of farmland next to the existing power stations to build Hinkley C; the next stage in this massive expansion, Hinkley D, would require buying even more.

If, as the CEGB expects, permission is given to build the Sizewell B PWR, then a planning application for a PWR would immediately be filed for Hinkley Point. The fourth station might well be another PWR or, even more remarkably, one of the controversial fast breeders. On local television that day, some councillors described the prospect as 'a nightmare'.

The new C station would be built to guarantee electricity supplies west of Exeter, and the D station to guarantee power to the West Midlands; the latter would also involve building a new pylon line from Severnside. A further station, Hinkley E, would then be built on the site of the present Hinkley A, as by that time, the A station would be 'partly decommissioned, only the core remaining'. Station F would be built on the present site of the Hinkley B AGR that has featured in recent accidents, when that was decommissioned. Hinkley residents will be world leaders in the concentration of nuclear power in one neighbourhood.

It appears that even the chairman of Somerset County Council's Planning Committee, who is also chairman of the liaison committee, is concerned about this exciting prospect. He said it was 'a bizarre kind of leapfrogging, building one station on top of another'.

Future developments are awaited with interest.

On 15 May 1986, the CEGB held a press conference to give the results of their inquiry into what went wrong at Hinkley B on 29 November 1985. The accident was caused, they said, by the failure of a quarter-inch retaining bolt which should have held a control drive shaft in a universal joint on one of the gas circulators. It had been badly fitted with, of all things, re-used tap washers, and the joint itself was not the type specified by the manufacturers. As a result, the bolt fell out, causing the drive shaft to blow out under a gas pressure of 380 lb per square inch, leaving a 1-inch hole through which coolant escaped very quickly. The amount of radioactivity released was within permitted safety limits. In spite of strong requests from Paddy Ashdown, who attended the briefing, the CEGB refused to allow the publication of the full report, issuing only its findings and recommendations.

Hunterston

So to Hunterston in Strathclyde with its Magnox A station and its AGR, the 'twin' of Hinkley B.

Hunterston A has been plagued by problems and has suffered three radiation leaks: in November 1978, in January 1979 and again in October 1984. This third leak came from a pipe which had already been considered faulty in both previous incidents, and in January 1979 much of it had been replaced. The third leak was found after a radiological survey was carried out, and it was discovered that liquid effluent from the pipeline had contaminated the soil as far as about three metres from the leak to a depth of 1.5 metres. The leak was inside the site boundary and was not, said the NII, a health risk. After this leak a temporary pipeline was installed to bypass the leaking section which, said the NII in its report on the incident, would need to be totally replaced.

In February 1976, after a long series of mishaps and delays, Hunterston B started up within half an hour of its rival, Hinkley Point B. Both stations ran for just an hour and then shut down again. In September 1977, technicians at Hunterston B rigged a makeshift pipe in the cooling system and then forgot all about it. Fortunately the reactor had been shut down for maintenance work when the temporary pipe delivered thousands of gallons of raw sea water straight into the stainless steel core of the reactor, which then had to be shut down for two years.

It was an extremely expensive mistake. It cost £15 million to properly clean out and repair the inside of the reactor vessel, this figure also including the cost of replacing its interior thermal insulation. During the time the reactor was out of commission, the South of Scotland Electricity Board had to 'buy in' its electricity from elsewhere. The cost of shutting down the reactor and buying in electricity was estimated by the SSEB in 1980 to be around £42 million and this was later uprated to about £50 million. All for the sake of a makeshift pipe which had been forgotten. (Had the reactor been running it would have been a different story.)

When Hunterston B was being proposed, customers in Scotland were told they were entering a new era of cheap electricity. After the accident the SSEB brought in a major tariff increase. Yet again, words become meaningless in the nuclear power business, for when the SSEB announced its first estimate of the cost of shutting down Hunterston B and buying in electricity, the press release said that the figure of £42 million 'demonstrates the relatively low operating costs of nuclear generation'. So, apparently, spending £42 million on a broken-down plant and buying electricity from somewhere else was supposed to be some kind of a bargain.

Wylfa

In 1984, hairline cracks were found in the supporting columns of the crane used to lift the 50-ton flasks of spent nuclear fuel (that 'waste' again) out of the Wylfa station ready for its transport to Sellafield. This caused so much concern that the crane had to be taken out of service.

The result soon became apparent. All the waste which should have been removed regularly began to pile up at Wylfa, and the CEGB had to ask permission from Anglesey Council to store far more nuclear waste on site than had ever been anticipated or than the local authority had been prepared to allow. In a statement issued in October 1985, the station manager said he hoped the station could remain in production at least until the autumn of 1986, after which it would completely run out of storage space. He hoped that a new crane would be in place by that time.

Problems with cranes were discovered as early as 1981 when there was what is euphemistically described by the CEGB as 'a near miss at another station'. It was then decided to fit new emergency brakes to the Wylfa crane, but this seems to have put extra strains on it with which it was just not able to cope, and this resulted in the cracks.

At the time of writing there are a number of fears locally apart from the obvious one that nuclear waste is being stored in such large quantities. One is that the electricity output will have to be severely reduced; another is that one of the two reactors will have to be closed down altogether. The Magnox station is worth £11 million to the island's economy, according to the CEGB. The CEGB admits that there are real problems and hopes to have the new crane installed before power generation is seriously affected. However, said the regional secretary Mr D. W. H. Ashton: '. . . it will be a close run thing.'

Trawsfynydd

No official records of mishaps at this power station were published before it was obligatory to do so in 1976. That year, there were several minor incidents, in 1977 there were two fires and a crane contamination, and in 1978 there was another fire.

On 29 June 1980, what the CEGB described as 'moisture' – and many others as 'water' – was found in the cooling circuit of the reactor when it was being brought back to power after a 'disturbance' which had caused an automatic shutdown the previous day. Environmental monitoring, said the CEGB, had detected low levels of radiation on grass and some slight radioactivity in milk samples, but these were all well within permitted safety limits, and it was expected that the reactor would be on-stream again within days.

In fact, the information was only made public after a reply to a parliamentary question on 10 July 1980 by the then Secretary of State for Energy, Norman Lamont. He expressed himself as being satisfied it was a very minor 'mishap' and that there was no hazard to health.

On 30 July 1980, Trawsfynydd still being shut down, D. B. Thomas MP asked whether there would be a full departmental enquiry into the 'accident' at Trawsfynydd. In reply, Mr Lamont said that the Nuclear Installations Inspectorate had informed him that the 'moisture in the reactor is greater than at first thought.' The drying out of the reactor had involved venting into the atmosphere a small amount of radioactive carbon dioxide gas and it might well be necessary to release more. Low-level radioactivity was still being found in the grass and in the milk, but both were within permitted safety levels. It was, in fact, some considerable time before the station was operational again.

On 18 October 1985, there was a fire in the turbine hall at Trawsfynydd, which shut the station down for a further two days.

On 21 February 1986, there was another accident at Trawsfynydd. A pressure-relief valve, one of 12 on the reactor, lifted off and 13 tonnes of 'mildly radioactive carbon dioxide' escaped in just 14 minutes. The valve had opened although it was only designed to do so if there was a fault in the circuit of the reactor, and it had lifted at a pressure that was 30 lb per square inch below its intended operating pressure. It appears, too, that the valve filter, designed to filter out radioactivity, had failed to function.

According to John Large, a former UKAEA senior researcher, the automatic shutdown system did not work, and the valve had to be closed down manually by an operator sent on to the 170-foot-high roof of the reactor building. He did not wear protective clothing, and later a small particle of manganese-56 was found on his nose.

The 21-year-old reactor had just finished its statutory two-year safety test and was being returned to service when the accident occurred. It appears that the valve had been incorrectly calibrated after the test. This could be compared to a vital test being omitted when a car went for its MOT.

The 'plume' area – that is, the area downwind from the reactor and from any release of radioactivity – is estimated to have extended between six and seven miles. The CEGB monitored for contamination from one hour and 40 minutes after the gas escaped, and continued to do so for about seven hours. Contamination was detected first on the roof, then in 11 places on the ground within the area of the plant itself. A single particle was found on private land about 765 yards outside the boundary of the plant. All in all, the CEGB say they monitored 56 particles, which were so small that the station manager, Keith Baddeley, told the *Guardian* a week after the accident that he would not mind eating one of them.

About 10,000 people live within a 6-mile radius of Trawsfynydd – 5500 in Blaenau Ffestiniog and 2000 at Penrhyndeudraeth. Mr Large said that this was, potentially, a very serious accident indeed, 'a dry-run' to disaster. If a more serious incident occurred in similar circumstances and the valve blew and the filter did not work, then highly radioactive fissile material could be blown on to the surrounding countryside. Plotting the plume of radioactivity at Trawsfynydd in such an event would be difficult, said Mr Large, because of the nearby mountains which set up their own air currents.

The same kind of valves are fitted at all twelve Magnox stations in Britain, and at the time of writing these were being tested to try and discover why the filter system failed to work.

Sizewell

On 17 January 1986, it was announced that one of the two Magnox reactors at Sizewell had been shut down during the previous week following a failure in its boiler tubes. This allowed several hundred gallons of water to leak into the reactor's gas-cooling circuit. The CEGB said that its engineers had controlled the problem by isolating that particular boiler, but that they still had to get rid of the water somehow.

Ten days later, on 27 January, the staff at Sizewell had to be evacuated following a leak of radioactive carbon dioxide from a pipe. This time, the CEGB said the workers were allowed back into the reactor building some two hours later. There was no danger to the public, they added.

One of the reactors had to be shut down on 14 May 1986 when a fuel can failed, releasing radioactivity into the gas-cooling circuit. The CEGB said it was only a small routine incident, and it was only made public because of heightened public anxiety.

Dounreay

The government is currently planning to build a new reprocessing plant at the Dounreay nuclear power complex on
Scotland's north coast, site of Britain's prototype fast-breeder
nuclear reactor. It is designed to reprocess waste from all over
Europe, although it is hard to see how it will be economic
since there are no plans to build fast-breeder reactors in
Britain or anywhere else in Europe, except for France, until
sometime in the next century.

Dounreay, says the publicity, is a trouble-free complex. Not
so. Like the Magnox and AGR programmes, it has been
plagued by incidents and accidents, and like the AGRs it was
years behind schedule coming into operation. In October
1974, a plane-load of journalists was flown all the way up to
the north of Scotland to attend the grand switching-on of
power from the prototype fast-breeder reactor into the
national grid. Nothing happened. Apparently a bad storm in
the Atlantic had loosened vast quantities of seaweed all along
the coast of the north of Scotland. The beaches near to
Dounreay had not escaped, and hundreds of tons of seaweed
had been blown inshore and had blocked the plant's cooling-
water intake meaning that the station could not be switched
on. The mystified journalists were flown back to England
again without any explanation as to why there had been no
switch-on.

On 23 October 1983, the *Observer* revealed that there was a
serious accident at Dounreay in September 1962. The accident remained unpublicised until then because the family of
Frank McClure who had been contaminated in a blow-back of
radioactive dust, had to turn to the media for publicity, after
waiting for 32 months for an inquest into his death at the
age of 54 in February 1981, of cancer of the pancreas and
stomach.

McClure had been a foreman at the plant and was a
Conservative councillor for the area. On 12 February 1963,
five months after the accident happened and after he had had
a number of medical checks, he wrote a confidential account
of the accident, in which he noted from the beginning that he
had been exposed to a dangerously high level of radiation.

The *Observer* had confirmation from another source that the story was true.

McClure's secret account of what happened was contained in a letter which he hid away. He told his wife that if anything happened to him later, she could read it. In the event, she finally saw it early in 1978 when the doctor confirmed that her husband had cancer.

Frank McClure was in charge of four men who assembled that morning in 1962 in Building D1206, which was a chemical separation plant where uranium and plutonium were separated from spent fuel rods by remote control. The men were asked to sweep the floor of a tunnel containing a conveyor belt which took highly radioactive material from the area where the separation took place. They had to sweep away pieces of uranium which had fallen off the conveyor and clear up spillages which included plutonium.

He wrote that a special safety tent to act as an airlock should have been put at the entrance to the tunnel to prevent the escape of radioactivity and that this had been suggested at a management meeting called to discuss the best way of cleaning out the tunnel. Instead, he was told to put a piece of PVC sheeting on the floor around the hole used as an entrance so that anyone coming out of the tunnel could step on it to avoid contaminating the floor. A ruling had been made that a tent was not necessary 'as time would be taken erecting it'.

At 9 a.m., the plug covering the entrance to the tunnel was removed and Mr McClure told one of the men to drape the PVC inside the hole as he thought it would be safer. At 1 p.m. a process worker in a protective suit and a mask went into the three-foot-diameter tunnel and began to try and clean it out, using an ordinary sweep's brush, but the brush jammed on the conveyor belt. He tried for half an hour to free it, without success, so McClure told him to come out. As he did so the PVC suddenly fused together inside the hole, which meant there was either back pressure or a blow-out in the working area. The air movement was confirmed by holding a piece of paper tissue in the tunnel mouth.

Both men were severely contaminated. Mr McClure's account said: 'When I was checked, I was found to be contaminated on my clothing, hair and face, inside my nose and mouth, greater than 1000 counts per second beta.' Sixteen years later, when Mr McClure was trying to get compensation he was told that his greatest contamination had been 30 counts per second. From the time of the accident Mr McClure suffered from slight aches in the chest and back, the back pains being in the area of the lungs and kidneys. Five months later he began to get frequent headaches, some lasting several days. He told his wife at the time that there had been a big blow-out and that a tent should have been erected.

In January 1978 he had to have most of his stomach removed, and although he had always supported the nuclear industry he began battling with the UK Atomic Energy Authority for compensation. On 3 August 1979 Dr D. G. Wilson, senior medical officer at Dounreay, finally admitted that an 'incident' had taken place on 3 September 1962 but disputed the seriousness of it and the amount of contamination Mr McClure had received. The highest reading (on the hair), he said, was 30 counts per second, the lowest (on the hands) was ten. He concluded: 'Personally I feel you are distressing yourself fruitlessly in pursuing your allegation that your illness has been caused by your employment at Dounreay.' The contamination, he said, had been so light that it was removed by a few washes.

Thirty-two months was a long time to wait for an inquest. At that time the Coroner's Office could remember only one occasion for such a delay and that was when a criminal was still at large. The inquest finally took place on 17 February 1984. Mr McClure's five-page account of the accident was read. 'Experts' from the nuclear power industry were called as witnesses. After hearing both sides the Cleveland coroner, Michael Sheffield, recorded an open verdict.

Other incidents at Dounreay include spent fuel pins being lost and probably reprocessed in error, according to Peter Bunyard in his book *Nuclear Britain*, and of eight workers becoming contaminated with plutonium because the samples they were handling did not carry any of the routinely accepted warning notices.

The 'flavour' of some of those accidents was, in fact, given in more detail by the *New Scientist* in its issue of 25 September 1980. On the night of 9–10 May 1977 a high-level waste silo exploded. The silo is in a deep shaft fifty yards from the sea and it contains much of Dounreay's most dangerous solid waste. The explosion occurred when the sodium used to transfer heat out of the reactor core came into contact with water, and it cracked a fifteen-foot-square, four-foot-thick block of concrete on top of the silo and hurled a five-foot-wide plug from the centre of this huge block against the fence. A man had just left, having checked instruments at the head of the shaft. The statement made by the UKAEA at the time spoke of the 'lifting' of a concrete plug, causing 'minor damage'.

There was no mention, said *New Scientist*, of a worker having been on site only moments before, or that sodium should not have been dumped in a high-level waste silo so close to water – 'For, as any schoolboy knows, there is a fierce reaction when sodium and water meet'.

It is also worth retelling in more detail what happened to the eight men who were handling waste on 25 July 1979 without being aware that it contained plutonium nitrate.

According to *New Scientist*, it had been an uneventful day for the day shift in Building 1208 where radioactive liquid waste is kept until it can be disposed of. (At present there is no safe way of disposing of it.) The four men on that shift had been handling the waste passing through the building. It was marked 'contaminated'. The shift changed, and four other men took over the job, pouring the liquid through funnels into flasks, a routine task.

However, somewhere along the line the certificate identifying the waste as containing plutonium was lost, and the error was only discovered when the night shift went off duty. They checked their hands as they left and there was a high count of 'alpha' contamination, the hallmark of plutonium. As every restricted area is equipped with air samplers, safety officials immediately took readings and found that the levels of plutonium in Building 1208 were ten times the normal average, and they evacuated the whole area. Men handling plutonium must wear heavier protective clothing, special gloves and, most crucially as *New Scientist* points out, respirators to prevent their inhaling plutonium. Because the eight men did not know what they were handling, they did not wear either respirators or the correct clothes. The response of the UKAEA was to say that the importance of the incident had been 'exaggerated' and that tests carried out on the men showed that 'the amount of plutonium found, the dose received, was not medically significant'.

In 1982 the Health and Safety Executive produced a 40-page report on Dounreay – marked 'for official use only' – which was circulated to a limited number of people in the July of the following year. It admitted that the number of accidents involving the release of radiation within the plant had increased threefold between 1977 and 1982, from just 70 'radiological incidents' of all kinds to 223. The number of incidents in the prototype fast-breeder increased from thirteen in 1981 to thirty-four in 1982, and included a number of contamination incidents – fifteen of surface contamination and eleven concerning skin and/or clothing.

There was one incident in 1982 listed as 'serious' when a plastic bag spilled its contents on the floor resulting in the release of plutonium. This was duly reported to the Nuclear Installations Inspectorate at the time. One worker was exposed to three times the annual safety limit of radioactivity and another received a dose which exceeded the three-month legal limit. Also in 1982, there were five breaches (compared to only one in 1981) of the 'conditions of criticality' which are supposed to ensure that there cannot be a runaway chain reaction. The report said that there was no real risk of an 'excursion', i.e. major accident.

Another problem dogging Dounreay is the release of radioactive 'particles'. From November 1983 these began to turn up on the beach nearby. By November 1985, sixty-one such particles had been found. At a meeting of workers and management in 1984, the workers pressed for increased monitoring of the beaches and surrounding areas, but they were reminded of 'the importance of avoiding causing alarm to the public by the sight of intensified monitoring activity'.

Admitting to the appearance of four new particles on the

beach at Dounreay in November 1985, the UKAEA said the level of radioactivity was 'very low'. Thirty-five of the particles, including the latest four, are twenty-year-old metallic fragments believed to have originated from a spill after a break in a pipe in 1965. The other twenty-six, seven of which were found on public beaches, were thought to have leaked out within the last couple of years.

On 5 November 1985, the government, the UKAEA and British Nuclear Fuels were making advanced plans for the new reprocessor. A Mr Alexander Bell had been appointed to run the local public inquiry which has a very limited remit indeed. At the same time a study was released, to selected journalists only, giving details of the proposed new plant. There will be a chimney 180 feet high for the release of radioactivity. A new port facility and a new rail link will need to be built to deal with the large amounts of nuclear waste brought into Dounreay for reprocessing, and the plutonium produced at Dounreay will be flown direct from the airfield to Europe's fast-breeder reactors. In answer to those critics concerned about the airlifting of plutonium, the UKAEA and BNFL have said, according to the *Daily Telegraph* of 5 November 1985, that 'there would be inbuilt safeguards against air crashes'. One can only hope that this knowledge is being shared with the world's airlines as it would be the answer to all their problems.

The plant will be a huge one costing £200 million to build. The authorities have apparently drawn up a plan 'in the unlikely event' that something does go wrong: to protect the public in times of danger, arrangements have been made with the Highland Omnibus Company to provide buses if an evacuation is necessary . . .

At the time of writing the inquiry is taking place although its findings will not be made known for some considerable time. Meanwhile those who object to the expansion of Dounreay are still finding it impossible to discover just what has gone on there already. On 9 December 1985 a spokesman for Dounreay, Mr T. D. Roberts, told the *Guardian* that annual reports of the Health and Safety Subcommittee – such as that leaked – are confidential. Writing on 27 December, Dr C. Wakstein, a Harley Street specialist and the only expert witness to give evidence on the history of accidents at Windscale at the 1977 inquiry, queried why this should be so.

What possible reason could there be for keeping safety reports from the public? If these documents really have nothing worrying in them, even the most vilely motivated, carefully orchestrated, sinister campaign in the world couldn't make anything of them.

The excuse – that the general public might not understand them – is simply not good enough; it is up to the nuclear experts to make sure they do.

Dr Wakstein pointed out that, as we know, the record of Windscale/Sellafield for accidents (or incidents as British Nuclear Fuels prefers to call them) is far from unblemished – something in the region of 177 in 28 years. Dounreay, it is now admitted, had *223 in one year alone*. He concluded:

Of course the number of accidents is not the whole story; the character, the flavour of the accidents is what really tells the truth about Dounreay, and this can be gained only from full access to the real reports, not the sanitised versions which was all that had hitherto been available.

At the beginning of February 1986 the internal health and safety documents about Dounreay were finally made public after a great deal of pressure from a number of organisations. They showed there had been a very substantial increase in the number of radiation incidents at the Dounreay plant during the last eight years. Workers, said the reports, had been found to have been contaminated by plutonium, alarms have been found to be faulty, there have been numerous radiation spills and in one instance a plant had to be evacuated. Spots of radioactivity have been found on seats in public buses.

The total number of 'radiological incidents' at the plant increased from 70 in 1977 to 194 in 1984 and the 1984 number of 'serious' or 'significant' incidents was eight – double that of 1983. They included a 'mechanical malfunction' causing a

119

spill of plutonium liquid in the prototype fast reactor reprocessing plant, a radioactive particle found in someone's shoe
and a 'finger wound caused by a plutonium-contaminated
needle'.

The worst problems arose in the materials-testing reactor
processing plant where a large proportion of the workforce
was approaching Dounreay's safety limit by the end of 1984.
Dounreay's own health and safety subcommittee said,
however, that the plant's generally high safety level had been
maintained, exposure to radiation had been well within internationally accepted limits and action is promptly taken when
incidents occur.

It is interesting that the reports show there has been a
substantial increase in the number of incidents over the last
eight years. On 1 February 1983 a report was published in *The
Lancet*. Four members of the Information Services Division
of the Scottish Health Service Common Services Agency
expressed their 'concern' over an apparent rise in leukaemia
cases around Dounreay during that period. According to the
information in *The Lancet* no cases of leukaemia at all were
registered within a 25 km radius of Dounreay between 1968
and 1978. However, between 1978 and 1984 the investigators
found five cases within an area of less than 12.5 km from
Dounreay. Four of these were in the town of Thurso, the only
significant centre of population within that area. The fifth
lived 3 km from the plant.

The report states:

The importance of this finding is difficult to evaluate. The
choice of radii and time periods is arbitrary and, although
there is an excess of cases over the whole period 1968–1984,
no cases at all were registered within 25 km in the period
1968–1978. On the other hand, the fact that all reported
cases within 12.5 km occurred within a five-year period,
were in children under fifteen, and that the five occurred
within 12.5 km of Dounreay, may increase its potential
importance. Similar findings have been reported from near
other UK nuclear installations (e.g. Sellafield, Hunterston,
Aldermaston and West Burghfield.)

120

The four investigators say they hope to report later on any further clusters in Scotland.

In June 1986, the Granada Television series, *World in Action*, broke the story of a serious incident at Dounreay which had been kept secret by the UK Atomic Energy Authority since the latter half of 1984. It only came to light because a former Dounreay employee, Stuart Duff, thought it should be made known, even though he himself is still very much in favour of nuclear power. Granada also interviewed a number of Dounreay employees, all of whom made sworn statements, and uncovered a tale that is yet another catalogue of blunders and human error.

Fuel for reprocessing is placed in a nitric acid dissolver which strips away all the solid fuel. What appears to have happened in this case is that the solid fuel quite simply did not dissolve, leading to a build-up of fissile material in the dissolver tank which exceeded criticality guidelines.

The first alleged error was the decision to reprocess un-irradiated fuel. The crystalline structure of unirradiated fuel is quite different from that of irradiated fuel from nuclear reactors. Because of this, it is claimed, the research and development department at Dounreay were asked if there would be any problems if such fuel were passed through the system. They were said to have expressed doubts and to have told the management that unirradiated fuel might well not react in the same way as the irradiated type. In spite of this, it appears that their advice was overridden by management, and operatives went ahead and fed the unirradiated fuel into the plant.

The fuel is dissolved in the acid to recover the plutonium. The resulting liquor is then passed through a centrifuge to check that the total amount of plutonium has been recovered, but on this occasion, something went wrong. Only half of the plutonium was recovered; the rest – said to weigh about 25 kilograms and about the size of a football – was left stuck in the reprocessing system.

Then another mistake is said to have occurred: no effort was made to trace the missing plutonium. The Dounreay management assumed that Sellafield had made a book-keeping error in the amount it had sent to Dounreay, and they did not realise that it was actually still in the dissolver. Brian Wynne, a nuclear scientist at Lancaster University who was interviewed on the *World in Action* programme, said this was very worrying as it suggested that a possible serious breach in either the accounting or book-keeping at Sellafield had been treated as if it were almost a normal occurrence.

Then the third error is said to have occurred, which, according to critics, could have led to a major accident – or 'excursion' as the nuclear industry prefers to call it.

More spent fuel from Dounreay's own reactor was introduced into the dissolving system, which, of course, already contained a substantial amount of plutonium, as used in atomic warheads. It was at this point that it was realised that something had gone wrong: gamma ray alarms went off, meaning that the safe level for undissolved plutonium had been exceeded. If all the plutonium in the tank had come together in a mass, the result could have been, according to Brian Wynne, massive neutron storms in the environment of the plant with severe radiation doses to the workforce. Urgent action was obviously necessary: some of the liquid was drained from the dissolver into another tank, and the criticality was ended.

Owen Pugh, who is in charge of reprocessing at Dounreay, confirmed to *World in Action* that there had been a problem connected with some fuel which did not dissolve and admitted it was unirradiated fuel, but he put the amount at only 5 kilograms. He denied that there had been any oversights or indeed any human error. Management had realised some plutonium was missing, they found it and that was that; anything else was supposition. As to how near the plutonium came to criticality, well, it might have happened 'in the very long term', but it was spotted by a system designed to identify such errors so there was never any danger. He denied that the missing plutonium had been put down to a book-keeping error or that staff had not realised it was in the dissolver. There are built-in systems at Dounreay against human error.

Brian Wynne pointed out that whether the amount was 25 kilograms, as employees have said in sworn statements, or 5 kilograms as admitted by Owen Pugh, it is still a very significant amount when you compare it to the Hiroshima bomb which contained between 10 and 12 kilograms of plutonium oxide.

Chapter 5

Windscale: Nuclear Dustbin to the World

The incidents and accidents at the Windscale nuclear plant and the growing concern and criticism over the management of safety there deserve a separate chapter. At the end of this section there are details of just some of the accidents beginning with the well-documented fire in 1957 and ending with the contamination of the Cumbrian beaches in 1983 which led to British Nuclear Fuels being prosecuted.

It is also necessary to give, however briefly, the history of Windscale and the two different, but closely related, worrying aspects of this plant. These are the accidents that have occurred there and the pollution which has come from it. Some of that pollution has been due to accidents but much has occurred simply because of its operation, particularly the discharges of radioactive material into the Irish Sea.

Although British Nuclear Fuels decided to change the plant's name to Sellafield in 1981, saying they thought this more 'logical', the plant has always been known as Windscale and was certainly known only by that name until 1981. It will probably be simpler, therefore, if I refer to it as Windscale throughout this chapter until we come to the Cumbrian beaches incident.

The Windscale site on the Cumbrian coast housed a munitions factory during the Second World War and was acquired by the Ministry of Supply in 1947 for the construction of two air-cooled reactors: the No 1 and No 2 piles. At the same time it was decided to build a reprocessing plant on the site. Those first two reactors were shut down after the major accident in 1957, and in the early 1960s the reprocessing plant was also closed. There is now a Magnox station at

Calder Hall (part of the complex) and a larger reprocessing facility.

In 1952 the Windscale plant was given the all-clear to discharge nuclear waste through a pipeline into the Irish Sea. The great proponent of this was John Dunster, then Windscale's chief health physicist. Six years later in a report he gave to a special UN Conference, Dunster told those attending that the

sea had always been regarded by coastal and seafaring people as the ideal place for dumping their waste and this is, of course, a very reasonable and proper attitude. Almost anything put in the sea is either diluted or broken down . . . or stored harmlessly on the seabed . . . not the least of the attractions of the sea as a dumping ground has been the lack of administrative controls.

It is well to note, when considering the history of Windscale, its accidents, discharges and the safety or not of its pipeline, that John Dunster is now chairman of the nation's watchdog body on nuclear safety, the National Radiological Protection Board.

In 1954 the Ministry of Supply handed over responsibility for Windscale to the newly-formed UK Atomic Energy Authority and it, in turn, transferred the whole operation to the commercial British Nuclear Fuels Ltd (BNFL) when that company was formed in 1971.

We shall probably never know just what did go on at Windscale until 1976 when, owing to publicity given to a major unreported leak at the plant, the then Energy Secretary Tony Benn ordered that in future all such incidents anywhere in the nuclear power industry should be reported immediately. The leak was found in the early part of that year and it was coming from a silo containing radioactive material. More than 20,000 gallons had escaped into the ground by 1981 and down, possibly, into the water table. At the time of writing no one has yet succeeded in fully plugging this leak. It is thought the accident happened when the alloy containing the fuel became so hot that it cracked the base of the silo in which it was stored. Zirconium is used as a cladding for fuel rods and it is highly explosive in certain conditions. Storing the rods for long periods of time, often only a few feet below the water level, presents an obvious hazard. Whatever the reason, the leak went on and on.

Also in 1976, BNFL announced that it wanted to extend its operations by building a new and larger reprocessing plant. By this time Britain was accepting nuclear waste from most of the other nuclear countries except the Soviet Union and India, even from Japan, thus earning ourselves the doubtful honour of running the world's nuclear dustbin. The subsequent public inquiry in 1977 was long and hard-fought. At that inquiry it was alleged that there had been 194 incidents/accidents at Windscale between 1960 and 1977 (when the inquiry was held), eleven of which had involved fires and explosions and forty-five of which had released plutonium. Although the case against the extension was well argued, particularly by the well-respected Peter Taylor of the Oxford Political Ecology Research Group, permission was granted.

In July 1979, following a fire in the fuel de-canning cave, where metal casing is stripped off spent fuel rods, eight workers were contaminated above the permissible levels. What was permissible had become a subject of debate, and on 6 April 1978 the NRPB had advised the government that current safety limits for whole-body radiation were possibly too high and they should be reduced five-fold. The Nuclear Installations Inspectorate looked into the 1979 incident and reported on 2 August 1980 in 'the strongest attack ever made on a public utility' according to the *Guardian* of that date. It said the management had committed breaches of the Nuclear Installations Act and 'only the previous good record of the plant and the prompt remedial action taken by BNFL saved it from a prosecution for negligence'. Regarding the leak, the NII estimated this at about 100,000 curies.

By this time there was considerable concern about Windscale. In 1981 the Health and Safety Executive published a major report, *Windscale – The Management of Safety*, a hefty slam at safety standards on-site, explaining how the plant was organised and looking in depth into some seven accidents. The report concluded that by the early 1970s 'the standard of the plants at Windscale had deteriorated to an unsatisfactory level. We consider this represented a poor base line from which to develop high standards of safety. We are strongly of the opinion that such a situation should not have been allowed to develop, nor should it be permitted to occur again.' However, BNFL had taken a number of steps to ensure matters would improve and would be taking more. 'Morale and confidence in management are also important factors and we were encouraged to find these evident throughout the workforce. This should provide the conditions under which high standards of safety can be achieved', was the rousing and optimistic conclusion which, with hindsight, leads one to mutter that well-worn phrase, you ain't seen nothing yet.

After the publication of the report I was asked to review it in the *Birmingham Post* which I did, detailing the catalogue of accidents over the years leading up to its publication and suggesting that the management of BNFL were far too complacent. This brought a brisk response from a senior official at Windscale, Mr J. A. Preece, director of public information. He pointed out that I had not emphasised the fact that the NII had said, 'we would not like to give the impression that Windscale is a dangerous place at which to work or near where to live. In our view, the company shares with the best of the British chemical industry the merit of devoting considerable attention to health and safety matters at board level.' Which, I suppose, is true in view of the problems in the pesticide and asbestos industries. 'BNF is not complacent about safety', complains Mr Preece, 'and recognises there will always be room for improvement. We totally reject the allegation directed at the Company of repeated failures to deal adequately with reports which are critical of safety standards.'

Two years later, in 1983, BNF received world-wide publicity for the contamination of the Cumbrian beaches, an accident for which it was later successfully prosecuted and details of which appear at the end of the chapter.

But outside the catalogue of incidents and accidents, there has been growing public concern over pollution from Windscale, both airborne and from the sea, apart from the leaking

127

sea-pipe accident. At the time of writing actual sea dumping in this country has stopped, thanks to the efforts of the unions, although the government is agitating for it to re-start. But in 1979 BNFL was dumping each week in the sea off Liverpool alone 1500 gallons of radioactive waste which contained americum-241 and uranium from the uranium enrichment plant at Capenhurst near Aldermaston. BNFL said such dumping was 'completely safe.'

Meanwhile the two-km-long sea pipe kept on pumping out radioactive material. Traces of caesium-137 (with a half life of 30 years) have not only been found off the coast of Ireland but in fish as far away as the Baltic Sea. In 1978 the Department of the Environment noted that there had been marked increases in the plutonium-241 discharged into the Irish Sea. They also noted 11 tonnes of uranium, and a rise in the amount of strontium-90 discharged, from 11,534 curies in 1977 to 47,928 curies in 1978. Most worrying of the radio-nuclides discharged are plutonium and americum.

Radioactivity discharged into the sea does not just break up and float away as John Dunster optimistically forecast in 1958. There is ample scientific and independent proof that it ends up in the sediment on the sea bottom. Some of it disperses in sea currents and travels long distances, as has also been proved. Some moves back to land and makes, for example, for the Ravenglass estuary. Some is carried back on to the beaches at high tide, remains above the water line, dries out and blows inland.

By the time of the 1977 Public Inquiry, Windscale was discharging about 1000 times more plutonium into the sea than did its nearest dirty rival Cap de la Hague, and a staggering *million* times more than the USA's reprocessing facility at Hanford. The Irish Sea is the dirtiest, most polluted radioactive sea in the world. The discharges from Windscale would not be tolerated by the USA. In a paper prepared for the Paris Commission on the subject in 1984, Peter Taylor points out the enormous difference between Windscale and reprocessing facilities anywhere else, ending, 'It can thus be seen that other countries operating within the same international framework have achieved very high standards of control: a design target of 0.5 person/rem maximum offsite dose (these designs also offer increased worker protection), and thus "zero" liquid discharges are clearly "reasonably" achievable in technical and economic terms.'

As well as the leaky pipe there are also hotspots on the beach. In 1975 I walked along the beach nearest Windscale with a research team from Lancaster University. When we got to the point where the Drigg brook flows down to the sea, the radiation level was so high that the pointer of the Geiger counter went off the scale. Later, when I spoke to Mr Ken Semple who had worked at Windscale and monitored health and safety and radiation in the plant, he told me that the leak was well known.

The village of Drigg, four miles along the coast from Sellafield, consists of a few houses and a caravan site. BNFL had been dumping radioactive waste for years even before 1975 Said Mr Semple: 'They dig a trench about ten feet deep and about thirty feet long. A dumper truck arrives and drops the containers off. The trench lies open until it's full – possibly two or three weeks – then they fill it in and cover it over.' From the guarded gate of the dumping site there was just a wasteland planted with conifers. A woman living in one of the caravans on the site summed up the general feeling: 'I mean we've always been told it was harmless. It possibly is. But you don't know, do you?'

Confirmation of the Drigg hotspot came in 1983. Dr Barry Matthews, an internationally known specialist in soil and a member of the Agricultural Research Council's soil survey team, was contracted by the Ministry of Agriculture to find suitable sites for measuring the residual activity left by the atmospheric nuclear testing programme, and he was mapping soil in the Ravenglass and Windscale areas as part of a soil survey. He came across the hotspot near the Drigg brook, presumably where I had also come across it, and mentioned it to the management of BNFL, who responded in a reassuring manner that it was well within authorised safety limits.

Dr Matthews was far from happy and wrote to his MP (now Lord Whitelaw), and the then Energy Secretary, Michael Heseltine, both of whom replied in almost the same words as the reassurances given by BNFL. Some time later, Dr Matthews found a family picnicking by the Drigg brook and warned

129

them that he did not think it a suitable place for children to play because of radioactive contamination. The family took their concern to their MP, Dr John Cunningham, and the net result was that Dr Matthews was warned by BNFL that his comments were unwarranted. In April 1981, Dr Matthews found himself in front of a disciplinary tribunal charged with a number of offences, the most serious of which were: posing as an expert and using his official position in an unauthorised way to give an unwarranted warning to the family on the beach; and making unauthorised approaches to BNFL over the Drigg hotspot. On 18 June 1981, he was sacked. He appealed against his dismissal, and on 31 November 1981 was found to have been wrongfully dismissed. But as late as 1985 he had still not been reinstated. In December 1983, he was amply vindicated in a report published by Manchester University which found radiation levels on that part of the beach to be up to 100 times that of natural background radiation.

Dr Matthews was not alone in his troubles. John Taylor, an analytical chemist with BNFL, produced a number of reports on radioactive waste and suggested measures for improving the situation. All the reports were rejected, and in 1981 BNFL accused him of producing reports which were 'difficult to understand'. Mr Taylor began murmuring about cover-ups and in September 1982, after a long series of arguments, he resigned.

BNFL and the United Kingdom Atomic Energy Authority before it have always maintained that no worker has died as a result of working at Windscale, but from the mid-1970s onwards, as we shall see in Chapter 7, there have been an accelerating number of out-of-court settlements to the families of those who have contracted various forms of cancer after working at the plant.

On 1 November 1983 Yorkshire Television transmitted James Cutler's documentary *Windscale – The Nuclear Laundry*. It was a shocking report in every sense of the word. It showed people living with radioactive house-dust inside their own homes. It pointed out that the annual discharge of waste from Windscale's pipeline had increased one hundredfold between 1958 and 1978. It described a deliberate scientific experiment which resulted in widespread low-level radioactive contamination of the Cumbrian coast. Yorkshire TV showed an increase to ten times the national average in the rates of childhood leukaemias and cancers in the village of Seascale.

This shook even the government and they immediately set up an inquiry chaired by Sir Douglas Black. Its subsequent report offered relative reassurance but, again, we will go into its findings in more depth in Chapter 7.

It was the attempt by Greenpeace to cap the long pipeline which led to the discovery of the 1983 leak. One can only surmise if this would ever have come to light had Greenpeace not discovered it and it is ironic that it was Greenpeace who received the far greater fine for their action which drew the attention of the country to the leak. In 1985, after a very low-key trial in the Crown Court, British Nuclear Fuels received fines totalling £10,000 (Greenpeace had been fined £50,000). The judge actually said that he felt this was a suitable fine as nobody had been harmed by the radiation discharged from the pipeline . . . a statement few scientists, even those working in the nuclear industry, would feel qualified to make. BNFL had faced a number of charges connected with the pollution from the pipeline. They pleaded guilty to two. They were found 'not guilty' on a technicality of another. They were found guilty of failing to keep adequate records, to keeping down the amount of radioactivity discharged to the lowest achievable levels and for their contamination of the Cumbrian beaches. Greenpeace, on the other hand, was fined for its tampering with the Sellafield pipeline.

Again, British Nuclear Fuels has promised to put its house in order and on 5 September 1985 it announced it would not be appealing against the convictions and that one million pounds was to be spent on a public relations campaign to improve its image. On 6 September 1985 the national dailies were full of half-page advertisements from BNFL explaining what a fine company it was. The £10,000 was mentioned, with a rider to the effect that the judge had specifically stated that 'no one had been harmed' by the release of radioactivity. The judge also emphasised, continued the advertisement, what high-quality people were to be found running Sellafield.

At the time of writing, British Nuclear Fuels still has permission to discharge between 4000 and 6000 curies of radioactivity into the environment every year. Hanford waste disposal plant in the United States is now employing a totally recycled waste system resulting in *zero* liquid discharges. There is no doubt that a similar system could be introduced here if there was a will to do so.

To date there have been 300 incidents/accidents at Windscale/Sellafield at least. Here are a few of them.

The accident of 8 October 1957

This accident was caused by an experienced physicist apparently in a moment of aberration. One of the plutonium-producing reactors threw a switch too soon. The physicist was carrying out a routine operation, known in the trade as 'releasing Wigner energy', which involved raising and lowering the power level. According to his instruments, he thought that the temperature in the core was falling without completing the Wigner release. He did not have a pile operating manual (which has a special section on the Wigner release that would have told him what to do) nor had he sufficiently detailed instructions. He decided therefore to give the power level another short boost to bring the temperature back up and complete the release. What he did not know was that the instruments recording the temperature of the core were not in its hottest part: temperatures in some places were much higher than the physicist thought they were. When, at 11.05 a.m., he withdrew the control rods to raise the power level again, the additional rise in temperature ignited at least one of the rods.

He had no idea that anything was wrong. Not until 5.40 a.m. on 10 October – 42 hours and 35 minutes later – was there any indication that something was amiss inside the core of Windscale No 1 reactor. The instruments then began to show radioactivity reaching the filters on the top of the cooling air-discharge stack. This stack was considered by many of those working at Windscale as rather a joke. In 1948,

Sir John Cockcroft, head of the Atomic Energy Research establishment at Harwell, had noted a stack and filters at a reprocessing plant at Oak Ridge in the United States and, having discussed how they worked, insisted they be built into the top of No 1 stack at Windscale, already 70 feet high. It was a difficult engineering process and expensive both to construct and operate, and was considered little more than a nuisance.

In an article in *New Scientist* on 18 November 1982, P. V. Danckwerts, who had worked at Windscale, replied to a somewhat light piece by Roy Herbert about what it had been like to be at Windscale during the accident. Danckwerts, as well as detailing all the clues which should have told those in charge that something was wrong long before it was discovered, pointed out just what those filters had done. He had sat, he said, through countless meetings where requests were made to remove them, and senior management used to refer to them as 'political filters'. 'The filters remained,' he says (and claims a part in arguing for their retention) 'and saved Cumberland from being showered with radioactive particles on the *dies irae*.' 'Cockcroft's Folly' had saved an all-out catastrophe.

By the time the staff realised that something was badly wrong, the fire in the reactor was a raging inferno and spreading. Nobody knew quite what to do. Molten uranium and its cladding, highly contaminated, burned fiercely, fanned by air. Tom Tuohy, who was to become the general manager of Windscale, recalled standing on the pile cap in protective clothing looking down through a viewing port; he saw flames shooting out of the discharge face of the core and burning against the concrete shielding of the outer wall, which had to be kept below a certain temperature or it would collapse. The staff were fearful of using water, not knowing what kind of a reaction might then take place, and worried that it might cause an explosion. Some wanted to try carbon dioxide, although Tuohy reminded them that at the present temperature of the fire, the oxygen component of carbon dioxide would feed the flames as effectively as air.

Nevertheless, a tankerload of fresh liquid carbon dioxide which had just arrived on site for use as a coolant, was utilised. Tuohy was right; it just fed the flames. So only water was left.

In the early hours of the morning of 11 October, the Chief Constable of Cumberland was warned that there might well be a full-scale emergency. The fire had been raging for twenty-four hours. Desperate attempts continued to put it out with water. Only three people now remained inside the plant. Gradually the fire was brought under control but during that crucial twenty-four hours an ominous cloud of radioactivity had escaped from the molten fuel. Some had been trapped in Cockcroft's Folly; the rest had not. How much there was or of what it was composed, nobody was sure, but the first concern was over iodine-131 because of its proclivity for attacking the thyroid. The iodine-131 would get into the food chain through the cows eating polluted grass, and thence into their milk. Two million litres of milk were finally poured away. It later transpired that 20,000 curies of iodine-131 had been released.

Up in Cumberland they were still referring to this event as 'the accident' ten years ago (i.e. almost 20 years later) when I talked to people who had lived nearby. A Mrs McVery who had lived near Windscale all her life told me that she remembered clearly how the milk for the whole of the Lake District plus half that of Lancashire had to be thrown away.

We knew something had gone wrong but not what it was. It was 48 hours before they told us about the milk during which time both my sons, who were babies at the time, had drunk it. We'll never know if they should have done. You see, they don't tell you very quickly if anything goes wrong.

No effort was made to keep track of people who were near to the Windscale plant at the time of the accident, but in Chapter 7 we will look more closely at the cases of those who allege they were harmed.

After the accident there was a full-scale inquiry and the No 2 reactor was shut down in order to discover if a similar fault could also occur in that. The full report is still secret, but what does seem clear is that no economic way could be found to make No 2 safe, and it and Reactor 1 remained closed down.

Twenty-five years later, it became known from a document in the House of Commons Library that there had also been an emission of radioactive polonium-210 during the Windscale accident. A study published by the National Radiological Protection Board estimated that there would probably have been about twenty cancer deaths as a result of the fire and possibly 230 thyroid cancers, but did not mention the emission of polonium or a number of other radioactive substances. In March 1983, Mr David Hunt, MP for Wirral and a senior Conservative government Whip, asked Mr John Moore, the minister responsible for nuclear energy, why the escape of these other substances had not been reported. A spokesman for the NRPB said it was embarrassed as it had not known that polonium had been released. However, it appeared that there had been two monitored measurements of airborne concentrations of polonium at the time, one in the UK and one in Holland, and *Nature* magazine had drawn attention to these on 6 September 1958.

BNFL said that the amount of polonium was very small and there was no evidence that it would do anyone any harm. Mr Hunt's effort to draw the attention of the NRPB to the polonium resulted in their revising their figures and adding another twelve possible deaths, later amended to 20, then 33, and now considered by experts outside government to be more than that. Despite this, BNFL said there was no proof that anyone in the UK had contracted cancer or died of it as a result of the 1957 Windscale fire.

The NRPB report did, however, bring to light many disquieting facts about just what did happen in 1957 and what hazards the workers were exposed to before and after. The *Sunday Times* of 23 February 1983 ran the story of Les Jenkins who had worked at Windscale during the clear-up after the accident. On his arrival at the plant he was given a plastic suit and head-covering and sent to the No 1 pile building. Facing him, he said, was a concrete wall pitted with fuel channels from which protruded plutonium rods. The men were given long poles and told to push the fuel rods back through the wall. 'No one knew quite what was happening,' said Jenkins. 'We just did what the people in charge told us. We presumed they knew all the answers.'

135

Next he was sent to an underground pool directly below the pile, which contained about 1000 rods submerged in ten feet of water. 'The whole pool was lit by underwater spotlights which made everything glow and look an eerie green colour. The men fished for the rods with the 18-foot poles. They told us the rods were safe underwater.' The radioactive rods were placed on a machine in the corner of the chamber where the aluminium casing was stripped off, exposing the heavy rods themselves. Another machine then broke each rod into foot-long pieces. Red and green lights kept flashing on and off and alarm bells rang. His 'film badge', used to monitor the amount of radioactivity, recorded so much that it turned black. When he complained, he was told the badge must be faulty and given a new one. 'After use, the film badges should have been sent to the health physics laboratory for testing, but I found hundreds of them strewn all over the place, lying on tables, kicked into corners.'

When he talked to the *Sunday Times*, Mr Jenkins, who was then 52 years old, was suffering from bone-marrow cancer, was blind in one eye and weighed only 8½ stone. He had taken his case to his MP, David Hunt. Mr Jenkins pondered on whether others had cancer without knowing how it might have been caused: 'I want my case to be a warning to the other men who are walking around today not knowing their days are numbered, because we all walked into hell and never knew it.'

The accident at the head-end plant, 26 September 1973

The B204 reprocessing plant at Windscale had been built by the UKAEA as a purely military plant, civil waste being reprocessed through B205. With the second wave of enthusiasm for nuclear power, it was decided in 1965 to convert B204 into a 'head-end plant' to cope with an annual maximum of about 300 tonnes of fuel from the new advanced gas-cooled reactors then being built. These use not only uranium fuel but also ceramic uranium oxide fuel, which was more difficult to deal with as it had first to be chopped up and then dissolved in acid before it could be fed into B205. But there were countless problems with the AGR programme, long, long delays and a whole series of mishaps, so the B204 plant was left without much to do.

In 1971, of course, Windscale went commercial. British Nuclear Fuels decided this reduced output would not do and so began taking in waste from all over the world. By 1973, BNFL were planning to reprocess 1150 tonnes a year, and more and more of it piled up in the cooling ponds waiting to be dealt with. It was also announced that the head-end plant was to be upgraded to cope with 400 tonnes a year, and Britain would then lead the world – in truth becoming the world's nuclear dustbin.

What BNFL did not, apparently, appreciate, although many experts did, was that fuel which had spent two years or more in a power reactor is much more radioactive than weapons-produced fuel. Radiation also damages the acids used to dissolve it, making it hard to dissolve and process. Also, the higher burn-up of power causes changes in the fuel itself, the chain reaction producing strange metals such as rhodium, which is inert. If enough of these accumulate in the fuel, they form into tiny particles of metal alloy that are very radioactive, very dangerous and insoluble even in hot nitric acid.

On 26 September 1973, the workers began feeding in a new batch of fuel just after the head-end plant had been flushed out. They did not know that the previous batch had left a thin layer of sludge comprising radioactive granules in the bottom of a process vessel. The heat from the granules had boiled away all the residual fluid and had left the vessel boiling hot. When the new amount of process solution reached the hot vessel, it reacted violently, spurting a spray of radioactive material past a shaft seal and into the air in the plant, contaminating 35 workers. The Nuclear Installations Inspectorate was called in and the plant shut down.

In the NII's later report, it was stated that there had been an appalling state of unreadiness for accidents at the plant. One of the most obvious and most important safety measures, recognised by everybody, is that if you have to deal with material which can result in a dangerous accident, then it is absolutely vital that there are clear and unambiguous warning systems and efficient plans for immediate evacuation of all personnel. Neither operated at Windscale.

Warnings of danger were totally unclear. For a considerable period, health physics personnel and senior workmen ran from floor to floor trying to find out if the alarms actually meant what they said. A general order to evacuate was finally given by workers shouting on each floor that the building had to be cleared.

During this time, every breath of air could have meant an early death from cancer of the lung. It later turned out that no proper record had ever been kept of those who were working in the building and so nobody knew who was there and who was not. Long after the building had been evacuated, two painters and two workmen were found still working there.

For the two years following the accident, BNFL repeatedly claimed that all was well and the plant was about to be restored to service once repairs and cleaning up were completed. Four years after the accident, BNFL finally conceded defeat: the plant was a write-off. In its entire life, the head-end plant had actually reprocessed only 100 tonnes of nuclear fuel.

Seven Accidents from the NII Report *'Windscale – The Management of Safety'*

In 1981 the NII published a blistering attack on the standards of health and safety at Windscale although they did concede that matters had been and were improving.

Silo leaks, October 1976 and October 1978

The silos at Windscale are large concrete structures used for the underwater storage of irradiated Magnox scrap. The original silo, with a total capacity of about 3600m, was brought into service in 1964. On 10 October 1976, radioactivity was found in a nearby excavation after heavy rain. It was subsequently shown to be due to a leak of contaminated water from the silo at some point below ground level. The NII found that some 50,000 curies of radioactivity may have escaped into the ground nearby.

On 31 October 1978, an abnormally high concentration of

hydrogen was detected in the first extension of the silo. This was due to a more than usually vigorous chemical reaction between Magnox and water. Although no radioactivity escaped, work in neighbouring buildings had to be suspended while remedial measures were taken.

Both these incidents, said the NII, were basically due to inadequate design of the silo, inadequate instrumentation for monitoring and inadequate arrangements for cooling and ventilation. The first rise in water temperature due to rapid corrosion between Magnox and water had been noted in 1968, and a similar rise in temperature in 1972 may have damaged the concrete sufficiently to cause the leak discovered in 1976. The design might have been better if there had been more basic information about the corrosion reactions of the silo.

Spillage of 29 July 1978

On 29 July 1978 about 200 litres of radioactive liquid effluent from a monitoring tank overflowed from a sump which had been provided to protect against such overflows, and about 15 litres spilled into a plant roadway. A high-level alarm, which might have given warning of the level of liquid in the sump, had been isolated for ten months, and an alternative level indicator had been taken off the regular monitoring schedule. Further contributory factors included the maloperation of valves controlling the flow of effluent, and a leaking valve which had regularly allowed significantly high levels in the sump. The maloperation was partly due to a confusing identification system for the valves, and the valve leaked because of corrosion as the tanks were originally designed to hold another liquid.

Fire of 4 February 1979

On 4 February 1979, a fire started in the disused separation plant building while oxy-acetylene equipment was being used to cut away obsolete pipework. Hot metal spray from the welder fell through a gap between the floor and the building's outer cladding, and then on to an archive store which caught fire. The incident was due to a failure to observe all the procedures governing an operation that presents such obvious fire risks. It was made even more serious as the archive store was not up to current safety standards, and because the workmen had difficulty in summoning the works fire service: a fire alarm had been removed and the single telephone line to the local fire station was engaged at the time! To deal with the situation, the electrical supply to the building was disconnected; this, in turn, meant a loss of electricity in adjacent buildings, which affected their ventilation systems. In fighting the fire, defects in the equipment and the training of the works fire force were also revealed.

The B701 leak

A leak of highly radioactive liquid from the disused B701 plant into the nearby ground was reported on 15 March 1979. A diverter in the process pipework allowed liquid to splash over and enter pipes leading to B701, where it overfilled a receiving tank and flowed into its sump. This in turn filled up, and the liquid subsequently leaked through the side walls of the building into the ground, releasing more than 100,000 curies of radioactivity over a period of time. Among the reasons for this accident were the following. The flow of active liquid through the diverter had been increased without the possibilities of an accident being considered. Throughout most of the 1970s, the ageing tank in B701 was full of liquid and there were varying amounts in the sump. In the early years, care had been taken to clean out the sump regularly, but this became less and less frequent and then ceased altogether; the main sump-emptying pipe had been removed accidentally, probably in 1971. The recording of liquid levels in the sump ceased in 1973 and only started again in 1977 when renovated gauges were fitted. There is evidence that the sump was emptied in May 1978, at which time the removal of the section of sump-emptying pipe was discovered. Despite the identification of at least three possible sources of radioactive liquid which might enter the sump, its contents were considered to be mainly rainwater, and by March 1979 about 3000 litres had been allowed to accumulate. During this time, the sump gauge went off scale and its pointer was travelling around the gauge on its second circuit before anybody noticed. In November 1978 when an unusually high level of radioactivity was detected in a borehole near B701, it was ascribed to a spillage twenty years previously. Any analysis of samples was postponed until February 1979, which led to a three-month delay in determining the important fact that the leak was recent and continuing. Although a spillover into the diverter in the B701 plant had been noticed in 1964, the possibility of this was not taken into account in the 1976 safety assessment. The NII in its report considered that

> the circumstances of the incident indicate that the operational system viewed as a whole has not been adequate to maintain the necessary control over radioactive liquors being handled in the area. The main weakness in this instance appears to arise as a result of management responses which were lacking in the level of judgement and safety-consciousness expected. The engineering part of the system, while not meeting present-day standards, would otherwise have been adequate to prevent the incident occurring.

Fire in the de-canning plant

On 16 July 1979, a fire occurred in the de-canning plant. During a routine dejamming operation, particles of uranium caught fire and fell into accumulated Magnox swarf (i.e. sludge), which should have been removed before the operation began; this also caught fire. It took 45 minutes to put the blaze out, during which time a small amount of radioactivity was released.

Fires of this kind had occurred before and had been swiftly dealt with, but on this occasion one of the hoses tangled and could not be directed on to the fire. The ventilation system was turned off briefly to try and starve the fire of air, but this did not work and instead blew back radioactive air.

Spill of 11 September 1979

On 11 September 1979, there was a release of airborne radioactivity from a low-active effluent treatment plant

141

during a planned movement of radioactive solvent. During the operation, liquid overflowed from the tank into its sump and spilled solvent evaporated into the building. A pump provided to empty the sump did not do so, and an alarm which might have warned the operators of the presence of liquid in the sump was not working. The main causes were: inadequate tank design, inadequate performance of the pump, insufficient understanding of the complexities of the plant by the staff concerned, failure of the sump-level detector system (possibly due to previous maloperation), lack of tank high-level alarms, and inadequate operating instructions.

The contamination of the Cumbrian beaches

On 11 November 1983 an alarm sounded out across the Windscale plant (now officially called Sellafield). High levels of radioactivity had been recorded from pipes leading from a building where waste from the annual clean-out of the plant was being stored ready for disposal down the notorious pipeline.

That alarm only reached the ears of the public on 15 November and this was not due to a speedy admission by BNFL. It was due to Greenpeace. For many years Greenpeace had been campaigning vigorously about discharges from Windscale in general and from the pipeline in particular and the publicity given to the leukaemia cases at Seascale finally prompted them to take drastic action and that action was to 'cap' or block the pipeline into the sea. A cat-and-mouse game was played with the authorities over the proposed action, but Greenpeace did finally make the attempt. On 15 November they announced that they had discovered a large amount of contamination in the form of a radioactive 'slick' off the end of the pipeline. Their boat was heavily affected, and their clothing had to be destroyed; both were contaminated with ruthenium.

At this stage, BNFL announced that they had had an incident connected with the pipeline.

At the subsequent press conference in December, Coningsby 'Con' Allday, chairman of BNFL, admitted that a serious error had been made. The manager in charge of that part of the plant had failed to read the logbook properly. This would have told him what was in the tank he was about to open into the sea tanks for final disposal down the pipeline into the sea. He did not realise that, as well as radioactive liquid destined for the sea tanks, there was also a large amount of what is known in the trade as 'crud' – a highly radioactive surface layer of solvent and scum. The crud should have been floated off the top of the tank before the rest of the contents were emptied. It wasn't. The sludge and crud passed, along with the rest of the waste, into the sea tank, whereupon the alarm sounded. After five minutes the staff shut down the valves and stopped further disposal.

According to Mr Allday, what happened next was that most of the sludge, containing 4500 curies of radioactivity, was caught and transferred back into the waste tanks, but a small amount was allowed out through the pipeline to flush out the system. 'This is the first time this simple but damaging mishap has been made at the plant. The mistake was neither the result of neglect nor was it culpable,' he said. 'I conclude it was a genuine misunderstanding between managers caused by a complex series of events.'

Two subsequent reports failed to put such a gloss on the matter. One was by the Nuclear Installations Inspectorate, the other by the Radiochemicals Inspectorate of the Department of the Environment. It later transpired that there had been three leaks – on 11, 13 and 16 November. Some six days after the first leakage and two days after Greenpeace made its announcement, the beach near Windscale was sealed off by armed guards as the slick hit the shore. However, two days later, on 19 November, BNFL firmly declared that the area was 'safe'.

The first report – from the NII in December – yet again severely criticised the Windscale/Sellafield management. It said that by the time the alarm went off most of the crud had reached the tank which was the last staging post before the sea. At first, on 11 November, BNFL tried to release the liquid into the sea but keep the crud and solvent in the tank. The residue was then pumped into another tank for safety, but the pipes used in the operation became highly radioactive. The management then decided to clean them out on 13

November by flushing the material in them into the sea through an old discharge pipeline. They had to be flushed out three times because, after each of the first two attempts, radiation levels in the pipes unaccountably rose again.

Among other things the NII report said that the Windscale management had failed to learn the lessons of its earlier report drawn up in 1981, previously referred to. (It was my review of this report which prompted BNFL to say 'we totally reject the allegation directed at the Company of repeated failure to deal adequately with reports which are critical of safety standards' . . .)

On 7 December 1983, the government issued a warning to the public not to use the beaches along the whole 25-mile stretch of coastline near Windscale. True to form, the Ministry of Agriculture had earlier carried out its own survey of the Windscale beaches, but refused to release the full report of its findings with comparative figures and Geiger counter measurements, though it was reliably reported that more than 1000 times the normal background radioactivity had been found on some parts of the beach. The government had finally acted after this report which also appears to have said that there was radioactive contamination of seaweed, pieces of flotsam, string and plants between St Bees Head (about 10 miles up the coast from Sellafield) and Eskmeals. The public were also advised to refrain from handling any material washed up by the sea. Asked why no warning had been given back in November, a government spokesman said that at that time the level was 'consistent with the level of radioactivity that would have been expected prior to the incident'.

By February 1984 more information was coming out. It appeared, from the report by the Radiochemicals Inspectorate, that an entry in the official logbook had been altered to conceal the extent of the discharge. It had previously been said (and logged) that about 500 curies of radioactivity had been flushed out to sea and about 4500 diverted into the storage tank. (Windscale/Sellafield was permitted at that time to discharge 15,000 curies over three months.) It now appeared that virtually all of the crud finally went into the sea which, although it was technically within the limit of 15,000 curies over three months, breached the principle that discharges at any one time should be kept as low as possible. As well as this alteration, there were also 'inexplicit entries' in the logbook and deletions made to instructions for maintenance technicians.

Right from the start, questions had been asked as to why BNFL had waited nearly a week before making public the details of the accident. Why had they said that there had been no breach of the limits? Why had they not even told the local liaison committee at Windscale of the leak, especially as it had met with BNFL officials only two days before BNFL finally made its announcement? When, shortly after the incident, Dale Campbell Savours, MP, had asked in the House of Commons if anyone had been contaminated by the leak, he was told 'No'. In fact, eight people had been contaminated with ruthenium.

In February 1984, the NRPB published a fuller account of the contamination of the beach, and in March 1984 it announced that more radioactive waste was being found on the beaches – a tar-like substance different from that which had turned up following the leakage. The NRPB said that there had been a drop in the amount of radioactivity on the beaches at first, but this had not been sustained after 18 February, when they had last reported on the matter. It was not known where the new radioactivity was coming from, whether from parts of the beach uncovered by tidal action or from radioactivity already in the sea brought in by unusual tides, or whether there had been a new discharge by BNFL. BNFL denied the latter. By April 1984, the Nuclear Installations Inspectorate had joined in and were suggesting that radioactive contamination had been present on the beaches long before the November leak.

The government has consistently refused to hold a public inquiry although this was even demanded by the Sellafield workers in December 1983, when a vote of no confidence in the management was passed by a hitherto docile workforce. However, in August 1984, after mounting pressure, the government announced measures to stiffen controls over firms dealing with radioactive waste.

Two days later, following a six-month police investigation, the Director of Public Prosecutions decided to press charges against BNFL, prosecuting them under the Radioactive Substances Act of 1960 and the Nuclear Installations Act of 1965. The DPP alleged that BNFL had failed to comply with its certificate of authorisation and the conditions of its site licence. It was also charged with failing to keep proper records, for failing to keep discharges as low as reasonably achievable and to keep radioactive discharges and material under proper control. Nobody knows why the government did not bring the charges itself, nor why the matter was turned over to the DPP. The beaches remained closed for six months.

The uranium leak

Following the contamination-of-the-beaches incident, BNFL's credibility as a safe processor of nuclear waste reached just about zero. In a Gallup poll published in December 1985, of those asked if they thought British Nuclear Fuels was doing a good job with waste disposal and keeping the public properly informed, only fourteen per cent said 'Yes'.

On 23 January 1986 there was another leak. This time nearly half a tonne of uranium was dumped into the Irish Sea following another equipment failure at the plant. (The first statement issued by BNFL spoke of 'a few kilograms'.) The presence of the uranium was discovered when engineers sampled one of the two seawater tanks from which the diluted waste is discharged over the beach and into the sea. Some 440 kilograms of uranium were found to have accumulated in the tank – a significant proportion of the three tonnes BNFL normally pumps into the Irish Sea each year. The fault has been put down to a malfunction in a faulty evaporator in a plant handling uranyl nitrate. British Nuclear Fuels did inform the Department of the Environment, and it was mutually agreed that, since the amount of radioactivity present – even in such a large amount – was still apparently within permitted discharge safety limits, the tank should just be emptied out into the sea.

The significance of this particular mishap is that it is so similar to that which resulted in the contamination of the Cumbrian beaches – even after British Nuclear Fuels had said, once again, that steps had been taken to see that it would not happen again. ('This is just what the west coast tourist industry needs,' commented a local hotelier . . .)

British Nuclear Fuels' initial response was that the amount of radioactivity involved was much less than that in the discharge of 1983. It could, said BNFL, have drained the tanks back into the plant instead of releasing the water into the sea, but the Nuclear Installations Inspectorate and the Ministry of Agriculture had both agreed that it was all right to let the uranium go into the Irish Sea.

The nuclear mist

On 5 February 1986 BNFL put its Sellafield plant on 'Amber' alert, only two weeks after the uranium-dumping incident. There are four stages of alert. Amber is the second, the other two are Red and Purple. The Amber alert indicated an emergency in one building and a threat to the rest of the plant. The next stage, Red, would have indicated that the site had become contaminated and there was a danger to the environment. Purple means the whole district around the plant is under threat. The previous Amber alert was after the 1973 'blow-back' incident at the head-end plant, that part of the plant which has never reopened.

The alert occurred at about 9 a.m. when warning signals indicated there had been contamination. The accident happened in Building 205 of the big de-canning plant where spent uranium rods are stripped down for reprocessing. After the spent fuel rods are fed into the system and their casing stripped away, they are dissolved in hot nitric acid and the uranium and plutonium separated. Small amounts of the chemicals are siphoned off during the process, and it was at an early stage in the process that the accident occurred.

A team of workers was repairing a faulty valve used to pump out some of the plutonium nitrate for testing, but before this was done the valve had been enclosed in a plastic container. When the leak began, it was not contained within the plastic enclosure, and monitors outside began registering increasing levels of contamination.

Seventy-one workers had to be evacuated and the plant was

shut down. It took staff two-and-a-half hours to find the source of the contamination, and BNFL said that, by the afternoon, staff had returned to decontaminate the building.

The first statement from BNFL was that the mist of plutonium nitrate released 'was contained within the plant'. Doubts were immediately expressed by outside experts as to whether the mist could be so contained and one source said that 45 microcuries had been released into the atmosphere. 'There are no implications for the rest of the site and none for the public,' said BNFL. The workers were checked for contamination, said BNFL, but initial tests using face and nose swabs were negative. 'No one' had suffered any contamination from the plutonium nitrate.

The next day BNFL changed its mind. Two workers, it said, had been contaminated by the leak: contamination had been detected in tests on nasal mucus. Jim Coote, a physics health and safety officer at the plant, said that the affected building sustained 'no significant exposure'. On the contamination of the two workers, he stated: 'The level detected in the nose tests was so small that it was most unlikely there was a real intake of plutonium, but even if there was the level of intake would be very small.'

BNFL also changed its mind as to whether or not the mist 'was contained within the plant'. A junior Energy Minister, Alistair Goodlad, told the House of Commons that a small amount of radiation 'may have escaped into the atmosphere'. The amount was estimated at about 50 microcuries.

All spokesmen for BNFL played down any possibility of hazard. Mr Con Allday, chairman and chief executive of BNFL, described the leak as 'a small contained release'. 'I am amazed,' he said to the *Guardian* on 7 February, 'it has hit the headlines.' Mr Allday had, until 1986, survived all the Sellafield incidents since he became a director in 1975, including the reshuffle of senior management in 1984, following the Cumbrian beaches incident.

On 12 February, it was reported that workers at Sellafield had been threatened with prosecution under Section 2 of the Official Secrets Act if they said anything more to reporters. Notices had been posted all over the plant reminding employees that they had signed the Act as a condition of their employment. It was employees from within Sellafield who had alerted the local press to the nuclear mist and the Amber alert.

On 15 February, Con Allday wrote a spirited defence of Sellafield in the *Guardian*. It was published the day after news had broken of yet another incident there – a fire in the waste dump at Drigg where the low-level waste is buried. Early tests on smoke, said BNFL, showed 'no significant increase in radioactivity'.

Mr Allday denied that Sellafield should be criticised for its safety record. 'To talk of the safety record of Sellafield as poor and to refer to hundreds of incidents is nonsense.' However, public records show that there have been over 300 (see Appendix 1). Mr Allday also complained bitterly of the way the media had attacked BNFL. The incident had been only a small one, he said, easily coped with, but the media had gone in for wild, inflammatory scaremongering, having been tipped off by someone inside Sellafield. He said:

> As is well known, the incident was minor; there was no risk to the public; and none of our employees were significantly contaminated. Out of 71 examined, two showed results at the 'limits of detection' which *may* mean they are very slightly, but not dangerously, contaminated.

Even as readers of the *Guardian* were contemplating his response over their breakfast tables, BBC Radio 4 news was telling a different story: BNFL had admitted that *eleven* workers had been found to be contaminated, and there was also a possibility a further four had been affected, not two. Of those, one had received the maximum permitted dosage for a whole year – 0.5 millisieverts. The others had received less, but tests would continue.

Whether or not there was a breakdown in communication between Mr Allday and his press office is not clear, but such conflicting statements do little to reassure those who feel worried about Sellafield's safety record.

Concern about Windscale/Sellafield is growing, not diminishing. The government is financing a scientific study to discover whether radioactivity from Sellafield is responsible for the disappearance of one of the country's largest colonies of gulls from a famous Cumbrian bird sanctuary. The colony has been known since Roman times and is mentioned in the Domesday Book; Ravenglass gulls' eggs used to be sold in Harrods. Until 1981 the Ravenglass estuary supported 16,000 pairs of black-headed gulls, but after three years of trying to raise chicks – and failing – the gulls abandoned the estuary.

Many eggs did not hatch at all, and if they did, those chicks which emerged had lost the instinct to feed and died within a few days. Tony Warburton, a warden at the sanctuary, said that it was not just the gulls; he had hatched oystercatcher chicks and used normal feed stimulation but these too showed no interest in food and died.

A spokesman for Greenpeace said that birds had always been a 'miner's lamp' for pollution. They had warned about DDT and now they had abandoned Ravenglass. An experiment carried out by the Canadian government 'had shown that nesting birds avoided areas close to radiation'. Scientists have found radio-nuclides right across the Ravenglass estuary and blame both the pipeline carrying waste out into the Irish Sea and the Drigg dump. Apart from its fire on 1 February there is much criticism of the Drigg dump which we will look at in Chapter 11.

The 14 February 1986 issue of the *New Statesman* published yet another story from inside Sellafield. According to what the Cumbrians Opposed to a Radioactive Environment (CORE) say is an 'unimpeachable source', there is a leak from the Pond 5 spent-fuel-rod storage complex, which has been leaking radioactive water through the floor ever since it went into operation in November 1985.

Pond 5 was officially 'launched' by Margaret Thatcher, in November 1985, along with the new site ion-exchange plant, and a good deal of media publicity was given to the Prime Minister's expression of her total confidence in BNFL. BNFL will admit only that there are some 'damp spots' in the concrete, but CORE's source says that there are cracks in the floor and that water is being caught in buckets in a basement. They add that a haulage contractor working on Pond 5 recently had to dump eleven tons of substandard concrete.

If you add to this the information contained in a confidential report leaked to the *Guardian*, which stated that some of the scientific staff working at Sellafield were said to be neurotic and unstable, that its management was outdated and that some of the armed police there were incompetent, then you might well think the time had come for a complete reappraisal of the worth of the place.

This report was prepared by Douglas Wilkinson, a clinical psychologist for the West Cumbria Hospital, at the request of Dr A. W. B. Lawson, chief medical officer for BNFL. Mr Wilkinson's brief was to look at the application of psychology to the nuclear industry.

During his investigation, Mr Wilkinson was concerned to find that some workers had deliberately exposed themselves to excessive levels of radiation in order to earn a few days off sick. He was also concerned and alarmed at what he thought might happen due to the apparent unpreparedness of some personnel in the police force, and wondered if they had been sufficiently well trained.

Staff from Sellafield, he said, passed through the psychiatric casualty system at the local general hospital at a considerable rate, and there could be still more in the workforce with psychiatric and psychological problems: 'This means a lot of people, with a lot of problems, daily travelling in and out of a plutonium factory.'

Some of the scientists, he said, appeared to be constitutionally 'unstable and neurotic', and he wondered how 'such obviously disturbed people were employed in the plant in the first place'.

Perhaps most interesting of all in view of the knee-jerk reaction of BNFL to all criticism, Mr Wilkinson said that those working at the plant showed evidence of an attitude which made it difficult for them to understand, or react appropriately to, public pressures and complaints about leaks, secrecy and so on and staff complaints about 'the system'.

'It is no way to run a modern industry,' he said, 'to take the attitude that "staff should be stretched and if we have to cause a few nervous breakdowns on the way, that's just too bad."' If the workforce was not handled in the best professional manner, there would be an increase in the possibility of 'human error', an important part of the total risk attached to the operation of nuclear power plants.

The findings of Douglas Wilkinson's report were immediately repudiated by the BNFL management, who said that it had been submitted some four years previously but never published.

At the time of writing the EEC Commission has asked for full details of the discharge of uranium into the sea and the Irish government is said to be furious about both that leak and the 'nuclear mist'. At the time of the mist, prevailing north-easterly winds would have carried any contamination over heavily populated areas.

The last in an almost daily series of revelations about Sellafield during the early part of 1986 came in the *Guardian* on 28 February, when it was revealed that BNFL had rejected a report which said two plutonium-producing reactors, one at Calder Hall (Sellafield) and the other at Chapel Cross (on the Solway Firth), have design faults. In fact each station consists of four reactors, making a total of eight in all.

In 1983, a team of structural engineers was commissioned to look into the safety of Magnox reactors run by BNFL, after BNFL and the electricity boards had decided to extend the working life of these reactors. Their report concluded that the reactors were in danger of destruction from even a minor earth tremor. Such a tremor would destroy the key bolts holding each of the reactors some eighteen feet above the ground. This would result in them crashing down, possibly causing an uncontrollable fire and discharging radioactivity into the surrounding countryside. The likelihood of such an accident happening, said the engineers, was between one in 100 and one in 1000.

In 1979, there was an earthquake fifteen miles away from the Chapel Cross reactor, the third strongest tremor in the British Isles this century. This led the industry to check if the reactors were vulnerable. If the bolts on the Solway Firth reactors were damaged in any way, there is no way of knowing since they are hidden behind five-foot-thick concrete shielding and cannot be seen. Radioactivity inside the shielding is too great for access without extreme hazard.

One of the team of engineers, Peter Phelan, said, 'The

findings shocked me. I checked and rechecked them. It meant that the kind of tremor that would rattle the windows but not break them could destroy this nuclear power station.' As the pressure vessel is eighteen feet above the ground and weighs 2000 tons, a quake might crack the concrete shield causing an immediate release of radioactivity. In any event the pipes cooling the reactors would break causing immediate over-heating and the pressure vessel might well burst as the heat builds up. Mr Phelan told the *Guardian* that he remembered someone from BNFL 'joking' when he made his findings known, saying, 'It would be a very brave man who recom-mended the closure of these stations.'

The report was sent to BNFL, and nothing happened for a year. Then BNFL asked a firm called Principia Mechanicia to construct other mathematical models. The latter said that BNFL wanted the engineers to prove that the whole thing 'would lock solid and not collapse'. 'We told them frankly that we did not accept their figures but they asked us to prepare the document anyway.' The engineers went away and reworked their study but added the proviso that they were sure the premise on which they were asked to do so was wrong. The report was then sent to the Nuclear Installations Inspectorate but, at the time of writing, it is not known whether the views of the engineers as to the validity of the second study were ever passed on to the NII. BNFL, said Mr Phelan, 'were using unproved, and as far as I know unprovable, assumptions. We pointed this out but were told to do it anyway.'

In answer to this, a spokesman for BNFL told the *Guardian* that the company had nothing to hide: 'Everything we asked the consultants to do was technically supportable. We never coerced them.'

BNFL admitted that the reactors had not been designed to stand seismic shocks – they were designed and built in a rush in the 1950s to provide plutonium for Britain's bomb. Peter Dickens, technical manager of BNFL at Calder Hall, said that danger from earthquakes was unlikely. Nor did he think that the pressure vessel would fall to the ground as predicted. 'Initial calculations, we felt, were not representative. There was some unusual behaviour which was not physically cred-ible.' He went on to say that if calculations do not 'reach your expectation or common sense, you altered them to represent the situation, to the best of your ability.' BNFL were satisfied that there was no problem. The Nuclear Installations Inspectorate said it had relied on the information supplied by BNFL.

Suggestions that these ageing reactors might be closed down are likely to fall on deaf ears as they produce the plutonium for Britain's highly criticised Trident programme, a programme which all the opposition parties are against and to which opinion polls show a majority of the public to be opposed.

Two other reactors at Bradwell and Berkeley, though of a different design, are also not designed to withstand earthquakes.

The story of BNFL and Sellafield, will – on present form – run and run.

Chapter 6

More Problems

As well as the USA and Britain, the other nations which have developed nuclear power programmes have also had their problems, a selection of which follows.

France

Opposition to the French nuclear power programme has grown steadily over the years, leading in some cases to massive demonstrations and even full-blown riots. The main area of concentrated nuclear activity is Cap de la Hague on the Cotentin peninsula. The reprocessing plant there is somewhat similar to that of British Nuclear Fuels at Sellafield. While it is thought of as a 'dirty' plant it is not considered by experts to be as dirty as Sellafield.

When the plant was first built, the local population were told it was to make light electrical goods – televisions, clothes washers, dishwashers and so forth. Cynicism set in when the light engineering factory not only apparently required a 300-foot chimney stack but also a very long pipe going out to sea. The French authorities denied there was to be a nuclear facility on the site until the nuclear scientists actually moved in.

Just as at Three-Mile Island and countless other sites, the local people were told it was totally safe, there was no danger, nothing could go wrong . . . Then an accident at the plant in 1966 released radioactivity into the atmosphere, including radioactive iodine-131. As in the Windscale accident in 1957 all milk had to be destroyed because it was contaminated and even the name of the local butter had to be changed. By 1975, local fishermen were complaining that fish caught in the area appeared to be affected by pollution and that their flesh turned black; a government survey confirmed that fish caught off Cap de la Hague were five times more radioactive than those caught off Cap Fréhel sixty-two miles away.

By 1977, officials of the main French union concerned with the plant, the CFTD, were expressing grave concern over the management of safety at Cap de la Hague. In an inquiry into health and safety, the union opposed any further extension of the facility until it could be proved that it posed no hazard to health. 'It is clear,' argued the union in its submission, 'that the management has chosen to consider the reprocessing of spent fuel as a simple commercial operation whose success is assured simply by obtaining a juicy contract. We are totally opposed to this concept.'

CFTD went on to detail the carelessness and general lack of concern shown by the operators of the Cap de la Hague plant. Accidents had become commonplace. During one four-week period, picked at random and monitored by the union, there had been forty-two incidents. Nine had resulted in complete stoppages lasting a maximum of eleven days; five evacuations had been necessary due to contamination; seven days were lost through decontamination during which ten incidents occurred. In an industry noted for saying how safety-conscious it is and how little prone to accidents, it appeared that there had been only one day out of the whole four weeks during which there was no nuclear incident of any kind.

The unions also made public that there were continuous leaks from the waste pipe which, like that at Windscale, took the waste out to sea. By 1977 it had broken thirty times and it still leaks with monotonous regularity. There were also leaks on the landward side of the pipe causing contamination both of the ground and fresh water. The union also got hold of a secret government report which said that dispersal of radioactive material into the sea was not very effective: large amounts of radioactivity had been found in concentrated sites up to sixty miles away from the coast off Cap de la Hague and it was clear that the waste did not disperse in the nicely ordered way that had been thought. The results of the research, said the government report, 'are a great lesson in prudence'. A lesson which has still not been learned, it seems.

On 15 April 1980, there was a short circuit in one of the two

90,000-volt transformers which fed the plant. This caused a fire which spread rapidly to the building that distributed the medium-tension 15,000 volts to the rest of the plant. It took two hours to bring the blaze under control, by which time the plant had lost all its electric power supply, the fission products were no longer being cooled, and the ventilation systems had packed up along with the entire plant intercom system. According to the unions, the only thing left working at the end of the incident was the electric fence around the perimeter, which had its own independent power supply.

What of the back-up equipment? Well, the plant had its own emergency generating system in the event of such an accident, but although there were four diesel generators available, only one was actually in working order and that failed because it immediately provided electricity to the building which was already burning. Unable to think of what to do next, the plant operators finally called in the army, and engineers rigged up a temporary system of electrical high-tension cables, all of which, say the unions, were then left trailing on the ground. Fortunately, there was no fuel being reprocessed at the time.

Two years later, a report by an American engineer claimed that the accident almost caused an explosion that would have led to the massive radioactive contamination of southern England, including London. (French safety experts have made much of the fact that, should there be an accident, radioactivity would most likely blow away from France – i.e. over England.)

The report, drawn up by Dr Arjun Makhijani, who holds a doctorate in nuclear fusion from the University of California, was submitted as evidence as part of a case against the building of a nuclear reprocessing plant in South Carolina. In the report, he claimed that if the French army had not been called in promptly with an emergency generator, there would have been a complete breakdown of the plant's cooling system, causing an explosion similar to that at Chelyabinsk which would have scattered the debris right across the Channel.

Dr Makhijani also detailed the long history of mishaps and accidents at Cap de la Hague. He revealed that the accident had happened only ten minutes before a new load of

157

plutonium was due to be loaded into the system. Plutonium without agitation, he said, goes critical. The subsequent accident would have been in two stages: the total breakdown of the cooling system would have led after a few hours to an explosion of the high level waste tanks; then there might well have been a meltdown in the reactor with all that implies. The doctor emphasised that the engineers who had built the Cap de la Hague plant had 'cleverly sited it' so that most of the radioactivity would automatically blow away from the French coast.

'Towns along the southern coast of England would have been in danger and London would have been in the cloud's path,' he said. 'There would have been massive contamination.' He provided figures to show that the plant had operated for substantial periods of time at only 10 per cent capacity and that there had been a serious accident every four months between January 1980 and June 1982, including continual spills of large quantities of plutonium and a fire in a radioactive storage trench.

There was immediate reaction from the French Atomic Energy Commission which dismissed Dr Makhijani's report as 'science fiction', 'irresponsible' and 'completely false', although the same spokesman later admitted that there had been a fire in a storage trench and a 'small accident' after a power failure in the cooling system. The reaction of the experts in the British nuclear industry was that the doctor's report bore 'all the typical hallmarks of an anti-nuclear pressure group'.

Like Britain, France has no real answer to the problem of disposing of high-level nuclear waste. At Cap de la Hague it is currently stored in steel containers 300 feet below part of the site. The building under which it is stored will have to be permanently air-conditioned and the steel tanks in which it is stored replaced every thirty or forty years. By 1983 Cap de la Hague had more nuclear waste than it knew what to do with, as more and more French nuclear power stations came on-stream. A French government report, quoted in *New Scientist* in January 1983, said there were no back-up facilities if any of the reprocessing plants broke down, and that there should be far more research into waste disposal. The report also criticised the excessive secrecy surrounding the French nuclear industry, and revealed that some 156 kilogrammes of plutonium had actually 'gone missing' from Cap de la Hague, sufficient to make between ten and twenty nuclear bombs.

There is no Nugget File to tell us about French accidents. What is apparent is that the French experience is similar to that of all the other nuclear nations. The French PWRs are manufactured by Framatome under licence from Westinghouse. The French unions revealed that cracks had occurred in components just after they had been manufactured, let alone put into use. This was due to the welding techniques used. Although the unions warned the management of what was happening nothing was said or done for 12 months. Anything between 30 and 200 defects were found in special metal plates used in the construction of a number of the PWRS. But it is known that some of the defective components are already in service and have already caused leaks in the cooling systems in several nuclear reactors. So far Electricité de France has denied that there is any risk. There have even been two leaks at the French demonstration fast-breeder reactor, Phénix, at Marcoule; both were caused by leaks in the sodium cooling system. Sodium leaks are hazardous because sodium reacts violently in either air or water. One leak was found on 29 April 1982 when a routine check on the sodium in the second circuit showed abnormally large concentrations of hydrogen in the liquid; this indicated that a reaction between sodium and water had taken place somewhere. The reactor was halted and a faulty generator drained. The next day the same generator sprang a leak and released several litres of sodium, which caught fire on contact with the air. A special powder was needed to bring the fire under control, but the operators had no knowledge as to whether or not it would work with a larger release.

The French are, however, continuing with their nuclear power programme.

Japan

The first nuclear reactor in Japan was a small British one. In 1965, the Japanese government embarked on its own nuclear power programme, and its first commercial reactor came on-stream in 1970. A short while after this Tsuruga No 1 nuclear power station in Fukui, about 40 miles north-east of Kyoto, came into operation, people living around nearby Wakasa Bay noticed that something odd was happening to the seaweed: it was growing very profusely near the outlet from the plant. Tests were carried out on shellfish, and cobalt-60 was found in them. It was also present in the sediment at the bottom of the bay.

The publicity put out by the company operating the reactor had stated categorically that there would be no radiation leakage. After the contamination was discovered this was changed to 'harmless amounts of radiation only'. In 1973 the Fukui Prefectural Marine Resources Laboratory warned that shellfish caught near the reactors should not be eaten and that fishing boats should keep out of the waters. However, as the warnings were not enforced, local fishermen still fished there – sending their fish to market but not eating it themselves. Most of them were poor men owning their own boats, and eventually the power station owners began offering them high prices in return for their fishing rights, thus forcing them to fish elsewhere.

On 8 March 1981 there was what has been described as a 'massive spill' of radioactivity from the Tsuruga nuclear power plant, and a research team from the Kyoto University School of Agriculture, which had been conducting con- tamination tests at Wakasa Bay since 1971, said that the amount of radioactivity released was far greater than was officially announced. The group took samples of seaweed from in front of the drain outlet on 22 April, and found 111 picocuries of cobalt-60 and 40 picocuries of manganese-54.

This was almost 250 times more cobalt-60 than the official announcement of only 0.45 picocuries. If, for instance, the seaweed had been eaten at a rate of 40 grams a day for a year, the take-up of cobalt-60 by the body would have been seven millirems – that is, 2 millirems more than the five millirems set as a safety level for residents living near nuclear power stations. Government officials, however, denied that such a health problem was likely, pointing out that seaweed from that spot is not usually eaten, but they had to admit that such a high level of radioactivity had not been detected at other nuclear power stations.

An inquiry was demanded, and in a report made to the Ministry of Trade and Industry, the operators of the Tsuruga plant admitted that in addition to a whole series of radio-active water leakage accidents there had been ten floor-contamination incidents and ten equipment breakdowns in the building housing the reactor. In one of the accidents, in September 1975, the report said, about ten tons of radioactive waste water leaked into a waste water treatment facility and contaminated 200 square metres of the floor. Another five accidents concerning the leakage of waste water had occurred in 1975, 1977, 1978 and 1981, all due to 'human error'.

It turned out that the accident in March 1981 had been caused by tons of contaminated water leaking into a drainage system for about three hours. Fifty-six workers were con-taminated to an unspecified extent, as well as sub-contractors called in to help dispose of the water. Some of those working on the clean-up operation did not even wear protective clothing and simply mopped up the water with domestic mops and buckets. The accident was then concealed for over a month by the power company, and it probably would never have been discovered had not the research team found the high level of radioactivity in the seaweed and sludge – a somewhat similar situation to that of Greenpeace and their efforts to block the Windscale/Sellafield pipe. Some Japanese scientists claim that the amount of radioactivity released could well have been higher than that released during the Three-Mile Island accident.

Nuclear power in the Fukui Prefecture can hardly be said to have been a success. By the middle of 1977 there were nine nuclear reactors operating there, and people had been told they were about to be provided with very cheap electricity into the foreseeable future. However, by the autumn of 1977 five of the reactors had had to be shut down for long un-scheduled periods, and only two were actually working. None of them has ever run at full power.

The Mihama No. 1 site in Fukui had hardly operated at all for six years. In June 1972 a significant amount of radioactivity was found in the cooling loop and the trouble was traced to the primary system. Close inspection showed that 110 of the 10,000 heat exchanger tubes were defective, mostly because of corrosion. Improvised repairs were made by plugging them with copper wire, and the reactor was run for a further six months, but by 1973 another inspection showed that 2000 tubes were defective.

A committee of inquiry was set up to look into the plant and it recommended six-monthly, instead of annual, inspections and that the reactor should only run at 40 per cent of capacity. The reactor was started up again in September 1973 and came on-stream at 40 per cent capacity, but the next inspection six months later showed still more fuel pipes corroding. After further repairs, the reactor ran for only 42 days before it began leaking radiation, and the rate of breakdown in the pipes accelerated. In July 1974 the Mihama No. 1 plant was closed down.

All three reactors owned by the Kansai Electric Power Company at Mihama were made by Westinghouse, although the heat extractor on the No. 1 plant had been built by another American company, Combustion Engineering. However, when the other reactors were inspected it was found that they all had similar problems. Then the cause of the corrosion was said to be a defective anti-corrosion chemical added to the water. A new one was tried, but by November 1974 corrosion had set in again.

In 1976, a group of workers at the plant announced that the Mihama No. 1 reactor had been closed down because of a near-disaster, not because of damage to the tubes, but this was denied by the electricity company and the government. In December 1976, however, the Ministry of Trade and Industry sent a team to look at the plant and publicly admitted there had been a fault right in the reactor core. The defect in the core and the consequent near-accident had been discovered in 1973, two weeks after a public inquiry looking into the siting of a similar reactor in Ikata had been told that the construction of the Mihama No. 2 reactor core was completely safe. The accident, according to the Kansai Electrical Power Company, was due to 'human error' in the handling of the tubes containing the fuel rods, two of which had split open releasing fuel into the cooling system. They had not considered the matter worth reporting officially.

On 19 December 1976, the local anti-nuclear pressure group found out that the Kansai Electric Power Company was going to transport the leaky rods by lorry along the main road from the reactor to the government research station at Tokai-Mura, instead of storing them until their radiation had diminished to a safe level. Local residents joined trade union members and political leaders in a sit-in blocking the road leading out of the site, and 250 riot police were called in to drag the demonstrators away. The official government report of the accident contradicted that of the company. It played it right down, did not mention any human error and said that the accident had occurred during normal operations and was due to the working loose of clips holding the tubes, allowing the tubes to vibrate. There had been no likelihood of an accident; the fuel in the core had not melted.

This has left the local activists far from satisfied: first, it took so long for them to be told of the accident that they are still by no means sure they know the whole truth; second, Westinghouse will not release any details of their reactor technology in Japan and only experts from Westinghouse carry out inspections.

Finally, we should not leave Japan without looking at the story of the nuclear-powered cargo ship *Mutsu*. As Walter Patterson has said, her voyage during September 1974 'probably did more to set back the cause of nuclear marine propulsion than anything in the industry's worst nightmares'. Nuclear-powered ships and submarines were not, of course, new. However, the American effort to build a nuclear-powered cargo ship was less than successful. The NSS *Savannah* was thrown out of every port she tried to dock in.

The *Mutsu* was powered by a pressurised-water reactor and was launched at Mutsu in 1969. She was not popular with the local population who were worried about radiation leaks ruining the fishing in Mutsu Bay, and public opposition stopped her sea trials in 1972. A fund of 100 million yen was set up to cover compensation in the event of an accident, but in spite of this, local fishermen tried to blockade the ship and prevent it sailing in 1974.

When the ship was 800 kilometres out to sea, the reactor was brought to criticality but as the power was raised slightly, a leak was found. It appeared to be only a minor one but considerable problems ensued as any repairs had to be carried out at sea. Those on board had to improvise, and the results were a true black comedy. First they boiled rice to try and make shielding cement, but this was only a minor success. Then they stuffed old socks into the leak. The obvious thing was to run for port, but by this time the local population on shore were so irate that the crew actually feared for their own safety.

For forty-five days the *Mutsu* drifted aimlessly off the Japanese coast before enough precautions could be taken to risk docking. The authorities had to agree to find a new port for the ship, to leave all the fuel in the reactor, to remove all shore-based nuclear facilities at Mutsu within two-and-a-half years and to turn over to the mayor of Mutsu the keys of the fuel-handling crane. Additionally, the government had to provide $4 million to establish a compensation fund in case the fishing industry was ruined. 'As an exercise in Japanese nuclear public relations,' says Patterson, 'the *Mutsu* episode picked up where the *Fukuryu Maru* had left off twenty years before.' The *Fukuryu Maru* (Lucky Dragon) was the unfortunate Japanese fishing vessel which was deluged with fallout from a US atomic test in the Marshall Islands. The crew became ill almost immediately after contact with the fallout, some were still ill six months later and the radio operator died.

Canada

On the whole, Canada comes off best of the nuclear powers. It has never transferred its attention from civil nuclear power to nuclear weapons and its CANDU (Canadian deuterium uranium) reactors are considered to be among the safest. However, it was in Canada that the first major reactor accident occurred.

The reactor was a research model of the heavy-water variety in use before the CANDU nuclear reactors and it produced plutonium which Canada then sold to the USA and Britain. Known as the NRX and sited at Chalk River, Ontario, it went critical in 1947, reaching full power in May 1948.

On 12 December 1950, a technician working in the basement wrongly opened three or four valves and this resulted in three or four of the reactor's 12 shut-off rods being lifted right out of the core. A red light came on in the control room and the supervisor went to see what had happened. When he got to the basement he realised what was wrong, reset the valves and phoned to his assistant back in the control room to press Buttons 4 and 3 to restore normal operations. However, in his haste he apparently said 'four and one' instead of 'four and three'. The assistant immediately did what he was told. For some reason, resetting the valves had turned off the red warning lights even though all the rods had not been put back fully. The assistant was quite sure that the order was to press Buttons 4 and 1, which he did and thus lifted four more rods out of the core. The power level of the reactor started rising. Twenty seconds later he realised something had gone wrong and pressed the SCRAM button. This should have pushed all the rods back into the core but it did not – only one of the eight withdrawn rods dropped back in, and it took ninety seconds to fall three metres.

The technicians then decided to get rid of the heavy water moderator from the tank as a last attempt to shut off the nuclear reaction. The heavy water took thirty seconds to drain out, and then the instruments showed that power had dropped to zero.

However, down in the basement the supervisor could see water pouring out of the system. He and other staff rushed in with buckets thinking it was the water from the moderator, but it was, in fact, the reactor's radioactive coolant. Above them, the reactor rumbled and spewed out water. The radioactivity alarms sounded, and sirens warned site personnel to take refuge indoors. A few minutes later the entire staff were told to evacuate the plant. From the start of the accident to the order to evacuate took just seventy-seven seconds.

The control room staff stayed behind to try and prevent matters getting worse. By lifting out the control rods the chain reaction had speeded up so that the heat released had melted some of the uranium fuel. The heat had also boiled the coolant, which formed into bubbles of steam which were less able to absorb the neutrons so that the reaction accelerated even more. Within seconds, the melting uranium fuel and its aluminium cladding reacted with the water and steam: the hot uranium metal stripped the oxygen from water molecules, leaving, says Walter Patterson, free hydrogen. This hydrogen in turn mixed with inrushing air entering through ruptured piping, and the resultant explosion flung a 4-tonne helium-gas holder to the top of its container and jammed it there.

The reactor core was more or less destroyed and it threw out radioactivity in all directions. One man was killed and five were severely contaminated. One million gallons of highly radioactive water flooded the plant, and about 10,000 curies of long-lived fission products were carried into the basement by the leak of 4 million litres of cooling water. According to Dr Rosalie Bertell, medical preparations on the site were inadequate, being orientated only towards small, routine decontamination and spillages. The problems were later detailed in a US Atomic Energy Commission report of 9 February 1951: doctors hesitated to inject people through possibly contaminated skin; the decontamination of wounds was complicated by the lack of a probe to tell from which part of the wound the radiation was coming; there were no criteria for making decisions on how much a patient should be decontaminated before being taken to hospital; and there were unprecedented problems in connection with the transport of the contaminated body of the man who was killed to an undertaker. As always, the accident was shrouded in secrecy.

Fourteen months later, however, after a massive clean-up operation the plant was back in operation, and by 1958 there was another reactor operating on the site as well. In that year an irradiated fuel element in the new reactor broke and caught fire inside the refuelling machine. One of the overheated uranium fuel rods then ruptured within the core, and in the removal process a piece of highly radioactive fuel fell into a shallow maintenance pit, spewing fission products to areas inside the reactor building and contaminating 400,000 square metres around the building. The radiation dose in the pit was estimated as high as 10,000 roentgens per hour, and some six hundred men were involved in the clean-up.

The subsequent report of this accident by Atomic Energy of Canada Ltd said that only a small number of individuals had been 'over exposed' and that there would be no danger to health. However, there was no follow-up study on any of the men involved to check on what happened to them afterwards. One of the workers, Barnie Paulson, developed cancer within six years of the accident and in 1966 he had part of his nose removed. Between 1966 and 1984 he underwent forty operations to remove cancers from his rectum, scalp, pubic and anal regions. He had kept silent about his exposure for 20 years as he had been sworn to secrecy, but finally, in 1978, he went public with the story in an attempt to get a military pension (he had been an Air Force corporal at the time of the accident). The Canadian pension board said there was no record of his ever having been at the Chalk River site. Eventually, under pressure, his records were released and they showed he had been checked for external gamma exposure only, not for other kinds of radiation which might affect him in other ways. No other worker was followed up. Since Mr Paulson's case was publicised, another ex-corporal has been found to have cancer of the throat, and efforts are now being made to trace the rest of the personnel.

Chapter 7

The Broad Street Pump

In 1979, Dr Richard Bates made a telling point in a paper, *Environmental Health Perspectives*, on the subject of occupational and environmental cancers. He related a classic episode in the history of disease prevention which took place in London in 1854, when an epidemic of cholera occurred around Broad Street. Dr John Snow studied the habits of the victims and found that they almost all drew their water from a certain well. It was immediately closed down and the epidemic subsided. 'One can imagine,' writes Dr Bates,

the reaction which might occur today if it were proposed to close down the Broad Street pump on evidence of the kind obtained by John Snow.

Many scientists would point out that it had not been demonstrated conclusively that the water was the cause of the disease. They would be troubled because of the lack of satisfactory theoretical knowledge to explain how the water could have caused the disease. Furthermore, other habits of those who became ill had not been adequately investigated, so it would not be possible to rule out other causes of the disease. The scientists would have been correct. Others would have pointed out that some members of the community who drank from the Broad Street well had not succumbed to cholera. Thus, even if there were something wrong with the water, there must be other factors involved, and if we could control these we would not have to be concerned about the water. These conclusions are also correct. Some who consumed water from the Broad Street well would have objected to closing it because the taste of the water from other wells was not as agreeable. Finally, if the pump had been owned by an individual who sold the water, he would certainly have protested against closing down his business on the basis of inconclusive evidence of hazard. Meanwhile, of course, people would have gone on dying.

The moral of this story is worth considering. As things stand at the moment the nuclear power industry shares with the pesticide industry an important advantage – neither has to prove beyond reasonable doubt that what they are purveying is not harmful to health. It is up to those on the receiving end – often disorganised, unsure and widely scattered – to prove that either low-level radiation, or pesticides, or both, are hazardous.

The early victims

Radioactive materials give off three kinds of radiation: alpha, beta and gamma. All are dangerous to living things, but they act differently. *Alpha radiation*, given off by plutonium, is the most dangerous but it can be effectively shielded by even a thick piece of card. It is not dangerous unless the substance emitting it is inhaled, eaten or otherwise ingested.

Beta radiation is less damaging but more difficult to shield and can easily pass through skin. *Gamma radiation* is the least damaging in itself, but it can penetrate almost anything, even steel.

Even the happiest optimists within the nuclear power industry would not deny that high doses of radiation can produce diseases, especially cancers. Accepted victims include early pioneers in the field such as W. K. Roentgen, discoverer of the X-ray, who died of bone cancer, and Marie Curie and her daughter, Irene, who both died of aplastic anaemia at the ages of 67 and 59 respectively. It is also likely that Enrico Fermi and J. Robert Oppenheimer contracted the cancers from which they died when working on the early nuclear weapons programme.

Then, obviously, there is all the data from the Hiroshima and Nagasaki atomic bomb victims and, linked with the early nuclear weapons programme, the awful death of Harry

169

Daghlian. Daghlian was a young scientist who on 21 August 1945 was assembling a wall of small bricks of uranium to act as a reflector around two very nearly critical hemispheres of plutonium. Each brick weighed about 12 lb. As the last one was being put into place it slipped and fell into the centre of the pile. Immediately, the whole assembly went critical and a blue ionising glow seared across the room. Daghlian tried desperately to knock the brick off. He suffered second-degree burns on his hands and chest, but those did not kill him. After a further three-and-a-half weeks of agony he died of radiation sickness, having received a lethal dose following the blue flash. Photographs were taken of him every day to show the progress of the sickness. His death was kept secret.

Later still came the victims of the atmospheric testing of nuclear weapons. The United States chose two sites: one was in the Nevada desert area; the other in the Pacific around the Marshall Islands. Some 1000 US citizens are currently suing the US government, and the first of many enormous out-of-court settlements has already been made.

To start with Nevada: between 1951 and 1963 the US government exploded more than 100 atomic bombs in the atmosphere above the state. In September 1982, 1192 residents and former residents of the area instituted a court case, claiming that they had been exposed to dangerous levels of radiation and that many people in their families had either died from or contracted cancer. They had been told that the tests were 'safe', the radiation level was 'safe', that they would come to no harm even though the fallout was so bad that it could be seen as a thin grey dust which had to be brushed off windows, cars and pathways and washed off vegetables. Some publicity surrounded the case for in 1955, while the tests were taking place, part of the film *The Conqueror* was shot there, and its stars, John Wayne and Susan Hayward, had both contracted cancer from which they had died, along with the director, Dick Powell, other actors, cameramen and technicians among the film crew.

The Nevada residents had tried to bring a test case before, but it had been dismissed by Federal Judge Sherman Christensen back in 1956 for lack of evidence. However, in 1982

Judge Christensen reopened the case and this time, thanks to the 1976 Freedom of Information Act, the authorities were forced to produce the material they had suppressed earlier. The judge said that he had 'naïvely believed lying government officials twenty-six years ago'. Now he was outspoken in his condemnation. 'The circumstances clearly and convincingly demonstrate a species of fraud upon the court for which a remedy must be granted.' On 11 May 1984, an award of £1.9 million was made to cancer victim Jacqueline Sanders and to the relatives of nine other victims who had all died of cancer during the legal proceedings.

In January 1984, the *Journal of the American Medical Association* carried a paper by Carl J. Johnson MD on cancer incidence in an area of radioactive fallout downwind from the Nevada test site. He looked particularly at the Mormons who had lived in the area. Mormons have a very low incidence of cancer, which they attribute to their healthy lifestyle (they neither drink nor smoke), and the clean environment in which they live. Johnson's survey showed that out of 4125 Mormon families, there were 109 more cancers than should have been expected, with leukaemia as the most common form. At the end of his study he also pointed out that the burden of radiation-induced cancer throughout the state can be expected to rise; an excess of childhood leukaemias has been reported statewide, and this observation is an early warning that other classes of radiation-induced cancer will appear later.

The other area to suffer was that around the Marshall Islands. Victims here included both US servicemen taking part in the tests and the unfortunate inhabitants of the islands. Argument and litigation in both cases continue. Among the previously healthy Marshall Islanders there was a rapid increase in diseases of all kinds including cancer, along with an unusually high proportion of miscarriages and stillbirths. There were also a number of birth deformities in babies born to women who had been exposed to fallout. Women told investigators they had given birth to things like 'bunches of grapes', and to 'jellyfish babies' whose hearts beat for between two to twelve hours and who then died. The 'bunches of grapes' could be explained as what happens when a dead

171

embryo collects grape-like cysts, or if what formed was not a foetus but a large hydatiform mole.

There are also, of course, similar cases pending among Australian veterans. The Australian government set up a Royal Commission, which came to Britain to investigate and to take statements from British servicemen who feel that they have contracted cancer or produced deformed children or both, following the British atmospheric nuclear tests in Australia and in the Pacific. These latter cases have become bogged down on what constitutes a 'safe' level of exposure to radioactivity, and this is also crucial to those who live near or work in nuclear power plants.

So what does constitute a 'safe' level? One would feel more confidence in the nuclear industry if they had not constantly moved the goal posts while continuing to assure everybody that the level set was safe. Below is the table of what has been considered over the years to be 'safe' levels.

1920s	73 rems during one year
1938	50 rems during one year
1948	25 rems during one year
1954	15 rems during one year
1958	5 rems during one year

Now, the International Commission on Radiological Protection (ICRP) recommend that the dosage should be as low as 0.5 rems.

There are now many respected physicists who question if there is any such thing as a 'safe' dose. Professor Karl Morgan, a Nobel Prize winner, worked in the wartime metallurgical laboratory in Chicago where plutonium was produced, after which he was put in charge of the new health physics division at the Oak Ridge National Laboratory in Tennessee. He was also chairman of the ICRP working group on internal radiation doses, so he can hardly be discounted as a crank who does not know what he is talking about.

The state of a cell when exposed to radiation was described by him as 'a madman loose in a library'. In an article in the *New Scientist* of 5 April 1979, Professor Morgan said:

From 1960 to the present, an overwhelming amount of data has been accumulated to show there is no 'safe' level of exposure and there is no dose of radiation so low that the risk of malignancy is zero. Therefore the question is not: is there a risk from low level exposure? Or, what is the safe level of exposure? The question is – how great is that risk?

Whatever brave words might be spoken in public both here and elsewhere about the safe limits of exposure to radioactivity, in private there were obviously growing doubts following the emergence of cancer cases both in the inhabitants of Utah and also in the inhabitants of the Marshall Islands and among those who had taken part in the tests there. Officially, however, the US administration, in company with all the other nuclear powers, has said that any radiation doses received were 'too low' to have caused cancer.

'Safe' at any level?

There were also some unpleasant industrial cases coming to light. Ted Lombard was involved in work on the Manhattan Project at Los Alamos, like his friend, Harry Daghlian. Ted's job was to transport enriched plutonium from the Hanford reprocessing plant in Washington State to Los Alamos, hundreds of miles away. He handled radioactive material without any protective clothing, breathing apparatus or gloves. He was not told it was dangerous.

While still working at Los Alamos, Ted developed stomach ulcers and a variety of infections. By the time he was discharged, his eyesight was getting increasingly worse and he was told he might be sterile. He was also told that if he became seriously ill, the fact that he had worked where he had would enable him to claim compensation. However, he was given no verification of the work he had done. Ted was not sterile. He and his wife already had one child born before he worked at Los Alamos who was quite normal. He then had two daughters and two sons. The first daughter was unusually prone to infection and was discovered to lack certain antibodies and enzymes, a condition which had never turned up in the family before; she also developed severe neuro-muscular problems

173

and became severely disabled. The second daughter had the same neuro-muscular condition but she did not become as disabled. However she appears to have passed what seems to be the responsible recessive gene on to her own children. The next child, a son, suffers from seizures, severe headaches and respiratory problems. The youngest son is epileptic, deaf and mute, and is permanently in a home for the severely mentally handicapped.

Over the years, Ted fought a battle with the US government for compensation, but he had no proof of the work he had done. By the time he was 57, he was totally disabled with four defective children, and tests on him had shown severe damage to his bone marrow and possibly his chromosomes. He finally received some compensation but this was given on the understanding that there was no liability to do so and that it did not constitute an admission that his problems could be due to exposure to low-level radiation.

Joe Harding worked for eighteen years at a uranium enrichment plant owned by Union Carbide – the company that brought you the Bhopal chemical disaster. Just before he died, in 1980, Joe testified that measurements and records for the amount of radiation the men received, monitored by film badges, were constantly falsified. He said that he proved it when he put his own badge on top of 'a smoking chuck of uranium for eight hours' and still the company did not react. By the time he died, Joe had severe stomach cancer, a massive tumour had been taken from his thigh, and he had nail-like growths on the backs of his hands, his wrists, elbows and shoulders. His wife testified that Union Carbide threatened to sue the doctor who said Joe Harding's illness was radiation-induced: 'That's how powerful Union Carbide is in Peduccah.' Union Carbide denied any responsibility saying that Joe's dosage had never exceeded 5 rems per year, the official 'safe' dose. Even if the monitoring tests had been properly conducted and the film badges read and recorded, it was obviously impossible for Union Carbide to admit that even 5 rems was too much when the whole nuclear industry is geared to using that as a 'safe' level.

In 1964, Dr Thomas Mancuso of the University of Pittsburgh, one of the foremost epidemiologists on health hazards, particularly on the health hazards of chemical pollution, was asked by the Atomic Energy Commission (AEC) to survey cancer rates among workers at the Hanford reprocessing facility. There had been growing publicity for what appeared to be a worrying increase among workers there. He undertook the Hanford study in all good faith, believing that the AEC actually wanted to know the true position from an independent witness.

Only later, under the Freedom of Information Act, was it possible to discover what it was the AEC really wanted: 'The study should allay fears,' the Committee on the Health Hazards of Radiation of the US House of Representatives was told in 1978. Various documents obtained under the Act show that the allaying of fears was paramount. A letter from Professor William Schull, a consultant to the then Atomic Energy Commission, to Leonard Sagan, AEC contact officer for Health Mortality study, dated 8 November 1967, said:

It seems highly probable that if one went through the mechanics of calculating the kinds of radiation effects which a study of the present magnitude might detect, one would be led to conclude that the undertaking is a hopeless one. However, as earlier recognised, it may have another merit in that it may provide a firmer base for settlement of claims against the AEC and a buttress against ill-conceived and opportunistic criticism which might be levelled against the AEC.

In a letter to John Totter, Director of AEC's Division of Biology and Medicine, S. E. English, AEC's Assistant Manager for Research, said (13 November 1967):

the study should neither confirm nor refute dangers but should permit a statement to the effect that a careful study of workers in the industry disclosed no harmful effects from radiation . . . the statement, supported by any appropriate documentation, would seem to justify the existence of the study. A corollary statement could presumably be made about other exposed populations.

In blissful ignorance, Dr Mancuso continued with his survey. In 1974, Dr S. Milham, an epidemiologist from the Washington (State) Department of Health, reported a cancer rate among Hanford workers five times higher than that expected. The AEC asked him not to publish his findings until the Mancuso study had been published as this was very near its conclusion, and Milham agreed. Milham met Mancuso's statistician, Dr Barkov Sanders, and the AEC, worried about Milham's data, sent it away to the government-funded Batelle Pacific Northwest Laboratory to see if they could fault it.

Batelle confirmed Milham's results. A draft note in the file obtained under the Freedom of Information Act says, 'We hoped to have a good answer to the Milham report but instead it looks like we've got support for it.'

The AEC began to get worried, and finally Dr Sydney Marks of the Energy Research and Development Agency asked Dr Mancuso to put his name to a press release refuting Milham's findings. This said that there was no significant difference in radiation-related effects between Hanford employees and their siblings, based on a scrutiny of 4000 death certificates, and that there was no more evidence of cancer or other deaths attributable to radiation than among any other members of their families. Mancuso refused.

Almost immediately, his grant was terminated and he was told his research would be taken over by the government's own research establishment. By this time it was becoming apparent that Mancuso's study, when it was published, would be even more devastating than Milham's. Dr Mancuso had detailed information on each worker's exposure to radiation; he was able to correlate that exposure with the cause of death; and, using a larger data base than Milham, could offer a more powerful argument.

The first reason given for Dr Mancuso's dismissal was his age. He was sixty-two, with eight years of his university contract still to go. Later, when that reason was questioned, ERDA said that a 'peer review' of his research was highly critical of his procedures. In fact only one person had been critical; the other five had praised his meticulous data collecting and extraordinary quality control.

Dr Mancuso is, apparently, a mild man but he became

extremely angry at his dismissal and contacted Dr Alice Stewart of the Queen Elizabeth Hospital in Birmingham, England. Dr Stewart was famous for her work on the X-raying of pregnant women and its connection with childhood leukaemias. Mancuso told her that he had found excessive rates of cancer of the pancreas and myeloma (bone cancer) and asked if she would give him an independent assessment of his data. She agreed, with the proviso that she would bring in her own statistician, Dr George Kneale. Kneale and Stewart's findings agreed with Mancuso's.

Strenuous efforts were made by ERDA to get hold of all copies of Mancuso's data, but fortunately he had kept a complete file of his findings in Pittsburgh. Government officials then set out to confiscate all of his previous research, including a radiation study of atomic energy installations.

Mancuso, Stewart and Kneale presented their first paper at a Health Physics meeting in 1976 and it was later published in the *Health Physics Review* of November 1977. At the same meeting Dr Sydney Marks of ERDA and a Dr Ethel Gilbert produced an analysis of the health risks of nuclear workers which came to a different conclusion. Mancuso's findings were that those working at the Hanford plant had a 26 per cent higher risk of dying of cancer than might be expected. More importantiy, the risk of dying of some specific forms of cancer already associated with radiation, such as bone cancer, was 107 per cent more likely.

Mancuso's findings were severely criticised by the nuclear industry and government agencies. Later, Mancuso was to find that a critique of his survey had been circulated in the USA and Europe before publication without his knowledge or consent. Mancuso, Stewart and Kneale submitted their findings for reanalysis and the results of this were given in a paper to the International Symposium on Late Biological Effects of Ionising Radiation, held in Vienna in 1978. In this paper they revealed that out of 3520 Hanford workers who had died, 670 had died of cancer; 66 per cent of these cancer victims had had one or more positive radiation badge readings; and 61.1 per cent of others with positive readings had died relatively early of other causes.

Since then, no effort has been spared to discredit Mancuso's careful work and that of Dr Alice Stewart who, called as an expert witness, was disgracefully treated at the Windscale inquiry in 1977, rudely questioned, verbally attacked and denigrated.

Brief mention should be made of two other US surveys. The first concerns the Big Rock Nuclear Power Plant in Michigan, owned by the Consumers Power Company, which came on-stream in 1962. It is part of a 600-acre site on the shore of Lake Michigan in a resort area where the main commercial activities are either tourism or farming, and lies within Charlevoix County, an area considered to be relatively free from pollution and thus a healthy place to live.

Dr Gerald Drake, who both lived and worked nearby, became worried about trends in public health near the site of the nuclear power station and reported his concern to the AEC in 1974.

He claimed that after ten years of operation, the number of infant deaths near to the station had risen by a small percentage, whereas the number for the whole state of Michigan had dropped. There was also an average increase of 21 per cent in low-birth-weight babies born to mothers living near the station, while the state-wide increase was only 1 per cent.

Cancer deaths had increased by about seven people in the 16,000 county population per year but the state average was only one person. Dr Drake felt this was statistically significant, since the probability of it happening by chance was less than 0.001. Although the leukaemia death rate remained the same throughout the state, it rose slightly in those living near the power station.

In response to his concern the AEC hired a government-funded laboratory to study the allegation that the trends could be due to increased exposure to low-level radiation. The laboratory, not surprisingly, came to the conclusion that they were not.

Dr Drake's wife, Martha, was extremely annoyed at the treatment her husband had received and she decided to carry out a second survey of her own for her master's thesis. Throughout 1976 she analysed death rates in populations near nuclear plants with boiling-water reactors. She took the three earliest reactors to come on-stream and investigated the six counties nearest each of them. She also picked out four different control groups: three samples of eighteen counties taken at random, none of which had nuclear installations, plus an analysis of statistics across the USA as a whole.

Nearly a million people (959,904) were involved in living, working, or both near the reactors. At the time the reactors started up, the leukaemia rate per head of the population was exactly the same in those areas as anywhere else in the USA. After five years the exposed population averaged an extra nine cases per year, higher than both the control counties and the US as a whole.

Martha Drake took as her base the assumption that the average exposure of people in the counties at risk was 0.0001 rem, and she multiplied this by 1 million people. This implied that 100 person-rems of exposure had resulted in the nine extra cases. The official estimate is 100 extra leukaemias for one million person-rems, so her statistics showed an average nine times higher than that.

But as American scientists and others – both pro- and anti-nuclear power – point out, statistics are very hard to prove as the numbers are only small increases against a background of other cancers, both natural and occupational. In the US one woman in four will contract cancer and one man in five. There is natural background radiation all around us – as well as the radiation still present from the atmospheric nuclear tests. Then there are the different ways that different types of radioactivity affect the body, how they are absorbed and which organs are most at risk from each type.

We will now look at the position in Britain. Apart from the much criticised Black Report, which will be discussed later, there have been few studies of the problem here. While it would seem that each British nuclear site now has a 'cluster' of leukaemia cases near it these are not considered statistically significant. We will start with Windscale/Sellafield, however, as British Nuclear Fuels, while not admitting liability, has paid out considerable sums in out-of-court settlements to ex-workers.

Windscale/Sellafield: The workers

You have a pretty nasty time of it if you die of myeloma, that is, bone cancer. Back in February 1975, I happened to knock on the door of a Mr John Troughton, whose name I had been given. I was told he was an ex-worker at Windscale who had developed cancer and was ill, and that he wanted to talk to somebody about what he thought were the origins of his illness. I had not known about him before conducting my own investigations in and around Windscale.

To my embarrassment I was greeted by his widow; he had been cremated the previous day. When I apologised and said I would go away, she said, no, John had wanted to talk about his cancer, and please would I come in?

John Troughton had worked as a plutonium process worker for fourteen years. 'He was always so healthy,' said Mrs Troughton, 'right up until the time he was taken ill three years ago. He was a man who never ailed anything. He knew he'd had an overdose before that, and he wondered how because he'd always taken all the precautions, worn the special clothing and so on. There were two others along with him. I don't know how they've fared.

'I was lucky they let me nurse him at home, even though he had been in hospital a couple of times. They thought it would be too much for me. His bones had completely gone, you know. First the vertebrae in the back, one at a time. He couldn't sit up or anything. If he sneezed it damaged him. He did once and it broke three ribs – he'd lie there propped up with his finger under his nose.

'They suffer really terrible pain in spite of drugs; it's a terrible pain. But he was a fighter and he said: "When I've gone, girl, you must carry on fighting whatever you feel like to find out what made me like this." In the last week he was so heavily sedated I don't think he knew much; he'd been alert until then. I spent the week literally kneeling by his bed giving him little sips of water. Do you know, he died without his long-service watch for twenty-five years' service? He was so sorry about that, but he was so brave – he had to be.

'I think I felt it worse immediately after his death. The doctor said, "Well, there'll have to be an inquest and a coroner and all that, and they'll be around to take him away in about two hours." Actually it was four, but it didn't seem very long. That was the last I saw of him. They had to remove a lot for the post mortem and then he was cremated. That was that. I hope I don't give up, I owe it to him to go all the way.'

Mrs Troughton did not give up, she became one of the first people to be awarded money in an out-of-court settlement by British Nuclear Fuels Ltd. Compensation was also awarded to a Mrs Connor whose husband had also died of myeloma when only thirty-nine. BNFL denied any liability; the payments were *ex gratia*.

Other cases have been settled out of court. In 1981 British Nuclear Fuels reached an agreement with the unions involved that workers would be compensated if BNFL agreed that their cases fulfilled certain criteria set up by BNFL and accepted by the unions. By the autumn of 1983 there were nearly a hundred cases of ex-BNFL workers awaiting investigation, and by 1985 this had risen to 174. The amount of each award is calculated by estimating the possible amount of full compensation which would be awarded in court and then dividing this by about one-half, to take into account the fact that proving the cancer was radiation-induced would be difficult and the case might well fail in court.

One of the first was that of Mr Thomas Watson who died of stomach cancer in 1973 at the age of 53, after working at Windscale for 23 years as a plutonium processor. His widow said he was sent home several times after being over-exposed to radiation. 'There were times when he came home late with his face all shiny and red. That was when he had been contaminated and he had been scrubbed to get the contamination off him. The company used to send a green chauffeur-driven car to our house to collect samples from his stools and take urine samples away.' The first payment out under the scheme had been to the widow of a man who had died of leukaemia in 1965. His widow did not wish to be identified.

In January 1984, BNFL announced that the records of 20,000 nuclear workers, going back to the late 1940s, were being examined to find out who had died from cancer and whether there was a link with exposure to radiation. The

20,000 figure comprises all who worked in the areas where radiation hazards existed and the study will also involve tracing relatives of those who died, some in the 1950s. The AUEW believe that up to 100 cases should qualify for compensation, but a spokesman for the union told me at the end of 1985 that, so far, only three cases had been settled under the 1981 agreement: one from the AUEW, one from the TGWU and one from the civil service union. It was proving very difficult for the cases to fulfil the criteria set by BNFL.

There have been many complaints over the timescales involved. BNFL had taken from three to six years before making any out-of-court payments which is why the 1981 agreement was set up. It admits that 'in a proportion of such cases occurring among radiation workers there could be a possibility that the disease was contracted as a result of occupational exposure to radiation.' But as these diseases could occur naturally it was difficult to distinguish between the two. All death certificates of those who worked for BNFL will now have to be examined and noted, but it is still obvious that proving any connection is very difficult indeed.

Windscale/Sellafield: Those outside

In March 1985 the population of West Cumbria discovered they had been taking part over the years in an exciting experiment – to find out how much radioactivity, *deliberately released*, ended up in the air they breathed, the fish they ate, the seaweed they might pick up and the sand on which they walked.

It appeared that in 1958 John Dunster (now, as already noted, director of the NRPB, our 'watchdog') stated in a paper to the Geneva Conference on Peaceful Uses of the Atom that

discharges from Windscale have been deliberately maintained . . . high enough to obtain detectable activity levels in samples of fish, seaweed and shore sand and the experiment is still proceeding . . . in 1958 the rate of discharge of radioactivity was deliberately increased partly to dispose of unwanted waste but principally to yield better experimental data.

Nor was the 1958 increase the only one. In February 1958 the chief medical officer for BNFL admitted to the local health authority that a release of radioactivity in 1952 had not been an accident: it had been a 'deliberate discharge' as part of the operations during early nuclear reprocessing under the military programme that resulted in Britain's first atomic bomb. There was a need for secrecy as a matter of national security, and information about the discharge has only recently been revealed. After the release of iodine-131, radioactivity was found in local milk and in the urine of two local children. 'The increased levels of iodine were released due to fuels being reprocessed after a shortened cooling period.' The finding of the radioactivity in the urine appears to have been completely fortuitous: researchers working on the effects of fallout from bomb tests tested their own children and found that they had been contaminated by the Windscale iodine-131.

As well as providing guinea pigs for BNFL, it seems that all the experts are agreed that at least some people contracted cancer as a result of the 1957 Windscale accident. The controversy is over how many. The first report published by the NRPB in 1982 estimated that there might be as many as twenty such deaths but in September 1983 they amended this to thirty-three. The re-assessment had been carried out, said the NRPB, following 'pressure from the media' which had suggested that major components of the fallout from the accident had been omitted from the board's first assessment.

The new report, therefore, took into account that polonium-210 was also released at Windscale. Polonium was not mentioned at the time of the accident nor in the first assessment of it carried out by Mr Dunster. The amended report said that the NRPB was right in saying that iodine-131 was the most hazardous of the radioactive isotopes released, but the presence of polonium-210 brought the figure to a higher total by about 65 per cent. Measurements taken at the time – five nanocuries of radioactivity per litre of milk at one farm and a measurement of polonium-210 at another – were 500 times higher than the amount officially calculated as being present in the food chain. Professor Joseph Rotblat, one of Britain's leading radiation physicists, said it was extremely unlikely, in his opinion, that an error as large as a factor of 500 could have occurred.

The only reason given for disregarding the higher measurements of radioactivity in the food chain taken at the time was that they were 'very much higher than could be reasonably expected on the basis of plutonium-milk transfer data'. In fact they did not fit the NRPB's computer model of the fallout pattern, the radioactivity involved and the pathways by which it reached human beings.

As well as the number of deaths resulting from the 1957 accident, it might also be that some thirty more unfortunate souls will contract cancer and die as a result of the continuing pollution from the complex at Windscale/Sellafield. The calculation was made by Mr Peter Taylor of the Political Ecology Research Group. The victims could contract cancer by eating fish contaminated by radioactive waste discharged into the sea. More alarmingly, his calculations also show that people all over the country could die if the pollution continues. His figures are broadly accepted by the NRPB's scientists, who also accept that a further thirty people might contract cancer but not actually die of it. If the discharges continue, Mr Taylor estimated, a further three people would be doomed to die of cancer every year and he also thinks he is underestimating the danger by at least three times. If this is so the number of victims would be 90, not 30. When he used another set of internationally accepted figures, the number rose to 150.

So if it is known that some people might contract cancer as a result of the 1957 accident or from continuing pollution, it should not be too much of a surprise if cancers show up near Windscale, but it appears to have come as a shock when, in November 1983, Yorkshire Television showed its documentary *Windscale – The Nuclear Laundry*.

This stated that in Millom Rural District (in which Windscale/Sellafield is sited) the official number of cancer deaths for those under twenty-five is two-and-a-half times the national average. In five coastal parishes there are four times the national average of cancer cases among those under eighteen, and in Seascale parish, slap next to Windscale/

Sellafield, the leukaemia rate in children under the age of ten is ten times the national average.

While BNFL have constantly asserted that the discharges are within the International Commission's recommended limits, for the last eight years the most exposed group of Cumbrian residents has been receiving a dose well above the maximum recommended limit for prolonged or lifetime exposure. Plutonium from the estuary at Ravenglass was found in dust taken from a sample of nine houses in the coastal villages. Neither the Ministry of Agriculture nor the NRPB had ever taken such samples, although the Royal Commission in 1976 had recommended that around Windscale 'it is necessary to conduct general monitoring of human food, water and air and the built environment.'

The YTV documentary asserted that children can absorb up to 100 times more plutonium than adults. BNFL responded by saying you would have to eat '20 lb' of house-dust to run an appreciable risk – a statement that ignores the main hazard which comes from inhalation. The annual maximum inhalation dose for adults can be achieved just by breathing in a few grammes of dried silt from the Cumbrian estuaries.

Cumbria's medical officers were also quick off the mark to say that no unusual cancer pattern had developed in the area, but official figures from the West Cumbria Area Health Authority showed a different story. In the area around Windscale the number of cancers in males had risen from 10 per cent below the national average in 1968, to 17 per cent above it by 1980. There was a similar pattern for cancers in females. Men and women under 45 showed stomach and digestive cancer rates rising at twice the national average.

More localised areas revealed a more sharply abnormal pattern. Between 1963 and 1970, according to the Census Office, there were 13 cancer deaths in Millom Rural District in those under 25 when only 5 should have been expected. This had been denied officially at first, but in fact the census figures used the old boundaries which gave quite a specific result. Researcher Michael Burke traced and identified all thirteen deaths recorded in official figures, and also discovered another leukaemia death which had been missed from the record.

185

The rate among under-18s in one tiny parish – four times that expected – plus the cancers at Seascale, caused the chief medical statistician from Christie's Cancer Hospital in Manchester to say that, having checked out the figures, the probability of this abnormal cancer pattern happening naturally was between one in 50,000 and one in 140,000. A local Seascale GP who checked his own files after the film said that record books had showed that 'our figures agreed with YTV almost exactly. We are unhappy that the District Medical Officer has not collated it. He has maintained that our incidence is normal. This may be right for the rural district as a whole, but it's not the case in our parishes.'

The reaction to all this from BNFL was that the cancers were an 'unexplained cluster' and there are other such. There certainly are and among places where clusters have occurred are Sizewell, Berkeley, Bradwell and other areas with nuclear power stations, as well as one or two places without (see pp. 194–7).

This time, concern was such that the government immediately set up an inquiry under the chairmanship of Sir Douglas Black. Right from the start it was criticised for its very limited terms of reference, and received even more criticism when its report was published in August 1984.

This stated that there was 'no obvious geographical pattern' in cancer rates in the area and that the apparent clusters were 'unusual but not unparalleled'; a link between the cases and Windscale remained 'unproven'. Sir Douglas was rushed on to television and radio to make reassuring noises about the situation. He said he believed the only problem with Windscale was that people perceived a risk from radiation – which presumably implied there wasn't one. He linked fear of radiation with fear of electricity a century ago, and said that people should accept radioactivity in the same way because it could be measured. In September, speaking to the British Association he said, 'common sense might lead one to believe that the comparatively high rate of leukaemia at Seascale is connected with British Nuclear Fuels' plant at Sellafield, but common sense is not science.'

Among those not happy with the Black Report was James Cutler who made the YTV documentary. He received confidential copies of the detailed evidence given to the inquiry which revealed a different picture from the reassuring one made public.

The evidence showed, without doubt, that more than half the cases of childhood cancer that occurred in Seascale and surrounding villages had been, quite simply, left out. The result was obviously an under-estimate of the numbers involved. Worse still, says Cutler, other polluted areas on the Cumbrian coast were found to have alarming childhood cancer rates but were never mentioned in the report as they were not within the area that was the inquiry's remit. Funny things happened to those cases the Black Report did look into; Cutler notes that Elizabeth Fox, who had died of leukaemia at the age of seventeen in 1964, is listed in the front of the report but unaccountably vanishes from the statistics analysing leukaemia deaths in the area in which she had lived. James Cutler found this particularly surprising because he had personally sent the inquiry a copy of her death certificate. This omission plus others produced a result that the leukaemia rate for Millom was actually below the national average.

The Black Report also omitted from its calculations William W. aged 9, who contracted lymphatic cancer in Seascale; Gemma L. who contracted the same disease at the age of 2, also in Seascale; Janet Walker who died of cancer aged 14, in Seascale; Diane W. who contracted brain cancer at the age of 12 and who lives in Bootle ward (next to the contaminated Ravenglass estuary); Geoffrey Runton who died of a bone tumour, aged 12, also in Bootle ward; and Phillip Hughes who died of a kidney tumour, aged four, also in Bootle ward.

All the statistics used by Black, argues Cutler, show omissions and distortions. Also the enquiry only concentrated on one limited period, from 1968 to 1982. If the study period had been extended by just one year, to 1983, there were two further leukaemia cases diagnosed in Seascale which puts Seacale at the top of the northern region for this disease. Fourteen-year-old victim Janet Walker was left out of all the studies, even though her cancer was diagnosed in 1975, well within the study period.

Cutler says that when all the missing Seascale cases are included and when the 'top ten' wards in the area are correctly listed by statistical significance (i.e. whether or not the cases could have occurred by chance), Seascale heads the top ten wards in the tables for all cancers and for leukaemia. Its rate – 24 times the regional average – is unlikely to have happened by chance 'since the odds against are a million to one and it is unmatched by any village so far found in Britain.'

The more detailed data also shows a definite geographical pattern. Missing out cancer cases resulted in Bootle ward being shown as having only one cancer case instead of four. Four of the wards in the 'top ten' for childhood cancer in the northern region are found on the Cumbrian coast: Seascale, Ravenglass and Wampool, both the latter being on river estuaries and Barrow Island, a plutonium hotspot, according to the government's own environmental radioactivity monitoring experts.

It rapidly became apparent that public anxiety was not allayed as a result of the Black Report, and James Cutler revealed in February 1985 that there had been a number of confidential meetings on the subject, including one on 22 October 1984 at the DHSS. Attending the Elephant and Castle headquarters were representatives from the Black Inquiry, the NRPB, the Ministry of Agriculture and other bodies. One of the bright but almost unbelievable ideas minuted at the meeting and leaked to Cutler was that Seascale children should actually be fed contaminated shellfish and then monitored to see how much plutonium was absorbed. This was rejected, but it was decided to monitor tissue from dead Seascale children, aborted foetuses, stillborn babies and the placentas of Seascale mothers.

It also transpired that the Black Inquiry had made a fundamental biological error in calculating the radiation dose received by Seascale children. Leukaemia occurs in the bone marrow where blood cells are formed. If damaged by radiation, these cells may become cancerous. The Black Report, according to Cutler, assumed that the blood cells targeted by the radiation are evenly distributed throughout the bone marrow, but, in fact, as a scientist told the DHSS meeting, recent research has shown that the target cells are concentrated in a specific place, on the inner surfaces of the bone. It is precisely those areas where deposits of plutonium, if either inhaled or ingested, occur, and the meeting had to agree that 'this is very important since radiation exposure could be different [i.e. very much higher] if the cells are concentrated close to the bone.'

More recently, new information has come to light which appears to give considerable support to those who have failed to find reassurance in the Black Report. On 16 February 1986, the *Sunday Times* revealed that discharges around the Sellafield site were, at one time, *40 times* higher than those stated in the Black Report, and that doses of radiation received by the local population for a period of three years during the 1960s were five times higher than officially recorded. This only came to light because of physicist Derek Jakeman who was employed at Windscale in the 1950s. In 1955, he and a colleague from the Research and Development Department took Geiger counters back to their homes in Seascale. The readings were very high, so high that both men immediately asked for more information on discharges from the site. Not only was this refused, but both were told that if they pressed the matter any further, they would be sacked.

So they wrote an unofficial report which they gave to the Atomic Energy Authority. It was ignored. Jakeman was so incensed that he resigned, left Cumbria and worked abroad for several years. On his return in 1984, he read the Black Report with interest. As he did so, it struck him forcibly that the figures given in it, provided by the National Radiological Protection Board, were wrong, so he wrote to British Nuclear Fuels telling them this. At first, BNFL refused to believe him, but eventually they checked back through their records and found he was right.

A report produced by Jakeman's own department in 1955 had recorded that the amount of radioactivity in grass, lettuce and milk was approaching the maximum permissible level, milk being a particular matter of concern in view of the possible effects on babies and young children. The figure given to the Black inquiry for the amount of uranium discharged into the atmosphere between 1952 and 1955 was 400 grams. In actual fact, it was 20 kilograms. We do not know why this enormous discrepancy arose in the NRPB figures. In a statement made to the *Sunday Times*, BNFL admitted that the figure was wrong: 'The figure that was assessed for the amount of uranium released was about half a kilogram. A release of 20 kilograms is now considered more likely.' They said that improved measuring techniques had allowed them to reassess the figure. One specific paragraph of the Black Report said:

If all the assumptions are correct, these calculations [of the Black inquiry] have demonstrated that, at most, less than 0.1 deaths from leukaemia would be expected from the discharges (accidental or planned) from Sellafield to the under-20-year-old population of Seascale born between 1945–1975, giving a maximum risk of death from leukaemia of about four in a million young people per annum. This is approximately 1/40th of the additional number of deaths found at Seascale. To attribute these additional deaths from leukaemia to radiation, it would require that the total discharges from Sellafield had in fact been at least *40 times greater* than reported and that monitoring and extrapolations of doses to the public were *in error by a similar factor* [my italics].

So, has Sir Douglas Black now changed his mind? At the time of writing, it appears not, even though the correct figure appears to be, uncannily, 40 times greater than the one he had been given, and the number of additional deaths was, in fact, 3.5 and not 0.1. He maintains that there is still no 'scientific' link. The new figures are to be published as an appendix to the existing report, but there are no plans to update the report in the light of this new information. Is it to be wondered that people are cynical?

But possible ill-effects from Windscale/Sellafield may not be limited to its immediate area. In the wake of the Black Report, doctors working on the west coast of Scotland reported an increase in cases of leukaemia among young people. Looking only at those under the age of twenty-four they found nearly twice the number of leukaemia cases that they would expect among those living near Hunterston nuclear power station in Ayrshire. They also found an 'outbreak' of 19 cases of myeloid leukaemia along the coast from the Solway Firth to Cape Wrath between 1971 and 1975, and identified significant excesses of the same type of leukaemia south-west of the Clyde estuary. These figures were prepared by the Scottish Health Service and the Cancer Surveillance Unit at Ruchill Hospital, Glasgow, and their report notes that the figure for Scotland as a whole is not significantly higher than for anywhere else.

Doctors at Fleetwood, lying almost due south of Windscale/Sellafield, also discovered an unexpectedly high incidence of myelomas (bone marrow cancer) in their area. Dr Nicholas Howarth of Blackpool's Victoria Hospital said he wanted an investigation into the cases to see if they could be connected with the 1957 Windscale accident: myelomas had appeared at double the expected rate in Fleetwood since 1979, and this disease takes 15 to 20 years to develop. Polonium-210, the highly carcinogenic substance released during the accident, is strongly linked with myeloma. Howarth and a colleague at Blackpool, Dr Neil Hague, had looked at the incidence of myelomas in the Wyre Health Authority area (which includes Fleetwood) since 1979, and while the highest rate they might have expected to find using official statistics was 19 cases, in fact they found 39.

Nor has cancer been the only concern. In the *British Medical Journal* of 12 November 1983, there was a short article by Dr Patricia Sheeham of the St Michael's House Child Development Clinic in Dublin and Dr Irene Hillary of the Department of Medical Microbiology, University College Dublin, expressing concern over an unusual cluster of babies with Down's syndrome (mongolism) born to former pupils of an Irish boarding school.

The mothers all had one thing in common. During the 1950s they attended the school in Dundalk, an eastern coastal town, and during October 1957 pupils at the school were afflicted with an illness similar to influenza. In 1974, one of the doctors who wrote to the *BMJ* had examined a child born to one of the former pupils and the mother mentioned that

Down's syndrome babies had also been born to some of her school friends. All 213 pupils who had attended the school in the 1950s were contacted and details of their obstetric and personal histories noted. This revealed that six babies born to former pupils had Down's syndrome. The pupils were matched against a control group of 128 other women which included 55 former pupils at the school, in which group there was only one Down's syndrome child, born to a woman over forty. It is known that women over the age of 35 have an increased chance of giving birth to a child with this condition.

None of the Dundalk mothers smoked, had used contraceptives of any kind nor had taken drugs during pregnancy. Only one had been exposed to X-rays during pregnancy and that was for a dental examination.

The six women concerned had gone on to have a total of twenty-six pregnancies between them and no other Down's syndrome babies were born to them. In each case tests showed that the parents themselves had normal chromosomes and the mothers had not been infected with rubella, hepatitis B or the protozoan *Toxoplasma gondii*.

'The number of affected children was far too high to be the result of chance alone,' write the doctors. 'The incidence of six babies with Down's syndrome in a total of 26 pregnancies is significantly higher than the overall incidence of one in 600.' While clusters have appeared before in specific areas and at specific times 'this unique cluster is related to neither space nor time; the babies were born in different locations. The only common factor is that their mothers lived in close association during their teenage years and had an illness similar to influenza in October 1957.

'Another possible tie-related causal factor was the nuclear accident at Windscale on 10 October 1957. Irish meteorological reports are consistent with radioactive fallout having reached Ireland at a time of heavy rainfall in the Dundalk area . . . we suggest that the levels of exposure to radiation in Dundalk were probably similar to those of the average population of southern England.'

There have been criticisms of this study in the *British Medical Journal* mainly consisting of complaints over lack of information on the methods used, and on the choice of the control groups, although some among the critics do say that the number of Down's syndrome babies is significantly higher than average. The authors responded by saying they had indeed contacted all the pupils in the school at that time (213) of which 107 were in the same senior classes in 1957. These were what they considered to be the 'at risk' group. Twenty-two of these girls did not wish to co-operate but the authors learned, after the publication of the first *BMJ* report, that two had had Down's syndrome children who had died. These two babies *are not* included in the original report. Of the rest of the group 28 were unmarried and had no children and 53 were married of whom six were infertile. This left 47 fertile women who had had 119 pregnancies resulting in 121 normal babies (two sets of twins). Other abnormalities in this group were two neonatal deaths due to congenital heart disease, two spina bifida, three miscarriages, nine spontaneous abortions, and one case of cystic fibrosis. 'Six cases of Down's syndrome occurring in 142 pregnancies is an incidence of one in 24 and is therefore unlikely to have occurred by chance', write the doctors. (*BMJ* 14.1.1986) 'We wish to emphasise that this study, which was started in 1974, was concerned only with looking for a possible infective cause in this closed community. The possible connection with radioactivity and therefore with Windscale could hardly be ignored in view of the coincidence in timing and the relevant information made available to us from the Meteorological Office's records.'

Meanwhile, among legal actions in the pipeline is one from a young woman who was a pupil at a boarding school in Seascale in 1957. She developed thyroid cancer four-and-a-half years ago, from which she is recovering, but blames the 1957 accident and the iodine-131 which could have affected her thyroid gland. A young couple, Christopher and Christine Merlin, are also suing after finding radioactive dust in their house at Seascale. They consider this to be unacceptable.

As a footnote to the Windscale story, in December 1983 residents of the area deposited a bag of radioactive silt from the Ravenglass estuary outside No 10 Downing Street. The effect was remarkable. 'Experts' called in to deal with it, while emphasising the dust was harmless, mounted a full-scale clean-up operation of a dramatic nature. They dismissed as facetious suggestions that one way of setting minds at rest would be to store some of the silt in the cellars under the Prime Minister at 10 Downing Street.

Other cancer clusters

We have already seen how a cluster of leukaemia cases had been found within a radius of less than 12.5 km of Dounreay (*see* pp. 120–1). In October 1982 the magazine *Time Out* announced that it had found a cluster of leukaemia cases around Sizewell nuclear power station in Suffolk. Three workers had contracted the disease and two had died from it (later two other cases were to emerge.) Another worker had died of haemolytic anaemia, a rare blood disorder also associated with radiation.

The first leukaemia victim was Ken Thompson, a welder inside the reactor area, who died in August 1980 at the age of 44. Leukaemia was diagnosed in November 1978, seven years after he started work at Sizewell.

For seven months after this diagnosis Thompson heard nothing from the medical staff at the power station and then, in June 1979, the CEGB sent him to a specialist. 'He told him', says Thompson's widow, ' "You know you've only got three years to live at most." My husband passed out like a light.' He died following a massive brain haemorrhage induced by the leukaemia. At the subsequent inquest the coroner was told by the CEGB that the dosage Thompson had received was 'fairly average', but he recorded an open verdict, saying that while it was unlikely radiation was responsible 'there was always an element of uncertainty'.

Michael Hope, who died in March 1982, had also worked inside the reactor area and developed symptoms of leukaemia within three years. While he was recovering from an operation to remove his spleen, two CEGB officials visited him and asked him to leave the nuclear power station when he recovered and take a job in a coal- or oil-fired one. 'I do think that was funny,' said his widow. 'If it wasn't dangerous, why move him away from the reactor?'

The third leukaemia victim investigated by *Time Out* was Bob Biddle; his wife worked in the station canteen, and died of stomach cancer in 1981. His job was supervising the radioactive pile cap and overseeing the transfer of the fuel rods from the reactor to the ponds where they are stored prior to being taken to Windscale/Sellafield. He was told he had leukaemia in 1981 but when interviewed by *Time Out* he maintained that leukaemia was not a serious illness at all. More than that; he told them: 'If I died of leukaemia and I had got it at Sizewell, I'd think it was worth it for 17 years' wonderful work.' He believed totally in the CEGB's pronouncements on reactor safety. 'They look after you so well . . . I don't think anyone could have more regard for safety than the CEGB.'

George Marjoram, the man who died of haemolytic anaemia, was foreman in the instrument section, which often brought him into contact with radiation. His illness lasted five years.

It soon became apparent that the *Time Out* findings were the tip of an iceberg. In 1983 Dr Michael Busy, district medical officer to the East Suffolk District Health Authority, showed that eight out of eleven leukaemia victims notified since 1967 had lived at Leiston, all within half a mile of each other. Leiston is two miles from Sizewell. Although the number of cases in East Suffolk was not above the national average, in three areas it was higher than would be expected. The incidence of the disease occurring in Sizewell's 500-strong workforce would, if normal, be one in ten-thousand per annum. Also, out of eleven cases in sixteen years it seemed remarkable that eight occurred in such a small area. Dr Busy called for further research. His report was immediately dismissed by Dr C. J. Schilling, the CEGB medical officer.

A year later a twelfth person died of the disease, in the same area. Altogether twelve people of whom five were Sizewell employees have now died of leukaemia since 1967.

Another cluster has been found in the area around Berkeley nuclear power station in Gloucestershire, where seven children have contracted leukaemia. Commenting on this, Dr Gareth Leyshon, the district medical officer, said that since 1980 five children in and around Lydney, across the Severn from Berkeley, had been found to have leukaemia, and of these three attend the same school, Woolaston Junior School at Netherend, three miles down-wind from the power station. There are two more cases in the villages of Cam and Dursley, on the other side of the station. Another nuclear power station, Oldbury, is within ten miles of the leukaemia victims.

Health officials have stressed that no definite link with the power stations can be proved as radiation levels are so low, but the father of one of the victims is less sanguine. Mr Hobman told the *Observer* that 'one tends to be sceptical of the CEGB. They say there has been satisfactory control of radiation discharges – satisfactory to whom?' Local people were open-minded, he continued, but the fact was that there were no leukaemia cases in the area throughout the 1970s and the appearance of such a cluster in such a short time was highly unusual.

The attitude of the CEGB is that such clusters are not unusual but in fact, cancer specialists can only recollect ten such in the last twenty-five years and the majority of these have been near nuclear power stations. Dr Alice Stewart said of Berkeley, 'If you find an outbreak of leukaemia occurring in a place where there is an observed increase in radiation, alarm bells should ring.'

In the town of Ferndown near Bournemouth, leukaemia is occurring at ten times the national average. The point was driven home to Mrs Carol Cooke who moved there from Leicester in 1977. In 1981 her five-year-old daughter Anna was diagnosed as having contracted the disease. Her GP told her it was very rare, but when she started attending the special leukaemia clinic she found 'an awful lot of children suffering from the disease'. Until she began making inquiries she did not know that radiation can be a cause of leukaemia, but then she began her own survey as she and her family live near Winfrith nuclear power station.

When she looked into the statistics she found that Ferndown, with a population of 15,549, should have one case of acute lymphoblastic leukaemia every fifteen years. She found there had been nine cases in nine years. The small village of Wool, next door to the power station, could expect to have one case in twenty-three years, but three children living there were suffering from it. Stephen Ross, MP, took up the matter and discovered that until 1971 the figures for that type of leukaemia in Dorset were the lowest in all England and Wales. By 1981 they were the highest. Winfrith went on-stream in 1964.

Health Minister Kenneth Clarke agreed that the statistics were correct but said, 'Great care should be taken in trying to draw any worthwhile conclusions from these figures.' Mrs Cooke's MP, Robert Adley, went further and told the media that she was a very clever lady running a sophisticated political campaign for her own ends.

In August 1985 a lengthy paper appeared in the *British Medical Journal* revealing the results of the biggest study of employees' health records ever undertaken by the Atomic Energy Authority. Researchers found that the risk of genital cancer among workers exposed to low-level radiation appeared to be fifteen times greater than that recognised as safe under current guidelines. It also found that the death rate from prostate cancer in one group was eight times the national average. Further cause for concern emerged when statistics showed that among the 40,000 people who had worked at seven of the AEA's plants including Dounreay and Aldermaston (the records at two other plants, Risley and Culcheth, had been destroyed), 937 had died of cancer. There were also more cases of and deaths from leukaemia, testicular cancer, thyroid cancer and non-Hodgkins lymphoma than the national average.

Two findings were particularly interesting. One was that men exposed to multiple sources of radiation, particularly tritium at the Winfrith plant, were up to nine times more likely to develop cancer of the prostate, and twenty-eight had died from that disease. The other was that women in the five centres covered by the survey were twice as likely to die from cancer of the uterus or ovaries.

'The excess of deaths from genital cancers is significant and

unexpected,' said Dr Valerie Beral, one of those involved in
the survey. What was also proved was that the number of
cancers increased in proportion to workers' exposure to
radiation, particularly in the case of prostate cancer.

The Atomic Energy Authority, however, said that it found
the results of the survey 'reassuring'.

Currently, there is insufficient research on low-level radiation and its effects, although many doctors and scientists are
now pressing for this. In 1985, Dr Alice Stewart was given a
grant by the EEC to compare the incidence of childhood
leukaemias throughout Britain with the levels of background
radiation to which they have been exposed. The results are
expected towards the end of 1986.

Probably the single most worrying aspect of this whole
subject is that reliable information is so hard to come by in
Britain. The point was made very well by the *Guardian*'s
science editor, Anthony Tucker, in March 1986 when he
stated that official censorship is gagging those involved in
crucial civil research into radiation in the environment, and
he described statements made by various spokesmen for the
nuclear industry – that fears of radiation 'are born of ignorance' – as 'insulting, cynical hypocrisy'.

Information generated by research projects, carried out in
areas of public health or safety, may never reach the scientific
journals and, thus, the public. There is, he said, a highly
effective, 'insidious and concealed form of systematic censorship operated by government departments in conjunction
with industry', and this has corrupted British science to an
unprecedented level. Nowhere is this more true than in the
field of radiation.

Government departments exercise complete control over
the information that results from contract research, and this
can lead to interference, delay or the blocking of publication.
Civil research is starved of funds and increasingly under
pressure to accept government contracts in order to survive,
and thus the 'multiple gag applied by the government' is
destructively effective. In addition, the selling off of public
assets to the private sector will soon result in Harwell, so
highly regarded by the whole world (although not apparently
by this government), becoming privately owned.

The government gag is most stringently applied to research into the effects of radio-nuclides discharged into the environment. It appears that civil research is showing that radioactive material is not distributed evenly but accumulates as 'hot particles' throughout the inshore marine sediments and generally in the environment over a wide area around nuclear plants, and around Sellafield in particular. These findings should have been widely published to encourage discussion, but this has not been the case. The health implications of these hot particles are, said Anthony Tucker, not clear, and there is, as yet, no firm proof either way as to whether the risk of cancer from them might be higher than from radio-nuclides spread uniformly over tissue. It also seems likely that these particles could cross the placenta and reach the foetus in the womb – how would that be affected? The National Radiological Protection Board has said that, as the foetus grows, the dose per unit of volume tissue will fall, but this is not, in Tucker's view, a theory that seems to make much sense.

Hot particles in the environment pose different problems to a uniform spread of radioactivity, said Tucker, and public safety rests on internationally established dose limits. (These, as we know, are now a matter of controversy.) Apparently, the figures published by the Ministry of Agriculture and Fisheries (MAFF) are, not to put too fine a point on it, fudged. Official 'safe' levels are based on 'mean' values – i.e. they take a figure somewhere halfway between the highest radiation figure and the lowest. In recent years, the figures from which the government calculations have been deduced have not been published, so all we get are the mean values. It would appear, according to experts, that the MAFF figures themselves left much to be desired even when they were published in full, and, as Tucker has pointed out, the mean values issued by MAFF might well result from the fact that half the people in an area received very little radiation and the rest twice as much.

Tucker said:

The anomalous measurements and the emergence of research indicating a potential, serious 'hot particle problem' in which even inter-tidal plants and coastal grass, let alone marine food chains . . . are associated with single, aggregated particles, make absolute nonsense of the procedures used to protect us. Official withdrawal of information seems to have coincided with the dawnings of acceptance that there is now a problem, resulting in a cover-up of the worst kind, stemming not from incompetence or inadequate monitoring but from a planned policy of deception.

If much of the radioactivity from nuclear plants such as Sellafield is in the form of 'hot particles', which can be inhaled or ingested, then the fate of these particles in the environment and their relation to human beings should be investigated as a matter of urgency and the findings made public.

Money that once funded independent science is now in the hands of government with all that implies in the way of direct control of a kind, said Tucker, 'which is sinister and has never before existed in this country in peacetime.' Independent radiation monitoring is crucial, he said, for both safety and reassurance, yet only the government has the funding necessary to do it properly. It is even getting very difficult for an independent viewpoint to be published in British scientific journals.

He called for a pitched battle between, on the one hand, the policy information machine of government and of the industrial lobbies and, on the other, all those concerned about environmental radiation and other problems. He demanded adequate funding, independent research and the publication of findings, whatever these findings may say. However, 'the chances under this government,' he concluded, 'are less than those of a snowball in hell.'

We have come back full circle. Nobody denies there might be some risk; what is in dispute is how great that risk is. Or perhaps that is not quite accurate either – what we are really talking about is an *acceptable* risk and that poses the question: acceptable to whom?

In 1982, a big row broke out in the United States among members of the Nuclear Regulatory Commission over whether 13,000 deaths per year was an 'acceptable risk' from nuclear power stations. This figure was arrived at by the use of statistics and concepts so abstruse as to be described by a member of the Commission as 'meaningless'. The general consensus among Commission members was, however, that this was really rather a good figure set against deaths from other causes.

What is needed, without any doubt, is the sort of independent, properly funded research on radiation in the environment called for by Anthony Tucker. It might be that no epidemiologist will ever be able to obtain absolute proof that a radiation event caused cancer in either a worker at a nuclear power station or a member of the general public. All that can be done, by careful research, is to find out the extent of the problem and to expose the possibility of adverse effects in some instances. If this is not done, there is little chance of the nuclear programme being halted in an attempt to stop possible illnesses and deaths.

It was all a lot simpler in the days of the Broad Street pump, when it was possible to stop the source of an epidemic.

Chapter 8

The Plane Crash on the Football Ground

So just what are the chances of a serious nuclear accident occurring in Britain and what might be the result? Those chances, according to which pro-nuclear expert you go to, are remote and are described in different terms. Our own John Dunster of the NRPB considers the likelihood of such an accident happening to be about the same as that of a jumbo jet crashing on to a football ground while a match is under way. (Possibly, since he made this statement some time ago, he might have changed his mind following the spate of air crashes in 1985.) In the United States they go for the analogy of a meteor hitting a city. When the UK Atomic Energy Authority toured its educational exhibition 'Atoms for Energy' in 1980 it favoured: You might have a reasonable chance of getting between five and ten O-levels, but how about twenty-five? That is unlikely and so is a nuclear accident.

The nuclear lobby still stoutly maintains that its record of building and equipping nuclear power stations is second to none. Yet, as we have already seen, that is hardly the case. Behind the competent façade lie a number of incidents bordering on black comedy: Quad Cities-2 (in the USA) which operated with a welding rig still inside the pressure vessel; Vermont Yankee with its control rods installed upside down; and Palisades where the barrel supporting the core worked loose and scrunched up the internal works of the reactor, eventually involving its operators in an indefinite shutdown and a $3 million lawsuit.

Possibly most telling of all is what was described in the American press as 'Boondoggle at Diablo – The 18-year saga of greed, deception and ineptitude'. What happened was also described by the Nuclear Regulatory Commission as a 'fairly significant engineering goof-up' and by one of those involved as 'an extraordinary cockup'.

The proposed nuclear power station at Diablo Canyon near Los Angeles had never been popular and it went through numerous court cases, demonstrations and problems. Not least among the objections was that it was built only two-and-a-half miles from the active and notorious San Andreas earthquake fault.

However, in spite of all this, in September 1981 the reactor was ready to come on-stream. Over a thousand objectors marched to the site to try and prevent loading of the fuel taking place, but they did not succeed and most of them were arrested. Loading commenced.

But just before the reactor was started up, a young engineer noticed something odd (and bear in mind that the plant was supposed to have been thoroughly and meticulously checked). He asked his superiors to look again at blueprints for the plant and they discovered the builders had mixed up those for Units 1 and 2. The seismic supports, installed to cope with possible earthquakes, had been put in the wrong way round, with the strong ones in place of the weak and the weak in place of the strong. The two blueprints were mirror images of each other, said Dick Davin, a company spokesman . . . While sorting that one out, it was also discovered that the wrong diagram had been used in the stress analysis of some auxiliary pipe systems in one of the domes that would help cool down the reactor during a shutdown. To date, the power station has still not come on-stream.

It was shortly after the 1979 general election that a special Cabinet meeting was held by the Prime Minister, Mrs Thatcher, and the decision was taken to build ten nuclear power stations in ten years, beginning in 1982. The design chosen was that of the pressurised-water reactor (PWR) similar to that used at Three-Mile Island and designed by the multinational Westinghouse.

It is now history that this much-leaked decision has been subject to delay. The public inquiry into the building of the first PWR, to be put alongside the existing Magnox station at Sizewell in Suffolk, did not finish until 1985. But right at the beginning of the decision-making process, in 1980, the government were given encouragement to go ahead with their nuclear programme by our own 'watchdog', the National Radiological Protection Board.

Yet there is something odd about the NRPB assessment of risk. Their assessment reports rely very heavily on the Rasmussen Report, a summary of which was first published in the United States in 1974. One report said that the 'best available estimate of risk due to a nuclear plant is that of Rasmussen' and John Dunster, in the first part of an interview on *World in Action*, transmitted on 4 August 1980, said that the Rasmussen Report was 'very useful, the most complete there is.' However, in the USA it was attacked fiercely by both scientists and congressmen as soon as its summary was published.

Altogether about four million dollars went into the Rasmussen study. Professor Norman Rasmussen, dean of engineering at the Massachusetts Institute of Technology, along with a staff of fifty, spent three years on a study funded by the US Atomic Energy Commission. The report came up with exactly what the AEC wanted to know: that a nuclear accident was just about the least likely accident that could possibly happen – just like a meteor from outer space coming down and hitting a city. Accidents involving meltdown were marginally more likely than had been thought previously, but their consequences were far less than expected.

One of the lesser-known and less-publicised aims of the report was to help gain renewal of the Price-Anderson Act, legislation limiting the liability of companies operating nuclear power stations in the event of a terrible accident. Also the AEC needed an optimistic survey to bolster up its flagging image. Most commentators and the media helped by taking the summary at its face value, and not examining the twelve detailed volumes from which the summary was made.

This was crucial. The summary spoke of the likely number of 'prompt' deaths in the event of an accident and left it at that. It said that, say, ten 'prompt' deaths would be about the same number as would occur if a meteor shower fell on a heavily populated area. However, buried away in the more detailed data was the forecast that in addition to these ten 'prompt' deaths there would eventually be 7,000 cancer deaths, 4,000 genetic defects and 16,000 thyroid abnormalities as well as the contamination of some 3,000 square miles of land. Among the scientists who disagreed fundamentally with Rasmussen was one who said that the figures for deaths and injuries were sixteen times too low, and another who said Rasmussen had under-estimated the numbers of cancers and genetic effects by as much as fifty times.

The critics then took apart the methodology behind the study. The team had used computer analysis to go through a wide range of possible defects or component failures. As Peter Pringle and James Spigelmann point out in their book *Nuclear Barons*, they had assigned a precise probability to each defect or failure. 'But a number of the "probabilities" are no better than guesses multiplied by guesses.' Scientists showed that the report had under-estimated the possibility of a single accident, 'like a fire or an earthquake, resulting in multiple failures to a number of back-up safety systems'. They stressed that the averages produced by the team for weather patterns at reactor sites 'were meaningless; they could vary by up to one thousand times in the rate of dispersal of a radio-active cloud'. The report made no allowance for the un-expected or unforeseen, such as defects in new materials or new chemical reactions between components, even though the entire history of nuclear safety was 'littered with such examples'.

The Rasmussen team had refused to adopt the views on the health hazards of radioactivity put forward by accepted experts, and instead produced from nowhere figures lower by about half than those widely accepted. They gave optimistic forecasts of evacuation and decontamination measures and they 'glossed over' the fact that components deteriorate with the passage of time.

The full report was published in 1975. By 1979, informed criticism had reached such a pitch that the Nuclear Regulatory Commission was forced to formally disown it. In an unusually frank and stringent criticism, the NRC spoke of the politically motivated promotional aspects of the report; the American nuclear industry had used the Rasmussen report widely as a massive public relations boost. The NRC said that 'the Commission does not regard as reliable the reactor safety studies of numerical estimates of the overall risk of reactor accident . . . the conclusions should not be used uncritically for public purposes.' Nor should the report be used as a basis for licensing decisions.

Yet eleven months after this statement by the NRC our own NRPB gave its optimistic forecast to the government based on this very Rasmussen report. Challenged about this on the *World in Action* programme, John Dunster did admit that leaving out the number of long-term deaths from the Rasmussen report and concentrating only on the 'prompt' deaths had been wrong, indeed 'inexcusable'. But he still, in general, stood by the report.

Three years after it discredited the Rasmussen report, and in the wake of Three-Mile Island, the NRC announced it was going to shut down two nuclear power stations operating in New York State because emergency evacuation plans for the area were inadequate. This was the first time it had threatened such a thing because of worries about coping with an accident. It appears that in March 1982 the Federal Emergency Management Agency had carried out a practice drill. Nearby Rockland County refused to take part altogether and there were severe problems in Westchester County as it looked as if there would be insufficient bus drivers available to drive away the evacuees. Some 290,000 people would be involved.

In July 1982, an article in the *New Scientist* noted that American experts now thought serious accidents were more likely than they had hitherto believed. A new look at old data concerning breakdowns in reactors between 1969 and 1979 showed that the previous assessment of the chances of serious accidents happening had been about a hundred times too optimistic. Nuclear engineers at the government's own Oak Ridge National Laboratory in Tennessee published new estimates which put the likelihood of an accident in which a reactor core was at least partly damaged as happening once in every eight, or maybe even every three, reactor years assuming there are 72 reactors in the USA. The chances of a core meltdown they put at between 1.7 and 4.5 per thousand reactor years. This completely overturned the Rasmussen estimate, which was one meltdown every 20,000 reactor years.

In November 1982, the NRC released a preliminary report pointing out the dangers of the rupture of the pressure vessel in a PWR, and concluded that some sixteen of those currently operating in the USA would need significant modifications before the end of their working lives. This is because the pressure vessel of a reactor reaches very high temperatures (550° F). An accident involving loss of coolant (as at Three-Mile Island) would mean that the vessel would have to be dowsed with water at about 50° to 90° F. Because the steel in the vessel housing the reactor core becomes more and more brittle as it is subjected to increasing radioactivity, a rapid temperature shock obviously makes it more likely to break, and a really rapid drop in temperature could cause uncontrollable cracking. Since no plant could gradually cool down a core in such circumstances, the result would be disastrous and a meltdown almost inevitable. The NRC estimated that the pressure vessels of some sixteen plants would become so brittle that they could not cope with even a normal emergency shutdown. There were 85 cooling or thermal shock accidents between 1968 and 1981, an average of about five a year. Of this number, 24 were found to have been capable of cracking the vessel wall.

Whatever views reach the public from our government for a long time now they, the CEGB and other agencies have been working out what might happen in the event of a nuclear accident. There is a special computer program for this, called the Tirion Program. All concerned kept the Tirion program hidden away until, after a great deal of pressure, it had to be produced during the Windscale inquiry in 1977. It was then handed over to Peter Taylor of the Political Ecology Research Group, who has run a number of possible scenarios through it.

One was featured in the *World in Action* programme already mentioned. This posited an accident at the proposed Sizewell B rector in Suffolk, a serious one – a partial core meltdown – but by no means the most serious that could happen. The Tirion program feeds into the computer the kind of accident that might happen, where it occurs and how serious it is, as well as data about weather conditions such as wind speed, cloud, rain, sunshine, and the time of day at which the accident happens. Particular attention is paid to the direction of the wind, for this will affect how quickly the radiation will spread across the country and where it will fall. Then population figures are added and cities, towns and villages identified. The computer then calculates how many people would die at once, how many would die within a year and how many would die more slowly. Those caught in the path of the radioactive cloud would get a dose of gamma radiation, and they would also breathe in and ingest other radioactive materials, all of which would make for the lungs, bones and liver and thyroid.

So let us posit this accident at Sizewell B – not too bad an accident but quite serious all the same.

The weather is warm and cloudy. Winds at Sizewell generally follow the pattern for the British Isles with prevailing westerlies, but averaged out over a year they blow in from the north-east about one day in six. Given a wind speed of about 13 mph (not very windy), it would take a radioactive cloud about eight hours to arrive over London.

The first people at risk would be those in the town of Leiston only three miles from Sizewell. The cloud would reach them in 15 minutes. About 5000 people live there and unless they were all evacuated promptly, more than half of them – 2,695 – would die within a year and 650 later on from radiation-induced diseases. At the Sizewell inquiry, it was revealed that evacuation plans only consisted of moving the population of Leiston a further two miles away for a few hours.

Next in line after Leiston is the tiny village of Friston. Sixty people live either in the village or nearby, and the cloud would cross over them in about twenty-five minutes, leaving behind twenty-two early deaths and five long-term cancers, thus wiping out about half the village.

The cloud would continue relentlessly on its way, arriving in Ipswich (population 120,000), 19 miles away, in about two hours. There would be 900 early deaths from cancer and 1900 later deaths. Three-and-a-half hours after the accident, it would arrive in Colchester, with a population of 79,000. The cloud would be becoming more dispersed by this time, and there would be no immediate deaths, although many people would be ill. There would be about 500 radiation-induced cancers.

Getting ever nearer to London, the cloud would pass over Chelmsford and its surrounding dormitory area where some 300,000 people live. Again, there would be no early deaths but there would be about 1160 later ones.

Finally, a little over seven hours after it was created, the cloud would reach London itself. The dose would be weaker still and so there would be no early deaths, 'only' about 13,500 fatal cancers.

But if a tougher scenario were fed into the computer – a complete meltdown along with the right weather conditions – then scientists estimate that deaths in London alone might run into tens of thousands, and that some 258,000 Londoners would die within a year.

Even if you are prepared to ignore the possibility of death and disease from such a catastrophe, the social and economic consequences of this kind of accident are almost incalculable. Much valuable research has been done on this aspect by Earth Resources Research, using the National Radiological Protection Board's own computer models, the results of which and the data behind them were published recently as a report by Francis Nectoux and William Cannell. It is difficult to summarise such a complex document in any meaningful way, and certainly it should be read carefully by all those who want to take the subject further. However, it does demonstrate that should there be a serious accident at Sizewell or at any other nuclear plant the cost would not stop just at the toll on life and the expense of treating the survivors.

All animal and plant life would be affected to a greater or lesser extent, and the ground in some places would be unusable for an indefinite period of time. Depending on the amount of radiation and which isotopes are released, milk would have to be thrown away across the country and possibly even as far away as Ireland. If an accident took place in June no cereal or other crops could be harvested. Water would obviously be suspect; meat and poultry would be contaminated.

The social disruption would be immense if there were evacuation on a large scale. The length of time people would have to live away from the contaminated areas would depend upon the scale of the accident but from five to twenty years would be likely. To evacuate or not would be an economic question. As the authors of the report say:

> One has only to consider the social, psychological and economic consequences of such situations to understand that long-term-relocation decisions would only in fact be taken if their implementation could bring a significant reduction in the number of late health effects.

The financial costs would be enormous. First would come the health care for those damaged by the accident, care possibly stretching over twenty years. Then there would be compensation for those whose crops, cattle, poultry, etc. would have had to be destroyed, plus the cost of importing food to make up the shortfall. Then the losses in industrial and agricultural output over years would have to be taken into account, as well as compensation for loss of homes, loss of jobs and relocation expenses, which would include providing homes, work and possibly schools and hospitals for a substantial number of people who have had to move. On top of that would be the cost of decontaminating the ground, removing tens of thousands of tons of topsoil and possibly having to close some areas off altogether.

As for the costs involved in decontaminating and decommissioning the nuclear power plant itself, this is very difficult to forecast as

> it is almost impossible today to estimate the cost of decommissioning a nuclear plant even under normal [i.e. accident free] circumstances. Decommissioning and clean-up after a meltdown would be expected to be far more expensive and uncertain.

Taking one of the report's scenarios (by no means the worst) as if it had happened at Sizewell, the computer came up with a total of some 3000 early deaths from cancer, 4.5

million people having to take shelter and 1.5 million having to be evacuated. The whole of the population of Ipswich would have to be evacuated as well as some parts of London, and the costs of all this would soon top £15 billion. This sum is considered to be a conservative estimate using the NRPB's own computer models and still does not take into account decommissioning and decontamination costs.

So where does it leave us in Great Britain now? On the face of it, still leaning on the Rasmussen version of events. It is worth, once again, emphasising what the US Nuclear Regulatory Commission said about this:

ACCIDENT PROBABILITIES

The Commission accepts the review group report's conclusion that absolute values of the risks presented by WASH-1400 [The Rasmussen report] should not be used uncritically either in the regulatory process or for public policy purposes and has taken and will continue to take steps to assure that any such use in the past will be corrected as appropriate. In particular, in light of the review group conclusions on accident probabilities, the Commission does not regard as reliable the Reactor Safety Study's numerical estimate of the overall risk of reactor accident.

Our own 'watchdog' body, the National Radiological Protection Board, has always been overstretched, but spending cuts have made the position far worse. Also overstretched and overworked is the Nuclear Installations Inspectorate which as far back as December 1979 was twenty per cent short of inspectors, and one commercial nuclear power station, at Chapel Cross, was without a nuclear site inspector for several months. One London-based inspector was trying to cover Chapel Cross, plus the reactors at Windscale/Sellafield, and in October 1979 40 inspectors from the NII advertised themselves in the *Guardian* under the heading 'NUCLEAR SAFETY ENGINEERS SEEK EMPLOYMENT'.

Many of the worst mistakes made during the construction of British nuclear power stations have been discovered by the NII. The rundown of staff of the NII which has continued is extremely worrying in the context of Sizewell B, for if the go-ahead is given (as seems likely) for the controversial Westinghouse design it will mean that there will be a real shortage of experts to monitor its progress. That way, as we have seen from an enormous amount of evidence, design faults, bad workmanship and faulty components may go unchecked.

Also shorthanded are those scientists working for the Ministry of Agriculture who monitor radioactivity levels. In 1982, according to the results of an investigation carried out for the government by Sir Derek Rayner, before the unions banned dumping nuclear waste at sea, there was such a shortage of experts that the monitoring programme for radioactivity in the environment, and especially in the sea, had almost collapsed. At that time, Britain was responsible for *ninety per cent* of all the man-made radiation being dumped into the oceans of the world. Work on analysing samples for radioactivity was held up for long periods, and reports were being published nine months behind schedule because of staff shortages in the Ministry's Lowestoft laboratories. The Ministry's failure to publish comprehensive data was criticised by Mr Justice Parker at the Windscale inquiry in 1977 and five new posts were authorised, but years have passed without their being filled.

The Rayner report said that the nuclear regulatory bodies should be properly staffed for three vital reasons. First, because of the scheduled expansion of the nuclear power programme at the rate of up to one new power station every two years. Second, the expansion of fuel reprocessing to meet the needs of the UK nuclear industry and the levels of waste imported from abroad. Third, the increased pressure from domestic and foreign sources for more rigorous assessment of new proposals and monitoring of current practice.

The survey rejected outright those suggestions that this side of the nuclear business should be handed over to the nuclear industry itself on the grounds that 'the activities of government in this emotive area operate as a check against what the public perceives as an over-powerful nuclear lobby'.

But in spite of the encouraging noises on nuclear safety

from all concerned in the nuclear lobby, the Sizewell inquiry showed that there was substantial public disquiet.

The publicity given to plans for the 'mass evacuation' of the population of Leiston up the road to Saxmundham produced considerable derision. It is obvious both from the Tirion program and the NRPB's own computer models that it is highly unlikely that such an evacuation would have any point at all. We would be talking in terms of tens of thousands of people being moved a long way away. However, Sizewell, like most nuclear power stations, is situated in an area with poor roads and diminishing public transport. There seems to be little possibility that sufficient transport could be brought into the area fast enough to move such large numbers of people. In addition, as was seen at Three-Mile Island, the roads can soon become jammed with people escaping in their own cars. Also, we would not be talking about putting them up in a schoolhouse for a few hours but of relocating them for years.

The result of this obvious lack of public trust seems to have been a re-think within government circles but only as a public relations exercise. In July 1985 two circulars were published, one from the NRPB and aimed at general practitioners living within forty miles of a nuclear power station, the second from the DHSS aimed at area and district health authorities.

Taking the GPs' leaflet first: it asserts that nuclear accidents are extremely unlikely to happen, and even the worst, a core meltdown, would not 'explode like an atomic bomb'. The scenario that follows is very optimistic, far more so than any that must be available to those involved from their own forecasts using the Tirion program. A serious release of radioactivity 'would probably cause no immediate harm [sic] to persons in the vicinity but, after a latent period of many years it might lead to a few extra cancer cases . . .' Such a serious release might lead to some people 'having to stay indoors for a period and having to shut their windows and doors'. It does concede that a large amount of radiation might lead to radiation sickness, which would manifest itself by vomiting and diarrhoea.

All nuclear installations, it continues, have to draw up emergency plans approved by the Nuclear Installations

Inspectorate, and these are circulated to the appropriate local authorities. However, if the scale of the accident exceeded that for which the plans had been drawn up, more extensive action might be required. An operational support centre (OSC) would be set up to co-ordinate crisis management, and the police would also be very busy indeed. They would be warning people to stay indoors, issuing tablets of potassium iodate to the public to counter the effects of iodine-131, evacuating all those living downwind from the site and assisting evacuees to return home 'when the emergency is over'. The mind truly boggles. What police force could tackle all that?

Once the incident becomes public knowledge, warns the leaflet, GPs might well be contacted by people who are worried about it.

> They should be reassured that they are in no immediate danger and that the police will tell them if they need to take any action. If they are worried they can be told they should remain indoors with windows and doors shut if living within a few miles of the plant. Those caught outside should take simple decontamination measures to wash off any fallout, like taking a shower . . .

This provoked a number of doctors to come out into print, including Dr A. J. M. Coates from Colesford in Gloucester who asked, in the *Guardian* on 16 September 1985, how people could collect their potassium iodate tablets from police stations if they had to stay indoors, or would the police be able to visit every individual household in spite of the radioactive fallout?

The circular to health authorities is a more detailed version of the same optimistic leaflet. It explains what Operational Support Centres are and what such a 'crisis' would entail. It does, however, accept that an area up to forty miles from the accident might be affected.

All the authorities would need to be involved – water, health, local government, and so on – and such a release of radioactivity might have an effect on the population and also on food, water and other resources but evacuation is still seen as temporary and involving only a handful of people living within a few miles of the affected plant. There is some suggestion that hospitals might have to accommodate an influx of casualties, but no discussion as to how this might be organised on such a large scale. Again, there is no sensible idea as to how a large population could be issued with potassium iodate tablets.

If you read the document, you can see that certainly the notion of an accident has been thought through and the different problems considered, but the conclusions would appear to be largely wishful-thinking. An accident requiring so little action – such a minimum evacuation and people only needing to stay indoors to be safe – is not a 'serious' accident as such an event is generally understood. If this is 'serious' by DHSS standards, how would a really bad accident be described? Is there, one wonders, a realistic plan available somewhere for action in the event of a partial or full core meltdown?

There is a special note on the DHSS circular concerning the news media which, it says, would be intensely interested in such an event.

It is intended that the OSC should be the single authoritative local source of information. Health authorities should channel media inquiries through the OSC and all staff should be made aware of this.

So we are left, in reality, still facing the unknown and hoping for the best. Nobody wants to put the Tirion program to a real-life test to discover if the computer predictions are, in fact, accurate. It will be little consolation to those affected if, after such an accident, the British government changes its mind over the Rasmussen report on which the two most recent circulars would appear to have been based.

What is one to make then of the remark made by Sir Walter Marshall, chairman of the Central Electricity Generating Board, during a discussion on the *Today* programme on BBC Radio 4 on 13 August 1985? The chairman of the SSEB had been saying that a recent paper published in the American journal, *Nuclear Engineer*, had criticised the safety record of pressurised-water reactors and had said that the advanced gas-cooled reactors (AGRs), the kind favoured by the SSEB, were more reliable. In answer to this, Sir Walter said: 'Reliability is not important'.

Chapter 9

Playing Politics

There is a large body of literature devoted to the politics of nuclear power and in a book of this kind it is only possible to look briefly at the subject. While it is not within the remit of this book to examine the nuclear arms race, it is also virtually impossible to discuss the question of nuclear power without mentioning the nuclear weapons programme: the two are inextricably bound up with each other, and have been since the beginning. One could not exist easily without the other.

When one reads all the material, speeches and information on state subsidies to the coal industry, British Rail, British Steel, almost any nationalised industry you care to mention, along with all that is said about British commercial concerns that do not meet their targets, it is obvious that the nuclear industry is unique. No other has so consistently got its sums wrong.

Both the nuclear industry and the Central Electricity Generating Board have consistently *over*-estimated the nation's electricity needs while at the same time *under*-estimating the costs of providing nuclear power. The nuclear power programme has soaked up massive funds needed for research into other fields of energy production, such as solar energy, wind and wave power and tidal reservoirs.

One of the main reasons for this, of course, is that the civil nuclear programme produces plutonium, and that plutonium is essential for the manufacture of nuclear weapons. Quite simply, the hidden principal product of the nuclear power stations is that plutonium which is so essential to us if we are to continue with our own nuclear weapons programme and also, apparently, to supply the United States as well.

If this were not the case, it is quite likely that the nuclear power programme would have been stopped by now, on the

217

grounds of both cost and safety. Walter Patterson provides an amusing parable for the latter. Imagine how you would feel, he writes, were a lorry to draw up outside your home and the driver lean out of his cab and say he had your winter fuel – nitro-glycerine – on the back of his lorry and where would you like him to drop it?

Patterson also makes the other vital point. Nowhere in the world is plutonium fuel economic and the cost of this has been borne not by the world's nuclear industry, but by the world's taxpayers. No other industry has been so featherbedded.

As we have already discovered, every forecast of the cost of a nuclear power station has been massively wrong. Nuclear power stations have been consistently late – years late – coming on-stream. They have had countless problems; there have been numerous mishaps; there have been a number of serious accidents. So far nobody has come up with the answer as to how nuclear waste can be made safe indefinitely, and how to set about decommissioning the power stations once they have reached the end of their working lives, which are comparatively short. Throughout 1984 and 1985 we heard a great deal about uneconomic coal pits. Nobody talks about uneconomic nuclear power stations.

It was after scientists both here and elsewhere finally lifted their eyes from contemplating the bomb that they turned their minds to civil nuclear power. It was to be the wonder fuel of the ages. It would provide electricity too cheap to meter. It would be almost given away.

They said.

The ultimate in nuclear reactors would be the fast-breeder reactors. They would burn plutonium to make electricity, while at the same time producing more plutonium which, in turn, could be used both for more nuclear power and for nuclear weapons. The plutonium for the fast breeders would come from the other kinds of nuclear reactors whose fuel would be reprocessed to feed them. It would be a neat circular process. Twenty-five years later, they are still trying to get the technology right.

It was in 1951 that Lord Cherwell promoted the idea of an independent body in Britain, a semi-governmental organisation rather like the US Atomic Energy Commission. In

1953 the then Prime Minister, Sir Winston Churchill, set up a committee under Sir John Anderson to transfer responsibility for the nuclear power programme to such a body. In February 1954, following legislation in Parliament, the United Kingdom Atomic Energy Authority was born. It was a semi-autonomous organisation under the control of a non-departmental government minister and it was designed to offer a balance between the civil and military uses of nuclear power although, as Sir John Hill, the AEA's chairman from 1967 to 1981, said, 'the facilities required for the manufacture of nuclear fuel [both military and civil] were virtually identical.'

The Authority took control over all the different bodies involved in the industry, its research into both civil and weapons programmes and their development. Ten days after its formation, it was decreed that nuclear power was to be used on a commercial basis by the then British Electricity Authority and since then the relation between the Authority and BEA's successor, the Central Electricity Generating Board, has been a close one. Transfers of top management began in 1957 when Christopher Hinton moved from the Authority to the Board, and has carried on into the 1980s when the Prime Minister, Mrs Thatcher, invited Sir Walter Marshall to leave the AEA (of which he was chairman) to take up the same position at the CEGB. Sir Walter was known popularly as 'Mr PWR' because of his passion for that design of nuclear reactor.

In those heady early days, however, it was hoped that private industry too would have a large share of the action, and commercial firms were encouraged to form themselves into consortia to undertake the design and construction of nuclear power stations. This plan was doomed to disappointment. In 1960 the initial five consortia merged into three; one of these collapsed in 1969; and by 1973 only one was left – the National Nuclear Corporation.

On 1 April 1971, British Nuclear Fuels Ltd (BNFL) came into existence and was given the task of handling the fuel side of the business in general and reprocessing in particular. As BNFL had to take over the production and reprocessing plants at Springfields, Capenhurst, Chapel

Cross, Calder Hall and Windscale (later Sellafield), the dividing line between civil and military nuclear programmes became ever more blurred. In 1973 the strictly nuclear weapons side of the AEA was transferred straight to the Ministry of Defence.

After the initial enthusiasm of the early 1960s there was a lull in nuclear expansion as problem began to pile on problem, but in the mid-1970s, following the oil crisis, there was a resurgence of enthusiasm for nuclear power – once again it was to be the real fuel of the future. However, by the mid-1980s that optimism had, once again, vanished.

In 1979 the incoming Thatcher administration embarked on a nuclear power programme designed, it said, to provide ten nuclear power stations in ten years. By 1985 the public inquiry into the first of these was only just drawing to its conclusion. It had lasted twenty-one months.

For by the early 1980s a good many different factors were at work apart from the past history of delays and escalating costs. First and foremost was the recession, which had hit all the industrialised world but which was particularly savage in Britain, arguably as a result of government economic policies. Demand for electricity, which had been dropping off since the late 1970s, became even lower. In 1979 the CEGB had to downgrade its forecast for growth of demand from 1.7 per cent per annum to 0.5 per cent per annum. By 1983 there was no forecast of growth at all. It was also apparent that after twenty-five years of massive expenditure on research and development, nuclear electricity could still not compete commercially with that produced either by coal or oil. From being a scarce resource, too, there is now a glut of uranium. On top of all this, reprocessing has proved to be far more difficult than was ever anticipated and far more expensive, leaving us again with the still insoluble problem of what to do with nuclear waste. Nor has anyone yet come up with a foolproof and economic way of decommissioning a nuclear power station. That cost never appears on the accounting systems of the CEGB.

In fact the disposal of nuclear waste is going to become one of the most crucial factors in any possible increased nuclear power programme over the next decade. In September 1985

Britain lost its fight to recommence the dumping of nuclear waste in the sea when the London Dumping Convention, in spite of strong pressure from the British government, suspended such dumping indefinitely. The convention is not legally binding but any resumption will put Britain in an extremely invidious position, not least because, for the first time, one of the grounds on which the decision was reached was that the nuclear industry could not prove that such dumping was harmless; hitherto the onus of proof had always been on those seeking to prove that it was harmful.

Public opinion appears to be in line with the London Dumping Convention, for the results of a poll published on 1 October 1985 showed that 76 per cent of those polled were overwhelmingly against further dumping of nuclear waste in the sea, and an equal majority was against shallow land-dumping. Sixty-seven per cent said that British Nuclear Fuels was doing a poor job, and 85 per cent said they should be more accountable.

But when we look at the politics of nuclear power, no one government can be blamed for the position we now find ourselves in. From the very start government ministers and Whitehall departments have been mesmerised by the nuclear lobby, blinded by science. The nuclear industry itself has become, in the words of Sir Kelvin Spencer, who was chief scientist at the Ministry of Power when the decision was taken to go ahead with the civil nuclear programme, a State within a State, 'preoccupied with self-preservation, the expansion of their interests and the self-aggrandisement of their leaders'. Also, both the nuclear industry and the CEGB are helped immeasurably by the lack of any Freedom of Information Act in Britain which would make them more accountable for the decisions they take.

However enthusiastic Mrs Thatcher was in 1979 to expand the nuclear power programme, this had been matched previously by Tony Benn. When he became Secretary of State for Energy in the 1974 Wilson administration, he was drawn to the nuclear lobby like a rabbit to a stoat, telling Parliament he had never encountered 'such a well organised scientific, industrial and technical lobby as the nuclear power lobby'. He never spoke truer words. By the time his tenure as Energy

Minister drew to a close he was becoming quite disenchanted with the nuclear lobby, but he left behind him a legacy to be remembered, not least the expansion and consolidation of a totally unaccountable, deeply secret police force – the nuclear police.

Mrs Thatcher's fascination was more practical. Even then, in 1979, she never again wanted to find a Conservative government held to ransom by the miners, and that was certainly one of the reasons behind her decision to go all-out for a new nuclear programme: there must not be a total dependence on coal.

But by the mid-1970s, careful reading of the CEGB's own reports shows that it was having doubts about its own energy needs. In 1975, it stated that it had no need to order any new coal- or oil-fired power stations until at least 1978, saying, 'the Board appreciates that this will have grave repercussions on its suppliers but sees no justification for consumers having to bear the extra cost of advanced orders.'

In 1976, a government statement made in Parliament said: 'As a country we have overcapacity in generation . . . and there is a general turndown in energy demand.' This was long before we in Britain hit the recession. The 1980/81 Annual Report of the CEGB showed a 33 per cent surplus of generating capacity over maximum demand. The result was that the Board speedily began decommissioning economically viable non-nuclear power stations while it was, at the same time, pressing for the full nuclear power programme to be implemented – a programme which does not make sense.

A report of a House of Commons Select Committee on Energy, published in 1981, concluded:

Having examined the economic case for the policy announced by the Secretary of State [i.e. the nuclear programme] and in particular the figures supplied by the CEGB, we have concluded that many of the underlying assumptions are open to question and that the justification for a steady ordering programme of 15 gigawatts over ten years rests on premises which are necessarily very uncertain.

222

Further backing for this viewpoint came, also in 1981, in the report of the Committee for the Study of Economics in the Nuclear Industry, chaired by Sir Kelvin Spencer and funded in part by the Rowntree Trust. Using the Board's own figures, published accounts and reports, it concluded that to go ahead with the new nuclear power programme was 'sheer economic lunacy'. Close analysis of the CEGB's figures, given in the report, shows how consistently it has got its sums wrong at every stage of every programme, how huge sums have just been written off without even the auditors commenting upon them, how the Department of Energy appears to be allowing coal-fired stations to be retired from service when almost all of them could produce electricity at less cost than the new nuclear power stations built to replace them.

In spite of all that, in spite of the unresolved safety and waste-disposal problems, the new nuclear programme seems set to go ahead. To go ahead, moreover, at a time when the American nuclear programme has virtually ground to a halt, and even the fast-breeder part of it has hit trouble. Back in October 1983, the US Senate rejected by 56 votes to 40 a supplementary Appropriations Bill which would have allowed its experimental fast-breeder reactor at Clinch River to continue in existence, even though terminating the contract would of itself cost a further 150 to 350 million dollars. Altogether some $1.6 billion had been spent on this useless project.

West Germany, too, has had increasing problems with its nuclear industry. By 1981 it was facing prolonged periods of uncertainty, with cuts in capacity and even complete closures of some nuclear plants. Its own fast-breeder programme had, like everyone else's, been subject to delays and escalating costs. The original development costs of its Kalkar reactor had risen from an estimated DM1.5 billion to DM5 billion. When in 1981 the French imposed a moratorium on the processing of other people's fuel rods at Cap de la Hague, this had an immediate effect in West Germany and led, in turn, to two decisions in West German administrative courts. The court in Lüneburg ordered an end to the building of a proposed store for highly radioactive fuel awaiting transport to Cap de la Hague, and the Darmstadt court ruled that no quantities of such waste should be stored around power stations which were there purely for the supply of electricity and not as a focus for a nuclear dump. By that time, West Germany had 535 fuel elements with a total weight of 191 tonnes waiting to be despatched to France.

The Sizewell inquiry lasted longer than had been anticipated, but even before it had begun, Sir Walter (Mr PWR) Marshall had assumed what its decision would be. So sure were the CEGB of the result that the pressure vessel itself was ordered from the French Creuset Loire Company before the inquiry even opened, although the CEGB knew that any cancellation of that order would invoke penalty clauses. By the summer of 1982, work could be seen going on at Sizewell clearing the ground for the new reactor. Back in April 1980, the CEGB had issued a letter of intent to the National Nuclear Corporation, which is dominated by Sir Arnold Weinstock of GEC, placing the manufacturing order for the nuclear core of Sizewell B.

The preferred design, that by Westinghouse, is similar to that of the ill-fated reactor at Three-Mile Island. PWRs in the US have run into so much trouble that David Freeman, managing director of the Tennessee Valley Authority, admitted in November 1982: 'What is killing it [i.e. the nuclear industry] is not the Nuclear Regulatory Commission or the media. It is time to confess we went too far too fast in deploying large-scale designs of a reactor type we knew too little about.'

But that still does not appear to worry the British nuclear Establishment who are still, at the time of writing, apparently determined to press ahead with a design based on a Westinghouse 1100 megawatt reactor currently in use at Trojan, Oregon. This PWR has had a disastrous record of faults and failures. Westinghouse, in fact, has a number of outstanding lawsuits against it in the USA for problems which have arisen in other PWRs with which it has been involved.

That first PWR design offered to Sir Walter in 1981 was far too expensive in materials, and he was asked to come up with a new one, which he did – in three months flat. This was based on nuclear power stations at Wolf Creek, Kansas, and Callaway, Missouri, both of which were ordered back in 1973 and neither of which had, at that time, even started to produce any electricity. Sir Walter reckons it will take about five-and-a-half years to build his PWR. Standard US designs have already been under construction for ten years, so the British PWR at Sizewell will be, like the fast-breeder at Dounreay, a prototype.

In February 1984 there came another piece of news about Sizewell. With the inquiry still in progress, we were told that the CEGB had been given government clearance to order key components, mainly steel forgings, for the PWR from the French firm, Framatome, at a cost of £12 million. But this was not all. In April 1985, long before any 'decision' was supposed to have been reached, Westinghouse itself proclaimed to the world that it was all set to build the reactor at Sizewell. The firm's spokesman, Thomas Murrin, was in no doubt that they would be officially chosen. Not surprisingly, Westinghouse is desperate for the order as no orders for any kind of nuclear plant have been placed since 1979 in any industrialised country, due to the escalating costs, reduced demand for electricity and, above all, safety hazards.

There is another political aspect to the nuclear power programme which is only just emerging. It now seems that governments and the nuclear industry have seriously misled Parliament and the public over the years as to the use made of British reprocessed plutonium sent to the United States. For years ministers of both parties assured the public that British civil plutonium was not being used in American nuclear weapons. The assurances were more or less believed although some people did have reservations.

The whistle was eventually blown by one of the CEGB's own employees, Dr Ross Hesketh. In a letter to *The Times* on 30 October 1981, he criticised a proposed sale of plutonium from Britain's civil nuclear programme to the USA. It had been openly acknowledged that as a result of this sale, American civil plutonium would be released for nuclear weapons. Between 1964 and 1971, plutonium from our civil programme had been exported to the United States under a barter agreement, which specified that it was to be used exclusively for military purposes. This was under a Mutual Defence Agreement which is still in force.

However, from 1971 the government had strenuously denied that any plutonium from our nuclear power programme had ever been used in weapons anywhere in the world; in July 1982 the US government supported this denial in a special statement. Dr Hesketh was sacked for his pains on 10 June 1982 but, after a long wrangle, had to be reinstated. In July 1982 the then Under-Secretary for Energy, John Moore, repeated the assurances that CEGB plutonium sent to the US was strictly for civil purposes and described where it was used – in the United States' fast-breeder research programme.

However, in a letter to John Dingell, chairman of the US House of Representatives Energy and Commerce Committee, the US Energy Secretary Donald Hodel made it quite clear that British plutonium could well end up used in American weapons and that the British government had known this all along. He said that the Mutual Defence Agreement

> stipulates that the plutonium obtained from the UK in exchange for US defense materials is to be used for defense activities. The Department's Defense Program has loaned this plutonium to the DOE energy supply research and development activities with the knowledge of the UK . . .

In the September 1985 issue of the magazine *Nature*, four scientists gave the results of their research into this subject. It appears that two tonnes of plutonium are 'missing' from the British civil reactor inventory, and that is sufficient to make 400 bombs. The scientists had started by asking just how much plutonium is made each year in Britain's civil reactor programme, assuming that this was something that could easily be discovered. Not so. The government only publishes subtotals of the amount produced by the Magnox reactors alone. In spite of the Hodel statement, the British government is still denying that plutonium sent to the United States is for use in its military programme.

The four scientists set out to calculate the total amount of plutonium from our own civil reactors to see if the government's denials could be believed. Some of the information they required was unavailable, but they finally devised three separate and independent methods to calculate the total, and all three sets of figures agreed.

All the figures show that there is a balance of plutonium in the civil stockpile of 6.3 tonnes (plus or minus 0.8). However, the scientists say that the amount of plutonium supposed to go to civil destinations only amounts to less than four tonnes of it, leaving at least another two tonnes spare. So where does it go?

Cross-examined at Sizewell about this 'missing' plutonium, the CEGB spokesman, say the authors, seemed neither to know nor particularly care how much plutonium its reactors produced. The Campaign for Nuclear Disarmament therefore embarked on a lengthy procedural submission, asking for information on plutonium produced, year by year, since 1971 (the date after which, according to the government, no civil plutonium was exported). The CEGB then admitted it could not supply this information for the years before 1977 because unfortunately the information had been erased from its computer tapes as it was of 'no further value . . . for operational purposes'. Recalculation of this information would cost £50,000 and to provide the information for the years after 1977 would cost £5000. (This should be set against the figure of at least £10 million which the CEGB spent on its Sizewell case.)

It was asked that the figures from 1977 should be provided, but the CEGB never complied with this request and nothing was done about it. The only information they made public was on the amount of plutonium sent to Windscale/Sellafield for reprocessing.

Now the Department of Energy has forbidden the CEGB to provide information on the amounts of plutonium from each reactor, year by year, after 1977. Why? Because that information is, like so much in Britain, 'Officially Secret'.

The authors of the *Nature* article say that anyway they could produce the information required for the years preceding 1971 at far less cost than £50,000, so the reason for withholding the information cannot be cost. They point out that civil Magnox fuel is reprocessed at Sellafield at the same time as fuel from military reactors in a co-processing system, so it is obviously impossible to ensure that plutonium from civil plants does not end up for military use. At Sizewell, the CEGB did admit that its definition of the difference between civil and military plutonium differed from everybody else's.

On 20 March 1986 in the ITV programme *TV Eye*, Lord Marshall revealed publicly that CEGB civil plutonium had been directed to military use. The evidence of that programme directly contradicts the statements made by the CEGB at the Sizewell inquiry in 1984 and 1985. In their closing evidence at Sizewell the CEGB reaffirmed their 'firm policy to support and maintain the principle of a clear separation between the peaceful and military uses of nuclear energy.' (Evidence 22.2.1985) This directly contradicts the statement made in the programme by Christopher Ardland, head of DG 17, the section of the EEC Energy Commission whose job it is to oversee the demarcation between civil and military nuclear materials. He says that he had been informed that material from Britain's civil plutonium stocks had been redesignated as military. Asked if CEGB plutonium had been used for military purposes Lord Marshall replied, 'I don't know what it [the plutonium] was used for, but it has gone into the military stockpile. There is no secret about that.'

In the same programme Harold Bolter of BNFL stated that there was no physical separation between civil and military plutonium. It was also pointed out that because military plutonium is involved, the Euratom Safeguard's inspectors are excluded from the Windscale reprocessing line and plutonium store.

At the time of writing the government has still not commented on this.

Since Britain joined the EEC, all our civil nuclear activities are supposed to be subject to the safeguards of the European nuclear watchdog, Euratom. But even Euratom does not know how much plutonium we produce each year or where it goes.

Asked by the Welsh Nationalist MP, Dafydd Ellis Thomas, if any civil plutonium from the civil reactors here had been sent to the USA, since the Euratom Treaty came into force, the government took a year to reply and, when they did, their answer was both ingenuous and ambiguous. No, they said, no direct transfer of such plutonium had been made to the United States since the treaty came into force because all such plutonium was sent to Sellafield for reprocessing . . . which, of course, we already know. It also transpired from information in the press during 1985 that Euratom and the government were at loggerheads because Britain won't let Euratom's inspectors in to see what is going on at Sellafield, and because of this Euratom does not think that the reprocessing line is adequately safeguarded. We do not let them in because of our famed interest in our own national security.

Finally in their paper in *Nature* the four scientists made several essential points as to what this whole argument is about. First, they wondered if they are the only people in the country with a reliable estimate of the amount of plutonium produced in our reactors. They would, they said, be happy to provide even finer calculations for far less than £50,000, given the necessary data.

It is already sufficiently accurate to be sure there must be UK civil plutonium in destinations other than those listed by the government and also that the CEGB's assertion that the cut-off date for the exchange was 31 March 1969 just cannot be correct.

The state of civil plutonium accountancy in the UK is scandalous. It is an appalling example for the UK to set the 130 other nations who have signed the Non-Proliferation Treaty. Plutonium is one of the most dangerous substances mankind has ever created.

A few kilogrammes in a bomb could destroy a whole city. A few tonnes are produced every year by the CEGB and the SSEB [South of Scotland Electricity Board] yet no one in government or the nuclear industry will say how much or what happens to it.

Chapter 10

Too Dear at Any Price

It is not possible to leave the subject of nuclear power without examining one final aspect of it – its effect on our civil liberties. That it does have a very definite effect is due, in part, to the fact that the military and civil nuclear programmes are so inextricably bound. It is also because the plutonium essential to the civil power programme is so dangerous in itself that it produces a whole range of hazards, not the least of which is the risk that it might get into the wrong hands.

Overshadowing both programmes, and indeed our planet, is the threat of nuclear war, and here the nuclear equation of 'The Bomb = Defence of Our Way of Life' has a devastating effect on civil liberties. If the revelations in the *New Statesman* during September 1985 are to be believed (and the government has not denied them), in the run-up to any future hostilities the powers drawn up by the present government would be draconian. Whole areas of the country would be sealed off; large numbers of people would be forced into work gangs. Anybody considered as subversive – in the widest meaning of the term – would be rounded up and imprisoned and, if necessary, summarily executed. As if this were not enough, it seems our entire defence initiative would be handed over lock, stock and barrel to the Americans. These plans have been kept secret even from Parliament, unlike those of other European countries whose legislatures have discussed and debated them. Significantly, nobody else in Europe would appear to be considering handing over its sovereignty so happily to another power.

This scenario would give us the worst of all worlds – a period of police and military rule worse than anything ever experienced anywhere, followed by the nuclear holocaust. One might well ask just what it was we would all die defending

230

– certainly not our democratic way of life as we know it. Yet it is all part of the logic of the nuclear programme.

The assault on our civil liberties through the peacetime uses of nuclear power is more insidious but growing all the time. It is obvious that nuclear installations and nuclear 'waste' in transit should be guarded at all times and, as we have seen, the latter has been all too carelessly left open to attack. Terrorists could not only hold the country to ransom by threatening to blow up a flask containing waste, but if such a group could get their hands on stolen plutonium it would be quite possible for them to construct a home-made atomic bomb. The technology is available to all, and the genie cannot be put back into the bottle.

Back in 1970, various US government departments received copies of the same anonymous letter. It contained a blueprint for a bomb, a statement alleging where the writer had obtained the necessary plutonium and a threat to use it. The letter was believed because the plan of the bomb was workable and because it was quite plausible that the amount of plutonium required had been obtained from the stated source. Frantic attempts were made to track down the terrorist who turned out, at the end of the day, to be a fourteen-year-old schoolboy playing a practical joke . . .

According to Peter Bunyard, author of *Nuclear Britain*, there have been other worrying amateur bomb designs; one by John Phillips, owner of a pizza parlour, whose published paper brought him interested inquiries from foreign powers; and others by a Harvard student, Dimitri Rostow, who drew up plans for making twenty-five different types of atomic bombs, all within the space of five months.

The Flowers Report gave a good deal of attention to the question of plutonium getting into the wrong hands. The section in which the Royal Commission looked into the various ways that this could happen, concluded:

. . . it is entirely credible that plutonium in the requisite amounts could be made into a crude but effective weapon that could be transportable in a small vehicle. The threat to explode such a weapon unless certain conditions were met would constitute nuclear blackmail. This would present the government with an appalling dilemma. We are by no means convinced that the British government has realised the full implications of the issue.

This was back in 1976.

The Flowers Report then went on to prophesy what has since become the case to a large extent. Many people were rightly becoming concerned about the implications for society of the kind of security arrangements which would become necessary in a plutonium economy. The Commission commented that security organisations would have to play an active role:

> that is, to infiltrate potentially dangerous organisations, monitor the activities of nuclear employees and members of the public and generally carry out clandestine operations. The fear is expressed that adequate security against nuclear threats will be obtained only at the price of gradual but inexorable infringements of personal freedom.

> The second issue is over the secret surveillance of members of the public and possibly employees who might make 'undesirable' contacts. The activities might include the use of informers, infiltrators, wiretapping, checking on bank accounts and opening of mail. They would be practised on members or suspected members of extremist or terrorist groups or agents of foreign powers who, it was thought, might plan an attack on, or theft from, a plutonium plant. We regard such activities as highly likely and indeed inevitable.

And inevitable it appears to have become. One of the worrying aspects of the matter that the Flowers Committee did not investigate was how wide would be the definition of 'subversive groups', 'extremists', and so on. From what we learned early in 1985 from the revelations of ex-MI5 employee Cathy Massiter, a subversive can be anybody who disagrees with the government's nuclear policy. She herself knew of phone taps put on legitimate protesters and infiltration of the Campaign for Nuclear Disarmament, along with surveillance of other nuclear protesters.

It was also in 1985 that journalists, following investigations into the murder of Sizewell protestor Hilda Murrell, discovered that a whole range of unsavoury private investigation agencies had been used to monitor the Sizewell objectors and that this was, presumably, considered acceptable.

To counteract what might be seen as straightforward terrorism – i.e. the hijacking of a nuclear flask, the stealing of plutonium from a nuclear plant – the then Energy Minister, Tony Benn, introduced into Parliament in 1976 a Bill which was to become the Special Constables Act. It licensed a special and separate police force just for the nuclear industry. It is still so secret that not even Members of Parliament are allowed to ask any questions about it. Members of the force are answerable only to their own chief constable and he, in turn, is answerable only to the Home Secretary. Their annual report is classified as a Top Secret document. They are not accountable either to Parliament or to the people. We do not even know how many there are in this force, but possibly around a thousand. All of them are positively vetted by MI5 and the Special Branch. The force's full title is the United Kingdom Atomic Energy Authority Special Constabulary, and it is known as the nuclear police.

They have their own police training college and they have enormous powers. They know no county or metropolitan boundaries and can cross freely into different police authorities without even the relevant chief constables being aware of their presence. They have rights of entry and search without warrant and on grounds merely of suspicion. They are armed, and what is more, they are authorised to shoot – also on mere grounds of suspicion. What we have acquired is an armed secret police force, totally unaccountable and without any public supervision, which has been forced on the public to do a job which, according to the now concerned Mr Benn, it was not originally set up to do.

Strikes cannot be tolerated in any nuclear installation for obvious reasons, which has meant that it is very difficult for such workers with a grievance to get a fair hearing. In 1976 there was a strike at Windscale. Changing-room attendants, who help monitor workers before they enter or after they leave a processing area of the plant and who have to deal with contaminated clothing and other materials, complained that they were not issued with protective clothing. They were told this was not necessary, so they asked for 'danger money' which was not forthcoming. Next they went on strike. The strike spread; other workers were laid off; finally workers picketed the main road to prevent supplies of the liquid nitrogen used in the reactor's cooling system being brought into the plant. At which point, Mr Benn flew up to Cumbria and told the strikers that if they did not get back to work at once he would send in troops. The strike collapsed.

Safely out of office three years later, in 1979, Mr Benn had apparently changed his mind entirely and saw the nuclear power programme as a grave threat to our civil liberties. In a speech called 'The Democratic Control of Civil Nuclear Power' delivered to a group of scientists, he said that he saw four major areas for concern: (1) the close connection with military policy regarding the development of nuclear weapons developed without Parliamentary control; (2) the link between military and civil use of plutonium and the risk of its falling into terrorists' hands; (3) the wide gap between expert understanding and the information made available to the public; (4) the high rate of expenditure which creates powerful vested interests in the industries which depend on nuclear power for their business.

He gave a number of examples of how information had been withheld, even from the Cabinet.

In 1977 the Cabinet were not told of the nuclear-waste accident at Chelyabinsk although it now appears that the United Kingdom Atomic Energy Authority might well have been aware of it.

In 1968, he as Minister of Technology was not informed that 200 tons of uranium had been hijacked from Euratom, although the AEA knew.

In 1969, when a severe problem concerning the corrosion of Magnox fuel cladding at Windscale was revealed because of the resultant release of radioactivity, although he was informed, he was told it would be best to keep quiet and not cause alarm.

234

In 1972, the Vinter Report on thermal nuclear reactors carried out by the Department of Industry was withheld from the relevant House of Commons committee for reasons of 'commercial confidentiality'.

In 1976 he was not fully informed of the major radioactive leak at Windscale.

It was because of this last incident that Mr Benn instituted the system whereby all nuclear accidents are now supposed to be reported.

At the end of his speech, Mr Benn asked himself the question to which, perhaps, he should have addressed himself in 1976: 'Could we back into a police state because of high technology?'

The problem with nuclear power is that it breeds a climate in which safeguarding plutonium becomes more important than safeguarding the rights of people. We have seen how scientists can have their work discredited or lose their jobs if what they have to say runs contrary to the received truth on the nuclear industry. But there is an even more sinister aspect. You can lose your job because of your opposition, you can also lose your life. There are as yet, no satisfactory explanations for the deaths of two now well-known nuclear objectors, Karen Silkwood in the USA and Hilda Murrell in Britain. There is certainly an explanation for the death of the photographer on the Greenpeace vessel *Rainbow Warrior* when it was blown up in New Zealand – the decision to sabotage the ship was taken at a very high level within the French government itself. People who stand in the way of nuclear progress can easily become expendable.

Let us take some lesser cases first.

Didier Anger

Nuclear protestors in France tend to be arrested under the Anti-Casseur Law which was brought in during the student riots of 1968. Under that law, if any damage is caused during a demonstration, those who organised it can go to prison even if they were not there at the time, along with those who took part in the event. Police can also arrest those who merely stand and watch or – if they want to arrest somebody active in an organisation – they can plant an *agent provocateur* to set up some activity which can lead to arrests.

Didier Anger was an organiser of nuclear protests in France. He was also a teacher, and in France you are not allowed to teach if you have anything against you on your record. Certainly you could be sacked for taking part in anti-nuclear activities. Time and again Anger saw the same man provoking police reaction and eventually Anger asked him outright if he was a police spy. Anger taught in Normandy, his home area, and rented a house from a local gendarme. Suddenly the gendarme was told to evict him by the chief of police. The gendarme protested, saying that Anger paid his rent regularly and kept the house in good repair. So the gendarme himself was transferred to another part of France and had to sell up. Anger, too, was transferred to another district, which ended his investigations.

Dr Gordon MacLeod

We have already seen that Dr Ernest Sternglass found what he considered to be a definite link between the rise in the rate of infant mortality around the Three-Mile Island site and the accident there in 1979 (*see* pp. 89–90). But he is not the only expert to have seen such a link.

At the time of the accident, the Secretary for Health for the area was Dr Gordon MacLeod who had only been in the job for a matter of days. Dr MacLeod is a highly respected medical man who had been chief of the Yale Diagnostic Clinic of Internal Medicine and who was Chairman of the Department of Health Services at the University of Pittsburgh.

It was Dr MacLeod who had advised the state governor, the day after the accident, that he should evacuate all pregnant women and preschool-age children. The advice was not, of course, taken until some time later, and later still the governor denied ever having been given it. Afterwards Dr MacLeod set about trying to find out if there were any ill effects from the accident and ran into trouble with the state government who did not wish him to do any such thing. After six months of acrimonious wrangles he was sacked on the grounds that his style was incompatible with his job. He returned to university life.

In February 1980, he received information that the number of infant deaths had increased along with the number of thyroid abnormalities and that this information had been suppressed. He was, however, able to get hold of the figures, and a year after the accident he told a meeting held at the First Unitarian Church in Pittsburgh that the infant mortality rate around Harrisburg had indeed increased sharply. For the corresponding six months of 1977 there had been twenty infant deaths. In 1978 there had been fourteen. After the accident there were thirty-one and this number was even more significant as the birth rate had dropped. He also told the meeting that this information was being kept from them.

The press branded Dr MacLeod a scaremonger, and the nuclear industry issued its usual statement to the effect that there was no way of proving that the Three-Mile Island accident had brought about the increase in infant mortality.

But Dr MacLeod, like whistleblowers in Britain, remained alive even though he was sacked. Not so the three people whose cases we will consider next.

Karen Silkwood

Karen Silkwood's story has, of course, gone around the world. After massive coverage in the press, the official inquiry into her death, two full-length books and a feature film starring Meryl Streep, she has been amply vindicated. Even though, to this day, nobody knows who killed her, it seems very likely we now know why.

The Kerr-McGee Company for which Karen Silkwood was working at the time of her death held a virtual monopoly on sales of uranium to the US Atomic Energy Commission. They had previously been in oil, but moved into uranium mining following the discovery of deposits of the mineral in the late 1940s by Navajo Indians high up on a cliff face in the Lukachukai mountains of Arizona.

Several small mines had opened, but Kerr-McGee bided their time and eventually bought out the small companies as and when they could. They then bought a second mine and a milling plant in New Mexico before opening up a processing plant in Oklahoma. This converted the uranium into uranium hexafluoride for enrichment at the Atomic Energy Authority's own plants.

As more became publicly known about the hazards of uranium so Kerr-McGee increasingly began to feature in criticism of the working conditions of the Navajo Indians mining the uranium for them, who were paid $1.50 an hour for their labours. At a Bureau of Mines hearing about Kerr-McGee, it was noted that the workforce consisted of 80 per cent Navajo, 2 per cent black and 7 per cent poor white.

It was already known that many uranium miners in Germany between 1875 and 1912 had died of cancer, as had some 53 per cent of those working in Czechoslovakian mines between 1929 and 1931. Miners themselves knew that working with uranium meant, at best, they would suffer from severe chest problems and that often these were followed by death. Kerr-McGee never told the Navajo there was any danger. A spokesman for the company told a reporter back in 1974: 'They wouldn't understand radioactivity. Outside the reservation, people may have understood it, but not here, not Indians.' The Atomic Energy Commission kept silent too.

After some regulations were brought in, Kerr-McGee were found to be cheating, measuring the pollution of the air near to the air intake and not where the workers were actually working. A further federal investigation proved that the company had reported contamination levels 500 per cent lower than was actually the case, and the miners had been breathing a hundred times the amount of radioactivity now considered 'safe'.

By 1980, Navajo Indians as young as 31 years of age were dying of lung cancer, a disease virtually unheard of in that area since these Indians do not smoke and live in an unpolluted atmosphere. Later, in April 1982, Dr Gerald Buker was to report in a monograph, *Uranium Mining and Lung Cancer among Navajo Indians*, that the risk of lung cancer had increased by a factor of 85 per cent among uranium miners. However, after various court actions Kerr-McGee was found not to be liable for the cancer deaths of its miners, although it closed down the Navajo operation so quickly that it did not even dispose of its waste dump or seal off the mine opening. No compensation has been paid to workers or to their families. This, then, is the company that later made every effort to blacken the name of Karen Silkwood after her death.

Karen had been a bright physics student at university but, like all too many girls, had thrown up her college course to marry and have children. Seven years later her marriage had broken down and she decided to leave her husband and children and make a career for herself. There is no suggestion among those who knew her that she did not care for her children. During the period between her joining Kerr-McGee and her death, she had several affairs, one a long-term relationship. It was later said, therefore, that she was promiscuous. She had also, from time to time, been given sedatives – a common enough occurrence particularly in the United States. So it was said she was hooked on drugs. Add to that that she liked a drink with friends, and a picture could be painted of an unstable, promiscuous, drug-taking alcoholic out to make trouble. How this squared with her good work record was never explained.

Kerr-McGee opened its Crescent processing plant near the Cimarron river in Oklahoma in 1968. Here the 'cakes' of uranium were mixed with ammonium hydroxide and made first into a powder, then into a paste and finally into the pellets which went into the fuel rods for nuclear power stations. The motto SAFETY FIRST was painted in giant letters outside the plant.

Conditions inside were, apparently, appalling. At the inquiry after Karen's death, Division Manager James Smith was to say: 'It was one big pigpen. If you ever walked past the door, you couldn't hardly breathe from the ammonia fumes and uranium.' Ken Plowman, a former Kerr-McGee health physics technician, said: 'There was contamination everywhere especially in the lunch room. The men were fairly well contaminated on their arms and hands. There was no way to get it off without peeling their hide so they went home like this every night.' Yet by 1974 Kerr-McGee had been named one of the best managed companies in the country . . .

Karen Silkwood joined Kerr-McGee in August 1972

to work in the laboratory which tested plutonium pellets. Workers visually inspected each pellet to see if it was cracked before it was put into the fuel rod. Karen's job was to carry out random checks both on the pellets and on the fuel rods. She also joined the union. In 1973 there was a strike for better wages and better safety regulations, and Karen took part. It lasted ten months before it collapsed, by which time Kerr-McGee were bringing in untrained farm lads, short of work, to do the dirty side of the business. Karen, one of the last to go back to work, was extremely concerned to see ignorant and untrained farmboys becoming regularly contaminated with plutonium which they treated like fertiliser. They had not been told it could induce cancer.

But this was not all. After the strike, Karen discovered even more serious activities being carried on at Kerr-McGee. The firm was deliberately falsifying data on the fuel rods. X-rays were being doctored to show that rods were perfect when they were, in fact, faulty; faulty welds were being ground down and painted over so that hairline cracks could not be detected. Under the worst scenario, of course, faulty fuel rods could lead to a meltdown.

Tony Mozzochi, the vice-president of the union to which she belonged, later testified that the charges she made were the most serious he had heard in a lifetime of trade union experience. Her union asked her to collect evidence of her allegations, and this she agreed to do.

By this time, without knowing it, she was under surveillance. An officer of the Oklahoma state police pretended to be a reporter and offered to help her with the information she was uncovering. FBI agents were carrying out full-time surveillance, and her telephone was tapped. On a number of occasions she was found to be heavily contaminated with radioactivity although those working with her were not.

On 5 November 1974, just over a week before her death, she was found to be so heavily contaminated that she was sent to the AEC facility at Los Alamos for a thorough decontamination process. While she was there, officials from the plant, dressed in protective clothing, broke into her flat, and proceeded to take it apart. A source of high radioactivity was traced to her refrigerator and, finally, to a piece of cheese.

How the cheese became so radioactive is still unexplained. Was it made so by Kerr-McGee to frighten her off? Did she do it herself to discredit Kerr-McGee?

When Karen returned she was very frightened, aware that such a high level of contamination could cause a future cancer. But her research material was, apparently, safe and she rang a union official to tell him that she had all the evidence she needed about faulty fuel rods and doctored welds. She made arrangements – by telephone as she was unaware it was being tapped – to meet union officials and a reporter from the *New York Times* on 13 November 1974.

She never lived to make the rendezvous. When she did not arrive, those waiting for her went to look for her and were finally told that there had been an accident. She had driven off the road and been killed, her body was gone and the car removed. But it had not been removed by the normal highway patrol but by a special wrecker service called by – whom? We do not know. The car had then been searched by Kerr-McGee employees in protective suits, who took away documents from the car after reading parts of them aloud to each other. The documents have never been seen again.

Kerr-McGee said that Karen had been in an emotional condition, had been drinking and taking tranquillisers. She was a poor driver, possibly she had gone to sleep and driven off the road . . . Yet an expert accident assessor said that she appeared to have been forced off the road. Nor was she a poor driver. She had regularly entered for what we might call in Britain rallying or motorcross. Within a few months the case was officially closed and in answer to questions from her family, her union and the National Organisation of Women, the FBI responded by saying that there was nothing sinister about her death and that 'they watched too much television'.

But a lot of people remained unsatisfied and in November 1976, two years after her death, Kerr-McGee were formally charged with contaminating Karen with plutonium. The case was to last for three years and during the hearings a story came to light of carelessness, deceit and cover-up of appalling proportions. It was proved without question that much of what Karen had alleged had been true. In the end, the jury at the Oklahoma Federal Court awarded $10.5 million in damages against Kerr-McGee plus a further $500,000 in personal-injury damages to Karen's children. By that time, the Cimarron plant had already been closed down. As well as the specks of plutonium discovered in Karen's cheese, a further 40 lb were found to be missing. Was it lost or had it been stolen?

Karen Silkwood's friends erected a monument to her near to the plant where she had worked. It said: KAREN GAY SILKWOOD. BORN FEBRUARY 19 1946. DIED NOVEMBER 13 1974. VINDICATED MAY 18 1979.

But we shall never know who killed Karen Silkwood.

Hilda Murrell

On the morning of 24 March 1984, the body of an elderly woman was found in a copse near Shrewsbury. It was that of Hilda Murrell, a 79-year-old internationally famous rose-grower. The body showed superficial injuries, and we are told that death was due to hypothermia, although nobody has ever been allowed to see the post-mortem report.

The police, who continually told the public in the early weeks that they were about to make an arrest, later announced that the motive appeared to have been burglary. The house had been 'ransacked' but only £50 stolen. The police force concerned, that of West Mercia, brought in Detective Chief Superintendent David Cole who had been involved in the Leslie Whittle murder case and also in the case of the spy from GCHQ Cheltenham, Geoffrey Prime.

Several weeks after her death, the police announced that Hilda Murrell had been sexually assaulted as well. Intensive inquiries were undertaken, and a surprisingly large number of witnesses came forward to say that they had seen her white Renault being driven through Shrewsbury about midday on Wednesday, 21 March, the day on which it was later assumed she had actually died. Other witnesses claim to have seen a 'running man' on the road between the lane up to the copse and Shrewsbury.

But police inquiries did not appear to get anywhere. During the summer of 1984, they interviewed many people, they re-enacted the running-man scene, they called in a hypnotist, they called in the FBI for the first time ever in such a case. A profile of the kind of person they were looking for was fed into the FBI computer and came out with just what the West Mercia police had said they were looking for – a local, unskilled man, a beer drinker, possibly sexually perverted and a loner.

The murder might have passed out of sight and into that limbo of unsolved crimes, except that by the end of the summer of 1984 a positive flood of strange facts began to emerge. First, Miss Murrell was not just an expert on rose-growing; she had also made herself an expert on nuclear power and on the problems connected with nuclear waste in particular. She was one of the very few private individuals who would be called to give evidence at the Sizewell Inquiry, and at the time of her death she was working on a paper in which she set out to prove that there is no safe or economic way of disposing of such waste.

Nor was that all. The police story of the finding of her body and of the events surrounding her death was full of contradictions. Her car had been seen on the lane near to where her body was found at lunchtime of the day she died, and it had been reported immediately to the police. It was reported again 48 hours later, and it was also seen by two young men who were later prosecuted for stealing its tax disc. Yet the police did nothing. Their accounts conflict as to why this was the case, one version saying it had merely been assumed to be an abandoned car and the other that they had put the wrong number into the DVLC computer at Swansea and wasted time trying to find the wrong owner.

On the evening of Friday 23 March a policeman called at Miss Murrell's house, received no reply but found the kitchen door open. He appears to have found nothing suspicious so he went away. He paid a further visit the next morning and spent over an hour in the house, also apparently without finding anything amiss, although there was post heaped by the door, rain on the floor from the open kitchen door, and signs of a struggle. Then, too, the owner of the copse in which she was found swore – and still does – that he visited the copse on Thursday 22 March while marking trees for felling, and that no corpse had been there at that time.

Finally, it seems her house had not been 'ransacked' but carefully searched, nor was she sexually assaulted. Her telephone had been disconnected, and a telephone engineer told me it had been done in such a way as to appear to be working to those ringing in. At first the police agreed that the wires had been cut in a 'sophisticated' manner; later they were to say they had merely been yanked out. Yet another strange fact emerged: the telephone in her holiday cottage in Wales was also out of order at the same time. Lightning had caused it, according to the Home Office. But there had been no lightning in the area at that time. Ah: well, the lightning hit the telephone exchange, knocking out only her relay. Then the Welsh holiday home was set on fire.

Hilda Murrell was finally cremated in August 1984 although there had still been no inquest. The police suddenly told the family they had to make arrangements for her body to be dealt with within days and they did so. The family did not know that they could have had an independent autopsy. At the time of writing they have still not seen the police's post-mortem report.

By September 1985 another factor had entered the case. Hilda Murrell's nearest relative, her nephew Robert Green, had played a crucial role in naval intelligence during the Falklands War and had knowledge of the signals traffic to the submarine *Conqueror* at the time of the sinking of the *Belgrano*. He had since left the Navy. It was at the beginning of March 1984 that Sir Robert Armstrong, Secretary to the Cabinet, had been trying to discover who was leaking information about the *Belgrano* sinking to Labour MP Tam Dalyell.

Most sinister of all, it seems Miss Murrell had herself been consumed by strange anxieties. She was not considered to be a fanciful person, yet she had told several people just before her death that she was fearful for her life. On 25 February, she had rung up an old friend, Mr Morgan-Grenville of the Eco Ropa organisation, in an agitated manner and eventually told him. If they don't get me first I want the world to know that one old woman has seen through their lies.' Who were 'they'? On the day of her death she seems to have called up a man named Laurens Otter from a public call box, saying she had papers she wished him to keep for her. She told him she had a lunch appointment that day and they worked out he could not reach her before she set off for it. Both she and Otter belonged to the Shropshire Peace Alliance of which there was a meeting that night, and she arranged to bring the papers with her. Of course, she never arrived.

At the inquest on 5 December 1984, only the police officer in charge, DCS Cole, and a Home Office pathologist were called to give evidence. The pathologist said that Miss Murrell had received superficial injuries, bruising, a broken collar-bone, small stab wounds, but had probably died of hypothermia, almost certainly where she was found. Later, in a television programme in June 1985, he was to say that the collar-bone break was on the opposite side to that which he had told the inquest, that there were fewer stab wounds and that the possibility could not be ruled out of the body having been carefully moved.

On 23 December 1983 Tam Dalyell, in the course of the Consolidated Fund debate, told the House of Commons he had it on good authority that Hilda Murrell had been killed when she interrupted members of the security services in the course of burgling her home. Certainly, had her telephone been tapped, it would have been assumed that when she left home on the day she died she would be out all day. As it was, she returned unexpectedly. Mr Dalyell's theory is that the agents were looking for leaked *Belgrano* material.

Further investigations by journalists in early 1985 uncovered the fact that Sizewell objectors had been under surveillance for a long time. In some cases, employees of private investigation agencies had been used, we do not know by whom. Some of those employed had, to put it mildly, doubtful records – such as the man who had served a prison sentence for procuring his own children for under-age sex and who was a member both of a neo-Fascist group and a Satanist cult.

In March 1985, ex-MI5 employee Cathy Massiter blew the whistle in a Channel 4 television programme when she revealed that members of nuclear protest groups, among others, had had their telephones tapped and been under surveillance. There had been authorised break-ins too, one of the units used for these being the AIA unit of MI5.

Following Tam Dalyell's statement in the House of Commons, an 'independent' inquiry into the investigations into Hilda Murrell's death was set up, headed by the Assistant Chief Constable of Northumbria, Peter Smith. It reported in June 1985. There was nothing to worry about. Some of the early investigations by West Mercia police could have been more efficient, said the report, but there was nothing to suggest that members of the security services had carried out the burglary. However, no evidence could be offered to support Peter Smith's view as the matter was secret since inquiries were still going on.

It seems likely that Hilda Murrell's name appeared on two sets of files: first, as a Sizewell objector, and second, as the aunt of Robert Green. At some point the lines crossed and she became a focal point. At the beginning of March 1984, when everyone was running around trying to find out the source of the *Belgrano* leaks, it was decided that somebody should go in and see if she had anything and possibly, while they were there, to see if she had anything on the Sizewell inquiry that might be of interest. Everybody is agreed that it was a burglary that went tragically wrong.

I do not believe that Hilda Murrell had any documents relating to the *Belgrano*. Nor, on the face of it, could she have had anything on Sizewell that she should not have had – all the information given in her not-quite-completed paper is freely available. But then we cannot actually know what she had, as whoever broke in had four days to search her house, unimpeded by the police. They also had four days to cover up their tracks and, if it was an employee of a security agency, to call in the professionals.

It is unlikely we shall ever know who did kill Hilda Murrell. But even if she was actually attacked by that lone, beer-swilling local burglar whom the police want to interview, and even if you believe all the coincidences, and in Santa Claus too, then what was found out during the investigations into her murder must give us all pause for thought. That is, that legitimate protestors against current government nuclear policy can be considered so subversive that they can have their telephones tapped and be put under surveillance by petty crooks working for sordid private investigation agencies on behalf of unknown bodies.

Rainbow Warrior

At least there is now no doubt about who was responsible for the sinking of the Greenpeace vessel *Rainbow Warrior* in Auckland harbour in New Zealand on 10 July 1985. Nor, therefore, for the death of the photographer Fernando Pereira, who was on board at the time. It was the French government.

Greenpeace have for many years staged spectacular protests in the South Pacific around Mururoa Atoll where the French conduct their nuclear test programme. The present Prime Minister of New Zealand, David Lange, is fiercely anti-nuclear, and he is particularly against the South Pacific tests, his reasonable view being that, if they are as safe as the French say they are, why don't the French carry them out on land in Metropolitan France?

On 10 July the *Rainbow Warrior* was in port making preparations to sail for Mururoa. There was a sudden explosion and the ship began to sink. Those on board began to scramble off, but Pereira returned to collect some equipment. There was a second explosion which killed him and the ship sank.

This time nobody could pretend it was an accident. Also, the only people who would benefit from the sinking of the *Rainbow Warrior* were the French. Pete Wilkinson of the British section of Greenpeace told me, however, that even though the operation was carried out in such an amateurish manner, those who undertook the job might still have got away with it had not, fortuitously, two people been sitting on a hill opposite the quay with binoculars trained on the harbour. They saw a rubber dinghy leave the hull of the ship shortly before the first explosion.

The New Zealand government immediately began to investigate, and both it and Greenpeace blamed the French. The French government strenuously denied the allegations. The New Zealand police quite quickly picked up a young Swiss married couple who turned out to be neither married, nor Swiss, but two French secret agents. Efforts were also made to trace some Frenchmen who had arrived in a yacht which had put in further up the coast; they were traced to New Caledonia (which is French territory) and then lost. It seems that they were picked up by a French submarine and their yacht scuttled.

The storm of criticism provoked President Mitterand to state on 16 August that he would order a full and public inquiry into the affair. Meanwhile the French press, particularly *Le Monde*, were in full cry and undertaking their own investigations. The trail was an all-too-obvious one. It not only led back to the French external secret service – the DGSE – but to people very high up indeed, and pointed to a Watergate-style cover-up. At one point, the trail led to Britain where French agents had actually bought the rubber dinghy used in the attack. In fact at this stage there was some suggestion that our own security services might have been involved, not least because of the ineptitude of the whole operation.

Bernard Tricot, a senior member of a previous French administration, was put in charge of the investigation. By the end of August, M. Tricot had not only fully investigated the affair; he had also published his report. It was somewhat inconclusive but, on the whole, it let the government off the hook. It was greeted with derision by the French press, and the slogan '*Tricot se lave plus blanc*' – Tricot washes whiter – was coined. It was a similar conclusion to that reached by cynics over the Northumbrian police report on the death of Hilda Murrell.

But unlike their British counterparts, the French press were prepared to devote large-scale resources to uncovering the cover-up, apart from which they seem to have had a chorus of moles. More and more details began to emerge. A number of agents had been involved. One was sent ahead to infiltrate Greenpeace and pose as a supporter. The two agents arrested in New Zealand had set the whole thing up and made the arrangements for when the yacht arrived. Among those on the yacht were a team of underwater sabotage experts from the military underwater training centre in mainland France, who had a supply of limpet mines. The operation was too large to have been carried out by a group of maverick secret service agents acting on their own initiative, and it appears that funds of £425,000 had been released – nearly half a million pounds to sink one peaceful vessel tied up in the harbour of a friendly nation.

On 20 September, the head of DGSE was fired, and this was promptly followed by the resignation of the man to whom all roads seemed to lead: M. Charles Hernu, the French Defence Minister. On 23 September, President Mitterrand finally admitted that the French government had been responsible for the sinking of the *Rainbow Warrior*. The head of the DGSE said he had merely been carrying out orders, apparently the orders of M. Hernu. The new Defence Minister, M. Paul Quiles, described what had been established as 'the cruel truth'. Facts had been kept from the unfortunate M. Tricot and also from President Mitterrand, who had only been informed belatedly after the event. As to how the order had actually been given, it seems to have been done in rather the same way as that of Henry II who, when speaking of the inconvenient Archbishop Thomas à Becket, asked around a crowded court: 'Who will rid me of this turbulent priest?' In this case the DGSE obliged.

New Zealand had been demanding apologies and compensation in the strongest terms right from the start, as had Greenpeace who had lost their boat and one of their members. You might imagine that Britain would have taken a strong line: after all, the *Rainbow Warrior* was a merchant vessel registered in Britain. But the reaction has been very muted: a mild protest, the suggestion of a possible claim for compensation, virtually no overt criticism. Imagine the situation had the saboteurs been Russian . . . In nuclear matters, nuclear powers stick together, and there are probably some in Whitehall who also consider Greenpeace nothing but a nuisance and that they deserved all they got.

If it were not so serious it would be almost funny, that picture of a whole team of Inspector Clouseaux ploughing around the South Pacific in frogmen suits, having left a trail behind them which could so easily be picked up, a trail which led searchers to England where the saboteurs had bought a dinghy from a small boatyard in such odd circumstances that the owner was able to remember the incident clearly months later and identify the purchaser.

In reality, of course, it is not funny at all and what happened is best summed up by David Lange when he said:

> There is no principle of international law which allowed the French government to say it was responsible for the bombing, but because the people who did it were acting under orders they can therefore escape justice. This is not war. This is New Zealand in 1985. The defence of acting under orders is clearly inappropriate.

On the 22 November 1985 the two French agents captured in New Zealand, having been found guilty, were each sentenced to ten years' imprisonment. So far, Lange has refused to consider any request for repatriation to France. At the end of December 1985 the French government agreed to compensate Greenpeace, the sum to be decided by arbitration.

As Lange put it: 'The saddest aspect of the admission of French responsibility is that the bombing is not a fortuitous Beau Geste adventure but, instead, a sordid act of international terrorism.'

Here he encapsulates the implications of the nuclear state. In the name of cheap power, people become expendable. In the name of nuclear security, a supposedly friendly government can launch a terrorist attack on a peaceful ally and somehow feel it was justified. The nuclear power game is too dear at any price.

Chapter 11

The End of an Era

I'm told that if you drink a pint of the effluent [from Aldermaston] that goes into the river [the Thames] – in radioactivity terms at least – it's no more dangerous than a pint of mineral water purchased over the counter of your local supermarket.

> Lord Trefgarne, Defence Minister, quoted in a Yorkshire Television documentary broadcast on 3 December 1985

In spite of the encouraging words above, the winter of 1985/86 was not a particularly good period for the nuclear industry. While I have been writing this book there seems to have been one prolonged series of 'mishaps' both here and abroad. Also, more information keeps coming to light.

On 4 September 1985, the *Guardian* carried a story saying that, according to John Rimmington, Director-General of the Health and Safety Executive, the Ministry of Defence has been breaking the law for twenty years by not telling its workers at the Polaris submarine base at Rosyth about radiation doses received during their employment. A thousand workers had left the MoD without radiation records. Mr Rimmington said the Ministry's behaviour was 'reprehensible', but the Crown was immune from prosecution and he could only remonstrate with the appropriate officials.

The breach in the regulations had only come to light when Alec Falconer, a former shop steward at the dockyard, left to become MEP for Mid-Scotland and Fife. He said his union had been assured five years before that all employees received records when they left the dockyard, and as he had not received his, he wrote asking for them. After a year of waiting

251

he asked again. He then discovered that the Ministry had failed to keep any records at all since the regulations requiring them had been introduced in 1965. Each worker should have received a copy when he left, a duplicate going to the Health and Safety Executive. Neither was done. The Ministry say they are now trying to rectify this and are investigating the complaint.

Meanwhile, in the USA, it was announced in the *Washington Post* on 16 January 1986 that the US Navy had had a far higher incidence of accidents and mishaps with nuclear weapons than had ever been reported. This had come to light as a result of a court action brought against the Navy by the American Friends Service Committee, a Quaker group which monitors Pentagon affairs, who had used the Freedom of Information Act. The Navy was made to reveal that between 1968 and 1985 there had been two accidents directly concerning nuclear weapons and 628 'incidents' relating to nuclear equipment.

The two serious accidents occurred in the 1960s. In 1965, a naval bomber carrying a warhead was lost in 14,400 feet of water in the western Pacific. In 1968, the nuclear-capable submarine USS *Scorpion* was lost in mid-Atlantic and has never been found.

Most of the 'incidents' are considered to be minor and are called 'bent spears'. More serious ones are 'broken arrows'. There is a category lower than these which takes in low-level mishaps, and this category showed a higher figure in 1985 than in previous years. The Navy put this down to training programmes employing older components which were wearing out. The most recent 'broken arrow' had been in Damascus, Arkansas, when an Air Force repairman dropped a wrench which struck a Titan II intercontinental missile causing a leak in the fuel tank. In the ensuing explosion, one man died and 21 were injured.

More information is beginning to seep out as a result of the Friends' action, concerning other branches of the services. This includes details of an accident in Spain twenty years ago, near the village of Palomares, and as a result local residents are now demanding a full inquiry as they no longer believe official reassurances. In January 1966, an American bomber collided with a refuelling plane in mid-air, dropping three hydrogen bombs on the village. A fourth fell into the sea. The bombs' in-built safety mechanism avoided a nuclear explosion which would have wiped out southern Spain, but the impact of the collision caused a shower of radioactive plutonium and uranium to fall on the area. It was three days before local people were told what had happened.

At a meeting held in Palomares on 21 November 1985, villagers revealed how they had heard an explosion and had seen black smoke and red fire and molten metal falling out of the sky. Children had played in craters made by the bombs . . . A vast clean-up operation had taken place – crops were burned, animals killed, 2000 tonnes of earth removed – then the villagers had been told by both the US and Spanish governments that they were no longer in danger.

'We were told to burn our clothes and take showers,' one woman said. 'I scrubbed my children, but we couldn't afford to burn our clothes.' Villagers said they had been treated like lepers ever since and nobody would buy their crops. The Spanish Nuclear Energy Board had shrouded all investigations in secrecy. At the meeting in 1985 a physicist from the Board, Francisco Mingot, told the villagers that there was no hazard from plutonium remaining in the environment: they would have to eat 'thousands of tons' of local produce for the effects to become 'serious'. But independent researchers from the Scientific Institute in Barcelona fiercely disagreed. One, Dr Eduardo Rodriguez Farre, said: 'Plutonium is one of the most toxic substances known to man. I find it inconceivable that the Board should say otherwise.' He is now calling for funds for an independent inquiry as 'this is the worst case of plutonium contamination known in the world and not one study of the disaster has ever been published, not even in Spain.'

Another 'broken arrow' was the major accident involving the burning and destruction of nuclear weapons at the US base at Lakenheath in East Anglia in 1956. US personnel were evacuated, but the local population was told nothing. This obviously slipped the memory of the MoD, for its pamphlet promoting cruise missiles states: 'Nuclear weapons have been stored in this country for many years. There has never been any accident or radiation leakage.'

Other revelations were contained in two major television documentaries: Yorkshire Television's *Inside the British Bomb* broadcast on 3 December 1985 – from which the foot-in-mouth quote at the beginning of the chapter comes – and Channel 4's *Waste Not, Want Not?* (John Gau Productions).

On 3 December, YTV broadcast the result of its investigations, *Inside the British Bomb*. It looked at problems inside military sites where there are reactors or where waste is reprocessed, and at apparent risks to health of those either working in them or living nearby. Sites included early Magnox reactors not covered by international inspection arrangements – at Calder Hall in Cumbria (part of the Sellafield complex) and Chapel Cross near Dumfries. Both are plutonium 'factories' working on a special nuclear fuel cycle to produce weapons-grade plutonium for Trident missiles.

At Sellafield, a special plant recovers weapons-grade plutonium from the 'waste' fuel rods, which is made into ingot-like billets and then transferred to Aldermaston for machining. They are then sent on to the Royal Ordnance factory at Burghfield in Berkshire. Other material arrives at Burghfield from the Ministry of Defence factory in Cardiff.

From a newly built plant at Chapel Cross comes tritium to boost the yield of atom bombs. It is quite hard to discover much about who provides tritium and why. It is accepted even by the industry that tritium causes birth defects in certain circumstances. Nuclear industry secrecy, enforced by the Radioactive Substances Act of 1960, makes it unlawful to reveal the sources of tritium. This featured in a story in the 6 December 1985 issue of *New Scientist* which said that companies west of London (presumably a euphemism for the Aldermaston area) were continuing to discharge it into the atmosphere although it is highly radioactive, and that this is causing the Nuclear Installation Inspectorate concern because the Thames Water Authority has refused to mix it with sewage and then discharge it into the sea. If the NII are unhappy about its unpredictable nature and its contamination of food, especially of growing crops, then perhaps we all should be.

According to YTV, three major naval nuclear sites also discharge radioactivity into the environment. At Faslane, Rosyth and Devonport, liquid radioactive waste from nuclear submarine operations is discharged directly into the sea.

The YTV documentary gave examples of some of the accidents to personnel at military nuclear plants. Early in December 1957, at the Aldermaston nuclear research establishment, a pipe to a smelting furnace broke and Douglas Whittaker was caught in a stream of molten lithium being used to test hydrogen bombs. He died two days later. Thirteen workers at Aldermaston are known to have suffered significant plutonium contamination to their lungs, four from plutonium elsewhere in their bodies. Five widows are currently suing the MoD, and sixty-one other workers are contemplating legal action.

At the Royal Ordnance factory at Burghfield, there have been five recent cases of cancer, and, in 1983, a major accident when an assembly worker accidentally ignited the fuel of a small decoy rocket used in a Chevaline warhead. Nobody was hurt although a fire started, but all witnesses were told not to breathe a word about what had happened.

Speaking of Aldermaston on the programme, Lord Trefgarne said, 'We can be confident that what goes on there is done to the best possible safety standards.' Yet the original plutonium-manufacturing buildings at Aldermaston became so contaminated that they were closed in 1978 and a new complex is under construction. After much pressure, however, the old buildings were reopened in 1982 to produce plutonium for Chevaline. From these operations, about 1 million gallons of plutonium-contaminated liquid is pumped into the Thames at Pangbourne. YTV has a copy of a secret specification which states that the waste treatment plant 'does not comply with current safety standards'. Lord Trefgarne happily proclaimed the liquid harmless but did not explain why, in that case, there were two signs on the bank at Pangbourne warning the public not to 'moor, anchor or bathe between these signs'.

There are 61 chimneys discharging air from radioactive

areas in Aldermaston and in five of these, a 1978 report revealed, the radiation monitors have been put in the wrong way round and can only measure radiation in the air outside, not that coming out of the chimneys. In fact, for a little extra cost, there need be no discharges into the atmosphere.

Up in Rosyth, in the West Tip area near the dockyard, caesium and cobalt-60 have accumulated on the foreshore. The dockyard generates about 600,000 gallons of radioactive effluent each year, and this is causing a steady build-up of radioactive sediment at West Tip. One solution – a new drainage system – is being held up awaiting decisions on Trident requirements. Of this build-up Lord Trefgarne said: 'There is no evidence to suggest these discharges are having any kind of effect . . . I think people can therefore continue to live in the areas around Rosyth in perfect confidence.' Quarterly records obtained from the Admiralty Records Centre show that some workers at Rosyth have received over seven times the permitted dose of radiation.

But it was when the documentary came to the possible risk to health of local residents around all these sites that the information tallied very closely with research into areas near to civil nuclear installations. Within a two-mile radius of Aldermaston there have been eleven cases of cancer and related diseases among people under 25. There have been eight cases around Burghfield, only four miles away. Of this total of 19 cases, fifteen are leukaemias and lymphatic cancers in children under ten – five times the national average over the same period. The overall leukaemia rate is five times the national average, and the cancer rate is three times as great. The number of lymphatic cancers in under-fives is *ten times* the national average.

At Rosyth, YTV found eight cases of childhood leukaemias in the previous twelve years, three times the expected figure for Scotland. These included a truly tragic case, that of the Lindsay twins. Stewart and Steven appeared to be quite normal when they were born but they failed to thrive. Specialists diagnosed leukaemia. This devastated their young parents who, when interviewed by YTV, told most movingly how they had fought for their babies' lives and tried to be hopeful when all hope had gone. One twin died at seven-and-a-half months, his brother four months later.

At Holy Loch, the researchers found that twelve cases of cancer among young people had occurred during the previous fifteen years, again three times the Scottish average. Figures for leukaemia among children living around the Loch are five times the normal rate, and in one village, Kilmun, with a population of 318, there have been three recent cases of childhood cancer. One of the victims, a seven-year-old boy, contracted a form so rare that it was the only case in his age group recorded in Scotland in 1983.

Research also showed an unnaturally high rate of harelip and cleft palate among children of the 300 men of Britain's first Polaris submarine, HMS *Resolution*. All those involved – from the Ministry of Defence to government Ministers – stoutly denied there was any 'provable' link. But it is clear that if we compare these figures with those in Chapter 7 there is close 'coincidental' similarity. The IBA threatened to ban the film from being shown, and then insisted that British Nuclear Fuels and the Ministry of Defence should be allowed to control their own contributions. Among other edicts was that YTV remove Lord Trefgarne's closing words: 'I think I can do no more than point to our record in more than twenty years of this kind of activity . . . we will make sure we maintain that record.' It appears the IBA thought his words might be misunderstood.

Two days later, on 5 December, Channel 4 launched a two-hour investigation into the disposal of nuclear waste, *Waste Not, Want Not?* Naturally, a large part of the programme was devoted to describing what nuclear waste is, and the different types, where it comes from, how it travels, how it is reprocessed and where it is disposed of – if it can be disposed of, that is. A string of experts from the nuclear industry was given ample time to put their case as cogently as possible and in great detail.

Yet, in the end, there was little in the film to shift the public distrust, shown so markedly by ordinary members of that public interviewed for the programme, and, indeed, as many questions were left unanswered as answered. Also, the film showed very clearly that in spite of everything, the nuclear industry remains extremely complacent. Examples abounded.

For instance, we were shown the waste burial site at Drigg near Sellafield. The site manager explained how the waste was put into the tip and covered with earth and how the water drained out from the site into a local river. The interviewer, having watched this, said it looked like 'any old rubbish dump'. The site manager said that the radioactivity in the water was monitored as it flowed from the tip. The interviewer rightly asked, 'What can be done at that stage if it is found to be higher than it should be?' Since it had already been stated that the site operators did not know what was there, then how could they find any specific source if necessary? The answer was that officials had 'a lot of experience about Drigg and we are certain Drigg is a safe disposal site.' The site manager went on to say that the beaches were carefully monitored for excess radioactivity and were well within safety limits. An independent researcher with a Geiger counter then took a reading: he was getting 40 counts a second, a hundred times the natural background level.

Another expert likened Drigg to a teabag with water being poured in and then flowing out containing particles of whatever was in the dump. At a similar site at Barnwell in the USA, opened in 1971, deposits of tritium had moved 21 metres down and 75 metres sideways – offsite – in ten years. Radioactivity has also moved offsite at Drigg, and industry representatives have admitted that the site would not get a licence if it were set up today. Assertions that shallow burial is a safe option have not been backed up by practical experience in the field, but only by computer models and scientific reports done at a desk or in a lab.

Even more significant was the response of a British Nuclear Fuels spokesman. Asked if he could understand why people were sceptical about the safety of Sellafield following so much adverse publicity about illegal discharges and leaks, the spokesman said: 'None of our discharges have ever been illegal.' But, pressed by the interviewer who said, 'You were *prosecuted* for one of them', the extraordinary response was: 'But we did not go above the authorised limit. We broke a "concept" called ALARA, but none of our discharges have ever been above the authorised limit . . .' Asked about a leak at Building 38, he told us it had now been stopped. Concerning the leak from Building 701 which consisted of high-level waste which had leaked for fifteen years, the answer was that the buildings had been constructed many years ago . . . And so it went on.

There followed interviews with a representative of NIREX about the proposed new sites for the burial of intermediate-grade nuclear waste. Again there were copious reassurances. The principles behind current techniques had been known since 'the Roman Empire, Hadrian's Wall, from the Greek Empire . . .' 'Do you really believe,' asked the interviewer, 'that one day you will be able to persuade people to picnic on top of it?' 'Oh absolutely,' responded the man from NIREX. 'I mean they could picnic on top from the first day of closure. I mean as soon as we have got the waste in there and covered over, there is absolutely no reason why we should not have people picnicking on top.'

Towards the end of the programme, the question of Britain as a reprocessing plant for the world was put under scrutiny. The reprocessing of nuclear waste from abroad and an expanding nuclear power programme in this country will mean that there will be 770,000 cubic metres of low-level waste and 59,000 cubic metres of intermediate- and high-level waste by the year 2000. We have plans to expand our reprocessing to take in waste from Spain, Italy, Sweden, Holland, West Germany, Switzerland, Canada and Japan – they don't want to do it. Reprocessing actually multiplies the volume of waste.

This, we are told, is in part to recover uranium. Yet there is a world surplus of uranium. The new reprocessing plant currently under construction at Sellafield already cost £1.3 billion and to try and recoup some of that it will be necessary to process a lot of waste. A spokesman for the industry said it would now be 'punitive' to go back on the contacts entered into to reprocess other nations' waste, more punitive than reversing the policy. Financially, that is.

Quite simply, the principal immediate benefit to the UK is the foreign earnings involved. There was no answer to the question why, if reprocessing waste is so profitable, are all the other countries not doing it as well? Why do they prefer just to get rid of it?

At the end of the film, the government's position was put by the Environment Minister, William Waldegrave. He expressed himself as happy with the way things were going, confident that nuclear power offered no real safety hazards nor did the disposal of nuclear waste. The view of the present government was the right one.

'Let me put a final question to you,' said the interviewer. 'Nuclear enthusiasts run the Central Electricity Generating Board. They run British Nuclear Fuels. Mrs Thatcher is a nuclear enthusiast. NIREX is full of nuclear enthusiasts. Who is going to be the champion in high places of ordinary folk who have fears about this [nuclear waste] coming near them? Is it you or are you one of the enthusiasts?'

The Minister replied: 'It is me. That is why my Department had been set up to control all this.' He, and his Department, are 'committed to a safe environment'.

And you? Are *you* convinced that the nuclear industry is preserving a safe environment? That the many interests involved from the scientific through the political to the commercial, are really objective, and have our best interests at heart?

For if, at the end of the day, it is discovered that the 'nuclear enthusiasts' in the industry and in government have been wrong, then it is us, the doubting 'ordinary folk' who have fears, who will be asked to pay the price, and the financial aspect of that price will be the least of it.

Epilogue

The safest form of energy known to man . . .
> Energy Minister Peter Walker in a press
> release, 17 March 1986

At 1.23 a.m. on 26 April 1986, the impossible happened.

That one-in-a-million chance materialised.

The one accident in 30,000 years of reactor life (or 10,000 depending on your choice of expert) actually occurred.

The jumbo jet finally crashed on the football ground.

On 26 April, the world's worst nuclear disaster took place at Chernobyl in the Ukraine in the Soviet Union.

The accident

For years, we in the Western world have been told that an accident of this dimension could not happen here. Make no mistake about it, the Russians thought it could not happen there either. In June 1983, B. A. Semenov, head of the Department of Nuclear Energy and Safety in the Soviet Union, said of the type of reactor used at Chernobyl: 'A serious loss-of-coolant accident is practically impossible.' Two months before the disaster, the Soviet magazine *Soviet Life* ran a massive spread on the Chernobyl nuclear complex, headed 'Total Safety'. The reactor was constructed in such a way, according to the magazine, 'that the possibility of a meltdown was incredible'.

It sounded like the view of the US Atomic Energy Commission in its 1975 report that the chance of a nuclear accident serious enough to kill 70 people was 'one in a million'.

The Chernobyl reactor complex is – or was – the jewel in the crown of the Soviet nuclear programme. It is actually a nuclear park alongside the Pripyat river, which (after it joins the Dnieper) supplies drinking water to the city of Kiev

261

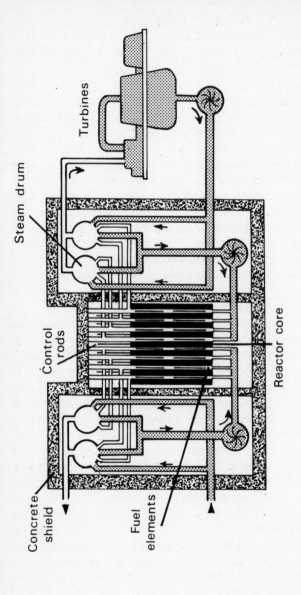

Turbines

Steam drum

Control rods

Reactor core

Concrete shield

Fuel elements

60 miles downstream. Between Chernobyl and the city of Minsk, 200 miles away, lies some of the finest farming land in the Soviet Union. The Chernobyl reactors were commissioned amid great self-congratulation on 26 September 1977. Brezhnev himself praised its builders for their speed and efficiency. It was, he said, 'an outstanding technical achievement'.

The Chernobyl reactor design is different from any in the West, as all our nuclear experts were quick to point out, but there are more similarities than we have been led to believe. The Chernobyl reactors use graphite as a moderator (as do our reactors) and water as a coolant (as do the American PWRs). In Western countries, when water is used as a coolant it is pumped around all the fuel rods together. In the Soviet system, dozens of alloy-clad pressure tubes carry the water through the core to the reactor's base, each one to an individual fuel rod. The water then re-emerges as pressurised hot water, which is used to run the turbines (*see* p. 262).

For an expert technical description, I turn to John Large, of Large Associates, who is an adviser to Paddy Ashdown MP, to Greenpeace and to Friends of the Earth. He says:

The Chernobyl reactor is of the generic RMBK (light-water pressurised-tube graphite-moderated reactor) design developed in the Soviet Union since the first USSR reactor at Obninsk. This type of reactor is in operation at Leningrad, Kursk, Chernobyl and at, or awaiting commissioning at, Smolensk, Ignalinsk and elsewhere.

In common with all types of reactors, the RMBK reactors share in-core neutron-flux control, in-core power-density control and regulation of each channel. In addition, the RMBK is provided with an emergency cooling system to cater for failure of the main coolant system and with an automatic reactor scram (trip) in the event of a primary coolant failure. In addition, individual fuel channels may be discharged and the defective pressure tubes sealed in the event of a localised tube failure. Containment systems beyond the reactor pressure vessel comprise several secondary systems, all designed to cater for a degree of pressure integrity, and include two separate reinforced

263

concrete structures serving as secondary pressure and radiological shields.

Clearly all these systems failed at Chernobyl. It is speculated that an explosive accumulation of hydrogen built up in the normally dry graphite moderator core upon contact with superheated steam leaking from an undetected pressure tube – the resulting chemical explosion was sufficient to penetrate all levels of secondary containment.

Mr Large points out that, in both Magnox and AGR reactors, carbon dioxide coolant is passed directly through a graphite moderator core. Contained within the reactor circuits of these are the steam generator units (boilers), which are conventionally maintained at higher pressure than the reactor gas-coolant circuit. A breach in the steamside circuit (a failed boiler tube) results in water penetrating the reactor gas circuit. Boiler-tube failures are not exceptional events in the UK reactors – witness that at Hinkley Point on 25 October 1985. In that accident the reactor remained in operation for *one hour* following failure of the boiler tube. AGRs have no secondary containment, relying on massive, reinforced-concrete pressure vessels, but the CEGB states that failure of one of these is not credible. Magnox reactors have what might be described as partial, secondary containment in the form of a reinforced concrete shield. Neither have secondary containment of the type that surrounds PWRs.

At first, John Large was a lone voice in the media when he stated that, in many ways, the Soviet reactor at Chernobyl was theoretically safer than many in the West. After the accident, we were repeatedly told of the lack of sophistication in Soviet technology, that this reactor would not have been licensed in Britain. However, on 20 May, Mr Large's assertions were confirmed when American nuclear experts admitted that they had exaggerated the dangers of the Soviet design. Suddenly they discovered that it had many features in common with Western reactors, just as John Large had said.

It was not a 'shoddy piece of Third World technology', as the US Nuclear Regulatory Commission had stated. In fact, the containment walls around the more modern Soviet nuclear reactors are designed to withstand more pressure than those in some US plants, and they have thicker concrete floors than those found in the US – and the thicker the floor the better chance of preventing a meltdown. As well as its massive and sturdy containment walls, Chernobyl also had a large basement pool of water designed to absorb any excessive steam pressure, a chamber around the reactor containing nitrogen (which is not combustible), duplicate and well-protected power cables and modern control equipment of the kind used in the West.

The first intimation in the West that something might have gone wrong came not from the Soviet Union but from Sweden. Over the weekend of 26/27 April, routine monitoring at the Forsmark nuclear plant in Sweden began to pick up exceptionally high levels of radioactivity, especially iodine-131 and caesium-137. On average, it was six to ten times the normal background level, but in a few hotspots it was 100 times higher.

The immediate reaction was that something must have happened at the plant, so staff were evacuated. However, when it was checked, there was nothing wrong. Then reports began to come in from Denmark, Norway and Finland of similar high levels, all of which suggested that there had been a major accident outside Scandinavia. Given the direction of the prevailing winds, it seemed that the contamination must be coming from the Soviet Union and that the most likely culprit was the Chernobyl nuclear complex in the Ukraine. The Soviet Union was immediately asked if there had been such an accident, and if so, could the fullest information be given so that the hazards could be quantified. There was no response.

News of the possibility of such an accident was first announced in Britain on the early evening news of 28 April. By this time, analysis of the content of the Scandinavian dust samples confirmed, because of the kind of isotopes that were found, that there had been a reactor accident, and not an atmospheric nuclear test. Radioactivity levels continued to rise.

From the Soviet Union came only a total and indefensible silence. It was later to become apparent that, for at least two days, the Soviet government itself had been kept more or less in ignorance of the severity of the accident, while those at the plant and local officials struggled both to contain the disaster and to cover up what had happened. However, there was no excuse for the continuing complete lack of information from the Soviets to the rest of the world.

Late on the evening of 28 April, the Soviet government finally issued a statement:

> An accident has occurred at the Chernobyl nuclear plant and one of the reactors was damaged. Measures are being taken to eliminate the consequences of the accident. Aid has been given to those affected. A government commission has been set up.

When this was read out halfway through their own news bulletin, there was nothing in the way the announcement was made to lead the Soviet people to think it was serious. They were told that two people had died in the accident as a result of an explosion, that there was no cause for alarm as the radiation situation had now been 'stabilised', and that some people living near the plant had had to be evacuated. At the same time, they were told how vital the nuclear power programme was and how superior was Soviet nuclear technology (a very similar reaction to the British government's when there is an accident here).

However well this might have been accepted in the Soviet Union, it certainly was not good enough for the West which, at the very least, needed to know the extent of the accident and whether or not steps needed to be taken to protect European populations. There was a chorus of fury, a positive outcry, from all over the world as governments demanded more information – hypocritically in some cases, as we shall see.

As levels of radiation outside the Soviet Union rose higher, the United States turned to its spy satellites for information. Later, they were found to have been somewhat less than totally accurate, but they did show that one reactor had suffered an accident severe enough to blow the roof off the building in which it was contained, and that it was still on fire. It also looked as if nearby reactors might also have been damaged. The pictures, when evaluated, suggested that the core was burning at 2000° C. This would automatically lead to a large release of isotopes, and one scientist estimated that the amount of radioactivity given off by the meltdown of a 1000-megawatt nuclear reactor that had been in use for a few years would be similar to that from a one-megaton nuclear weapon.

At the time of writing we do not know (nor apparently to the Russians) exactly what went wrong, although the accident is being blamed on 'human error'. There are various expert theories, the most likely (and the one to which John Large subscribes) being that it began with a failure in a weld, possibly in a pipe joint at the base of the reactor, which sent superheated steam into the normally dry graphite core. This led to an accumulation of hydrogen, and the resulting chemical explosion was sufficient to penetrate all levels of secondary containment. Another possibility is that there was a catastrophic failure of one of the huge welded pressure vessels known as 'steam drums' (each the size of a double-decker bus), which led to a large explosion and total loss of coolant within seconds, then to rapid overheating, fire and vaporisation of part of the core.

The explanation finally given by Soviet President Gorbachev himself on 14 May, 18 days after the accident, did not add very much:

> The reactor's capacity suddenly increased during a scheduled shutdown of the fourth unit. The considerable emission of steam and subsequent reaction resulted in the formation of hydrogen, its explosion, damage to the reactor and associated radioactive release.

The scenes at Chernobyl over that terrible weekend can only be imagined. The reactor was burning totally out of control, and those involved knew there was every possibility of a full-scale meltdown, even of that often mocked 'China syndrome' when an out-of-control reactor burns its way downwards towards the earth's core. Those working in the plant must have been doing so in lethally high levels of radiation: a reading of 200 rads an hour was registered above the damaged core during that weekend, an amount which would kill after two hours of exposure.

We now know that, to avert an even worse disaster, on the night of the accident plant workers in wetsuits actually dived into radioactive water to drain the basement pool beneath the reactor – acts of almost unbelievable bravery. These true heroes – for such they are – are among those now dead or seriously ill in hospital.

It also seems that those in charge of the plant did not immediately realise how serious the accident was, and when they did, they tried to cover it up. The result of this was that those living near the plant and most at risk were not evacuated for a full 36 hours, during which they were subjected to constant high radiation from the radioactive plume passing over them.

On 30 April, the Russians finally described what had happened as 'a disaster', but still gave very little further information. The same day, the Swedish Nuclear Power Inspectorate were contacted by the Soviet technical attaché to Sweden for advice on what to do next.

'We told them to do three things,' said a senior official of the Inspectorate. 'Shut down the other reactors in the vicinity, make supreme efforts to cool it down and attempt to contain the spread of radioactivity.' By this time, radiation levels in Sweden were running at 100 times the normal level in some areas and the Inspectorate reckoned that some Swedes had received up to three times the yearly permitted 'safe' level.

Sweden also suggested that the Soviet Union contact the UK Atomic Energy Authority for advice because of Britain's experience with the graphite fire at Windscale in 1957. They did not do this. A cartoon in the *Guardian* at that time showed two Russian scientists sitting outside Chernobyl: one asks if the other had rung British Nuclear Fuels for advice, and the other answers: 'Yes, comrade. They suggested we change the name . . .'

Soviet experts now admit that, four days after the accident, the reactor did come within an ace of the 'China syndrome'. It seemed inevitable that it would burn through its own base and into the ground beneath, with consequences that could only be imagined. In an attempt to contain and dowse the fire, they dropped sand, lead and boron (a non-metallic element that absorbs neutrons) from helicopters flown by volunteers working in shifts around the clock. While all this was happening, the Soviets were keeping it secret.

The public in the USSR was told that nearby towns had had to be evacuated but not how many people were involved or about the raging fire at the reactor. The implication was that both fire and radiation had been successfully dealt with. Soviet viewers were shown people apparently going about their normal day-to-day tasks in towns and villages quite near Chernobyl and preparing for the coming May Day celebrations in Kiev. Along with shots of the countryside around Chernobyl, they were also finally shown a somewhat fuzzy black-and-white photograph of the plant where it could plainly be seen that the top had been blown off one of the reactors. 'The accident did take place,' said the bland commentator, 'but you can see for yourselves, comrades, that it was not really disastrous.'

It was a different world from the reality. While the reactor was burning out of control, nearly 50,000 people had had to be evacuated from around Chernobyl, including 24,000 from the new town of Pripyat, which had been built almost entirely to service the nuclear park. The mass evacuation had begun at 2 p.m. on 27 April, but workers in essential services were told to stay and were not evacuated until 29 April. Some of them were thus condemned to death.

When the Soviet Union's great celebratory occasion of May Day dawned, there was a 'zone of death' with a radius of 19 miles, with Chernobyl at its centre. Those who entered it spoke of its eerie silence, of the strange beauty of the meadows and apple orchards heavy with blossom, all the while radiation continued to leak from the damaged reactor. Later, we were to see television film of pretty houses standing in large gardens full of spring flowers while white-coated officials and soldiers in protective clothing walked the silent and deserted streets of the small towns.

In an effort to fill the information gap, the United States turned to evaluation from the Pentagon experts. Their view, from which they later hurriedly backtracked, was that there had been meltdowns at two reactors and that thousands of people had died immediately or soon after. The Soviet government stuck to its figure of 'only two dead', but privately, Soviet officials were telling Western journalists that between 300 and 400 people were facing death from radiation.

Television news on 1 May showed jolly Russians enjoying May Day parades throughout the land including in Kiev. Unofficial reports spoke of thousands of people taking to the road with their children, while the inhabitants of Kiev jammed railway stations and bus terminals in a desperate effort to get out.

However, on 2 May a truly fascinating report was published in newspapers in the West. It appeared that the nuclear industry in the Soviet Union has more in common with that of the West than we thought – shoddy workmanship, careless construction and cost-cutting.

Almost exactly one month before the accident, on 27 March 1986, a senior manager at Chernobyl, Lyubov Kovalevska, had written in a Kiev newspaper that the inhabitants of the area were 'sitting on a time bomb'. She alleged that there had been sub-standard construction, incompetent workmanship, carelessness and bureaucratic incompetence. (Her report reads like a critique of the building of Dungeness B.) She also accused the Ukrainian state government of corruption. She wrote: 'The failure will be repaid, repaid over decades to come.' In their race to construct reactors, she said, corners had been cut, poor materials used and there had been insufficient supervision. She lived in the new town of Pripyat.

By 5 May, the Soviet government were saying that the radiation leak had been 'almost sealed', but people in Kiev were still voting with their feet, and the state government announced that school holidays would start early and 250,000 children would go off to summer camps elsewhere. Radiation from the core had dropped from 200 rads an hour to 100 rads. Attempts were being made to de-activate the soil, and all livestock inside the danger zone had been slaughtered.

A group of United Nations experts had been allowed in, and an American doctor was helping with those requiring bone-marrow transplants. There was, in fact, good international co-operation. In all, 15 countries sent drugs and equipment, and in addition, Britain supplied protective clothing as well as (eventually) expert advice.

On 6 May, Soviet officials gave their first proper press conference, although even then, only a limited number of questions were allowed. They spoke of the chaos at local level as those involved tried to deal with an accident whose implications had not sunk in. 'Only volunteers' had been allowed to work on the site, and they were still there trying to put out the fire. As well as the two dead, the toll of those in hospital had now risen to 204. The accident, they said, had been due to 'human error'.

It was on 9 May that British newspapers began carrying reports that there was a threat of a 'China syndrome', but this the Soviets immediately denied. Western experts pointed out that, if there was a 'China syndrome', the burning reactor would go through its base and pollute the Dnieper, one of Europe's greatest rivers, and it would also affect the water table, posing a threat to a sizeable proportion of the Soviet people.

On 11 May, the Russians announced that they had reached the turning point, and finally admitted that the reactor had come near to a 'China syndrome'. They had had to cope, they said, with a disaster for which there was no previous experience. With such a huge quantity of fuel and graphite in an incandescent state, there had certainly been a real chance that the core could have melted through the base of the reactor and into the earth.

By 13 May, we were told that strenuous efforts were being made to encase the damaged reactor in a thick concrete shield. The ground around it was being frozen to prevent water contamination in case the core should melt, and plastic was being laid over the area around the plant to try and avoid further land contamination. Western experts expressed doubts as to whether it would be feasible at this stage to insert a thick layer of concrete under the reactor.

And all the time the death toll was rising.

Throughout the two-week period of the crisis, experts in the West opined that there had been a meltdown or a partial core meltdown, although this was denied on several occasions by the Soviet authorities and initially seemed to be ruled out by the visiting UN delegation. But on 16 May, speaking on the BBC Radio 4 programme, *The World at One*, a Norwegian scientist, Rolf Linyarder, said that Scandinavian experts were quite sure that there had been a full core meltdown and that, indeed, it might still be going on. The amount of plutonium and other trans-uranium elements in the fallout which had been monitored in Scandinavia was so high that it could only have come about as a result of a full meltdown. He said that, in statements given to the Swedes, the Soviets had virtually admitted it, and that the UN delegation too now seemed to think it had happened.

Linyarder thought that nobody could know what was going on at the core. Radiation readings taken the previous week from a helicopter 400 metres above and 800 metres away from the plant were so high that those working inside would receive a lethal dose within minutes, and it must still have been impossible to get near enough to the reactor core to find out what state it was in. He thought that totally sealing off the entire reactor would be almost impossible.

Writing this so near to the event, it is impossible to know properly what the full situation is. If we think our nuclear industry is secretive, the position in the Soviet Union is many times worse. Although, over the days of the crisis, gradually more information did come out, there are still far too many unanswered questions.

For our own good, we need to know exactly what happened, especially when we read the CEGB's complacent report on the safety of its AGRs – 'a major failure of the pre-stressed-concrete pressure vessel is not considered credible because of the method of construction', and

> no credible fault sequence has the immediate outcome of a significant release of radioactivity. In most fault sequences, there is a long time interval before fuel overheats, giving ample time for operator intervention to restore cooling.

I will end by letting some of those involved in or concerned with the crisis speak for themselves:

> Western engineers still cannot explain what happened at Chernobyl because, on paper, it could not happen. The combination of a graphite core and water as a coolant should provide a reactor system which – above all – could not fail. [*Guardian*, 5 May 1986]

> The accident developed in an unusual way, not as scientific knowledge predicted. [Soviet scientist quoted in the *Daily Telegraph*, 9 May 1986]

Finally we come to Dr Richard Gale, the American doctor who worked himself to the point of exhaustion dealing with Soviet radiation victims. In a television interview, he turned wearily to the cameras and said:

> The lesson of Chernobyl is our limited ability to respond to a nuclear accident. We were hard pressed to deal with 300 radiation casualties – and so it is evident how inadequate our response would be to nuclear war.

The reaction

Let us start with Britain. The first reaction from the Prime Minister, Mrs Thatcher, was characteristically robust. On Tuesday, 29 April, when hardly anything was known about the Soviet accident except that it was very serious, she informed the House of Commons during Prime Minister's Question Time that there would be no danger from radioactivity to Britain.

Then the experts from the nuclear industry were immediately wheeled out and on to every possible radio and television programme. For the first few days, we were repeatedly told that the large release of radioactivity was due to the fact that the Russians had no secondary containment around their reactor. Some just implied that our reactors did, others actually stated it outright; according to the *Guardian* on 29 April, our reactors did have secondary containment and were therefore safe.

American PWRs do have such secondary containment, but as we have seen, Britain's present nuclear reactors do not. The reason why is that, when they were designed, this was not considered necessary.

There was also, quite rightly, a loud chorus of disapproval for the secrecy surrounding the events at Chernobyl, but this rose to proportions of unparalleled hypocrisy when we were continually treated to comparisons with the openness and lack of secrecy of the West. Openness? – when it took 26 years for us to be told that polonium had been released during the Windscale fire of 1957, and that several hundred cancers may well have resulted from it! Lack of secrecy? – when it was only by chance that a radio reporter found out that there had been an accident at Three-Mile Island, when the local population were still being told that there was nothing to worry about as the radioactive plume passed over their heads?

Zealots such as Lord Marshall appeared on every news programme to tell us that, of course, it could not happen here – but if it did, our superior technology would be able to deal with it. There was no mention of the fact that luck had played a very large part in diverting disaster both at the 1957 Windscale fire and at Three-Mile Island. The Windscale accident, like Chernobyl, resulted in a graphite fire, and we have already seen how difficult it was to bring it under control, while at Three-Mile Island, no one knows to this day why the huge (and dangerous) hydrogen bubble deflated – it was certainly not due to any sophisticated techniques undertaken by those involved.

However, as more and more details of the Chernobyl accident filtered through, there were some signs that the certainty which had always pervaded every statement made by the nuclear industry was showing signs of wear and tear. On 29 April, Lord Marshall appeared on BBC 2's *Newsnight*. He did not entertain us by shaking a cocktail of radioactive water – the highpoint of a lecture he gave at Westminster School in December 1985. Instead, his performance was, for once, less than sure, and it was well reported by Hugo Young in his *Guardian* column of 1 May 1986.

274

. . . but the second message from Lord Marshall's various appearances derived from the lameness of what he had to say. Suddenly one noticed the qualifications in his words and felt obliged not to give him the benefit of the doubt. Could there be a similar meltdown here? He did not think there was 'any reasonable chance' of it, i.e. yes, there was a chance even though only in unreasonable circumstances. Later he averred that 'almost any reactor' could be made safe by spending money. What was that about 'almost'?

Those who were by now thoroughly alarmed by the possibility of such an accident here could hardly have been reassured by a statement made to the *Daily Telegraph* on 5 May by Eddie Ryder, Chief Inspector of the Nuclear Installations Inspectorate. Speaking of the old Magnox reactors, he said, 'They probably wouldn't be licensed today,' and he then admitted that they lacked secondary containment shields.

It also transpired that, while the British government was joining in the chorus of disapproval over Chernobyl, it had had amnesia about an accident that had only just recently occurred in the British nuclear plant, Dungeness A. On the Sunday after Chernobyl, the *Observer* revealed that an explosion had taken place at Dungeness A on 31 March 1986, when staff were commissioning a new piece of equipment designed to treat gas used as a coolant for the No. 2 Magnox reactor. This resulted in a gash in the by-pass system measuring 9 inches by 2 inches, and 110 lb of mildly radioactive gas were released.

The *Observer* had received this information in an anonymous letter. The informant wrote:

Only by immense good fortune was a large release of reactor gas avoided. How did a piece of nuclear equipment that had been subject to all the CEGB's current design evaluation and independent analysis fail so spectacularly?

Geoffrey Lean of the *Observer* rang the CEGB on 2 May at the height of the furore over Chernobyl. He was told that they had put out a press statement about the explosion and the letter writer must have seen a report of it in the *Folkestone*

Herald. However, there had been no press release, nor had the local press run any stories. The CEGB continued to repeat its story until, after being asked several times for a copy of the press release, a spokesman admitted that there had not been a 'full' press release, more of a 'press statement', but the incident had not been considered important enough to send it out. The *Observer* was refused permission to speak to a CEGB expert on the grounds that 'these people are obviously vulnerable when dealing with people like you. They tend to be too straightforward and trusting.'

Aware that the *Observer* would run the story, the CEGB then presumably got in touch with other journalists, since the *Sunday Times* of the same date said that the *Observer* story was 'scurrilous', and the *Sunday Telegraph* alleged that the news of the accident had been run in the local papers following the CEGB press release. Neither was true. So much for openness and lack of secrecy.

Meanwhile, in spite of the hot air rising from Mrs Thatcher's statement that there was no hazard to Britain from Chernobyl, the cloud of radioactive contamination was relentlessly crossing Europe. At first, the winds had been blowing it back into the Soviet Union, but then, towards the end of the week following the disaster, they changed direction as winds do, in spite of the statements of politicians. In addition, at least some of the radioactivity must have passed through the atmosphere into the layer above – the troposphere – and this would also ensure its wider distribution.

The immediate brunt was felt by Poland, and as levels rose, children there were given potassium iodate to help counteract the effects of iodine-131, and milk was thrown away. Levels of radioactivity in European countries varied not only between countries but also between different areas within those countries – from between ten to as much as 1000 times the background radiation level. All affected countries quickly assured their populations that there was no danger to health. Two groups of British students who had been in Minsk and Kiev were flown back and were found, on arrival in London, to have received some slight contamination.

On 2 May, the day the cloud finally reached Britain, the

Daily Telegraph ran a headline: 'NO NEED TO TAKE RADIATION STEPS IN BRITAIN'. However, we shall see that there are now glaring discrepancies between what was considered a 'safe' level of radioactive contamination in this country and in others.

The amount of radioactivity precipitated over Britain probably was relatively small, but it soon became apparent that the situation for monitoring it was, in the words of a DHSS spokesman, 'a complete shambles' (*Sunday Telegraph*, 4 May 1986). There was no overall responsibility for monitoring foodstuffs as no single department had assumed such a responsibility. The DHSS had said, on 2 May, that there was 'no risk to health', and that 'no raised levels of radioactivity had been detected.' Two days later, when they said that the task of monitoring levels was to be done by the Ministry of Agriculture, the latter were angry that the DHSS had 'passed the buck to them'. The DHSS told inquirers: 'Testing is being carried out by the EEC, and we would be informed on the Common Market hotline if any serious problems arise. It is a good system.'

It is a non-existent system. When the *Sunday Telegraph* contacted Brussels, they were told that the EEC has no food-testing facilities of its own. 'All checks will be done by the member states themselves,' said a member of the EEC Commission. 'We have no mechanism for administering these controls.'

Over the weekend of the 3/4 May, the public were treated to a flood of reassurances from a number of spokesmen about the lack of any possible hazard. That particular weekend was a bad one for dealing with the outcome of a disaster, for the Monday was a Bank Holiday and many of the people who should have been monitoring radioactivity and/or passing on information were simply not there.

The information which did emerge was both vague and contradictory. As radiation levels rose irregularly in different parts of the British Isles, we were advised to stay indoors if it rained, and those living in Scotland, North Wales and parts of northern England with a high rainfall were told not to drink rainwater. Radiation in some areas, we were told, was running at ten times the normal amount, and some radio-nuclides were now being found in milk. At all times, the refrain was that there was no danger to health.

By Monday, 5 May, it was apparent that such reassurances were falling on deaf ears as callers jammed the switchboard of the National Radiological Protection Board at Abingdon, Oxon, which only has one external telephone line. When I finally got through on 6 May, after hours of trying, the spokesman, while reassuring me that there was no cause for alarm, refused point blank to reply to my questions about which radio-nuclides were being found and in what proportion. It was apparent that iodine-131 must be one of them as it was being found in other countries, but how about caesium-137, lithium and so on? There was no answer.

Some of the reasons for that lack of response became apparent when, on 13 May, the Department of the Environment finally released all the monitoring data it had received both from government departments and from bodies of the nuclear industry, but this, like that which had trickled out earlier, was a mish-mash of old and new technical terms and the data were imprecise – for example, the information from the Department of the Environment spoke of concentrations on a square metre of grass instead of the amount in a kilogram of grass. The answer to how much grass exists in any random square metre is no doubt similar to that for how long is a piece of string. There were no figures showing how much radiation had accumulated over the period of time that had elapsed since the Chernobyl accident, which meant that there could be no estimate of the total amount of fallout. In addition, the mixture of different types of units of measurement made it all very confusing.

In fact, right from the start, the information given out by government bodies was hampered by the flood of jargon in which it was couched. Although there have recently been changes in the terms used for some measurements of radiation, these have not been standardised, so information was variously given in rads, rems, grays, curies, becquerels and sieverts without any explanation as to what these words meant and still without hard facts about the proportion of radio-nuclides being monitored.

Whatever measurements were used, by the end of the Bank

Holiday the flood of anxious callers showed no signs of abating, and on 6 May, five days after the accident, the government set up a special hotline so that members of the public could ring and have their fears allayed. Perhaps it is not surprising, in view of what had gone before, that those ringing the number then received a strange response: they had been routed through to the drivers' rest room at the Department of the Environment . . . In the end, there were nine hot-lines, and they were all permanently jammed; those who could not get through all seemed to ring Friends of the Earth and Greenpeace, who tried to calm fears.

By that time, rainwater in some parts of Britain had reached 50 per cent of the danger level. This, it must be emphasised, is the *British* danger level. In Britain, the upper limit of the 'safety' level for iodine-131 in milk is 2000 becquerels per litre (bpl). In Austria it is 1000 and in West Germany it is 500 . . . The British limit for water is 2400 bpl. Initially, we were told that the amount found in milk was between 200 and 270 bpl, which was safe, but those drinking rainwater were told that if they drank it for a week, they might take in the equivalent of a year's 'safe' dose. Some experts did point out, however, that the safety level for babies could be less than one-tenth of that for an adult. Radioactivity was found in the breastmilk of Swedish mothers within 48 hours of the disaster.

One strange piece of information repeatedly given by both government spokesmen and scientists, particularly on the radio, was that, even if the level in water rose, it would not affect cows' milk. Asked on some occasions why this should be, the answer given was that cows acquire most of their liquid intake from moisture in grass, not water. There was no explanation as to how the grass would remain uncontaminated.

It was later discovered that very high levels of radioactivity indeed had been found in parts of Scotland. Radioactive iodine-131, four times above critical levels, was measured in water. In Glasgow, 9000 bpl were found during heavy rain over the weekend of 3/4 May and 9400 bpl were found in some parts of the Highlands, while the very highest level of all – in a puddle near the Dounreay nuclear research establishment –

was a staggering 28,000 bpl. (Perhaps it might be useful to inquire why . . . ?) However, on 8 May the Scottish Office did give the actual amounts of iodine-131 monitored in milk: on 5, 6 and 7 May, iodine-131 in cows' milk was 220 bpl, 225 bpl and 125 bpl respectively; nearer to Dounreay, goats' milk registered 450 bpl, 357 bpl and 224 bpl on the same dates.

Some of the advice given seemed either naïve, ignorant or both. Immediately after the news broke of the accident, we were told that staff at the British embassy in Moscow had been advised to boil their water as a safeguard! This would have been more appropriate as a way of combating typhoid during the Crimean War.

People were told to wash all fresh vegetables to avoid any possible danger. Apropos of this, there was an interesting letter in the *Guardian* on 13 May from the Department of Radiation Biology at St Bartholomew's Hospital in London. Its writers said that they had picked spinach and measured its radio-iodine content before and after thorough washing, and had found that only 20 per cent of the radioactivity had been removed after washing. The spinach retained this level of contamination even after cooking, 'which might imply systemic rather than surface contamination'. ('Systemic' means that the pollutant is taken into the substance of the plant itself, which is what is designed to happen with many pesticides and herbicides, some of which are themselves under suspicion as a danger to health.) The amount of radioactivity found in the spinach was very small indeed, but the writers felt that the implications were obvious and they hoped the authorities would not allow the importation of vegetables with a higher level of radioactivity on the assumption that people could decontaminate them.

When the Department of the Environment finally released information on 13 May, it said that the measurements for iodine-131 in milk varied between 200 and 400 bpl. However, Anthony Tucker, writing in the *Guardian* the day after, said that if the fallout data summarised by the NRPB was correct then the officially announced amount of radioactive iodine in milk was just not correct – it is too low by about a third. John Dunster, head of the NRPB, put this down to cows being fed supplementary feeds as well as grass.

By the middle of that week, we were told that any possible dangers had passed as the radioactive cloud had now moved across and away from the British Isles, but by the end of the week, it had returned, although it was far weaker and more diffuse.

Among the political fallout of that week was the announcement on 8 May by the Environment Secretary, Kenneth Baker, that the government was no longer considering the dumping of medium-level nuclear waste in the proposed new waste dumps. He insisted there was no 'scientific' reason for this; he was merely responding to public concern over the issue.

If the position in this country left much to be desired, the reaction of the French government was even worse, hooked on nuclear power as it is. Initially, it was little better than that of the Soviet Union.

The French Federation of Nature Protection Societies, meeting in Limoges over the weekend of 10/11 May, called for the resignation of Professor Pierre Pellerin, director of the Central Protection Service Against Radioactivity. This was because he had waited until 10 May to reveal that radiation readings in some parts of France were 400 times higher than normal. Hitherto this had been denied, and statements had been made to the effect that no special steps need be taken to alert the population about the accident and that precautionary measures were unnecessary.

Cynics had already refused to believe that the radioactive cloud had thoughtfully stopped at the French border, noting that West Germany was taking active measures on one side of the Rhine while the French did nothing on the other bank. On 11 May, French and West German protestors joined forces on both sides of the Rhine some 15 kilometres from the French nuclear power station at Fessenheim. They then marched towards it, preceded by two cows and a wheelbarrow full of vegetables, all said to be affected by radiation.

In Austria, parents had been advised to keep their children indoors if it rained and sales of fresh vegetables were halted from 5 May. In Belgium, cattle were brought in from the fields and people were told to wash all fresh vegetables. Denmark banned imports of cattle feedstuffs and said there was 'some danger' to children and pregnant women from imported milk. Luxembourg banned all sale of fresh milk, and Holland took in its cows and told people to wash vegetables. In Switzerland, with radiation running at four to ten times the normal amount, people were recommended not to drink rainwater and to avoid giving fresh milk to children under two, and unwashed fruit or vegetables to women of childbearing age. In parts of West Germany, cattle were brought in, and people were told to avoid outdoor swimming pools and eating green vegetables. It took the EEC two whole weeks from the time of the Chernobyl disaster to agree to ban the importation of foodstuffs from the Eastern bloc.

As a coda to what went on in Europe, some highly embarrassing information emerged at the time from the United States. It appears that it too came dangerously near a Chernobyl-type disaster in 1985, a year described by a congressional critic as 'having the worst safety record since Three-Mile Island'. Nuclear Regulatory Commission member James Asseltine said incidents had taken place at the Davis–Besse plant in Ohio and at the Rancho Seco facility near Sacramento in California.

The Davis–Besse accident has already been discussed on pp. 91–2. At Rancho Seco, a 26-minute loss of power led to overcooling which could weaken the reactor, and was said to be one of a number of such incidents which could have led to serious consequences. Mr Asseltine said both of the accidents of Davis–Besse and Rancho Seco came perilously near to mimicking the breakdown in safety systems at Chernobyl.

Following these admissions, White House Chief of Staff Donald Regan was asked about evacuation-plan procedures at some plants, and he admitted that, in many, they were as non-existent as they had been at Chernobyl. Told of the concern of those living near a nuclear power station on Long Island, who were asking how they would be evacuated if there were to be an accident, he replied, in his merry way, 'Perhaps they should start building more bridges.'

On 2 May, Senator John Glenn cited a report prepared in the US the previous September, which had been classified until he publicised it. It had been prepared by the General Accounting Office in Washington, and said that nuclear power plants in 14 countries had experienced 151 'significant' nuclear safety incidents since 1971. This figure includes only those reported to international atomic energy organisations and excludes those that may have occurred in the Eastern bloc.

What is sure is that ordinary people all over Europe, in the United States and certainly in Britain now show a great deal of hostility towards nuclear power. A majority want nuclear power plants to be phased out, according to opinion polls, and nearly as many would like them to be shut down at once.

Perhaps the general view is best summed up by a photograph that appeared in the national papers on 12 May 1986. It showed a demonstrator standing outside Trawsfynydd nuclear power station in North Wales, holding a placard on which he had chalked: 'Trawsfynydd – Twin Town Chernobyl'.

Health

The first two victims of the Chernobyl accident were two employees at the plant who were killed outright by the initial explosion, and for days the Soviet government insisted that this was the sum of the casualties. This provided propaganda for all those who wanted to play down the accident, both inside and outside the Soviet Union – after all, an accident which only killed two people could hardly be considered a disaster.

No unbiased person believed it would stop there. By 15 May, the death toll had risen to eight and there were a further 35 gravely ill people. No one thinks it will stop there either: there were 299 other people in hospital at the time of writing.

Early exaggerated reports from the United States had spoken of 'thousands of deaths' within days of the accident. This was not true, but it is more than likely that there will indeed be thousands of deaths as a result of Chernobyl over the next few decades.

Deaths from this kind of accident occur in five waves. First come those from severe and immediate high-dosage radiation which overwhelms the system. Next to die are those affected by slightly lower doses, who do not die of the radiation itself, but of gastro-intestinal injuries within two or three weeks. Those who received lower doses might recover from the latter, but their bone marrow is so damaged that they succumb a month or two later. Leukaemias appear in children within two years, peak at around ten years and tail off after 25. About ten years after the accident come the cancers – breast, thyroid, lungs, liver, stomach, large intestine, bone, oesophagus, small intestine, urinary tract, bladder, pancreas, rectum and lymph glands, in that order of frequency. There will also be an unknown amount of genetic damage to those unborn, resulting in miscarriages, stillbirths, malformations, disease and disability.

We have no way of knowing, at the time of writing, just what the outlook will be for those who lived around Chernobyl – who were not evacuated for a crucial 36 hours – nor for all those living further away who were in the path of the radioactive plume. However, Swedish experts estimate that, on the basis of the isotopes found in their own food chain, there could be tens of thousands of additional cancer deaths in Europe over the next 20 years, though it will not be possible to prove that a single one is linked to Chernobyl. John Dunster of the NRPB put the number of deaths in Britain as 'probably in tens'.

Some early government statements were made to the effect that the Chernobyl disaster would cause no injury to people outside the Soviet Union. To quote Anthony Tucker in the *Guardian* (6 May 1985): 'These statements are false.' Compared to what will happen to the Soviets themselves, the effects of the radiation will be relatively small, but they will certainly not be trivial. Anthony Tucker described one statement made by a CEGB spokesman – that the risk was like 'smoking half a fag a day' – as typically foolish. (On *The World at One* on 14 May, the leader of a team of scientists from Dounreay who were offering to go to the Soviet Union to assist in the clean-up said it was in the region of 'smoking five fags a day for life'.) Nor, continued Tucker, are the risks 'much less than background radiation,' or 'insignificant'. 'A small individual risk', he said, is a term more appropriate to a congenital gambler in a small-time casino than to a human life.

From what is known about iodine-131 alone, said Tucker, it can be estimated that there will be some hundreds of additional cases of thyroid cancer outside the Soviet Union, largely in children.

Among the children now playing, there is a scattered and unidentifiable group, several tens large, at whose necks the Chernobyl cancer pistol is now unwaveringly pointing. Earlier accidents, even though the scale was much smaller, provide an indication of health significance. Recent dose commitment calculations from measurements made at the time of the Windscale reactor fire in 1957 indicate that, averaged over the 20 years after the accident, the incidence of thyroid cancer in Britain will have risen by about 1 per cent. This may sound small, an additional risk of only one in 10 million, but it means that about 20 people, most of them children at the time of the accident, were not, and are not, 'at some slight risk'. After great distress and sickness, years later – they are dead!

He concluded:

The problems in Russia over the next 30 years arising from the wide spectrum of isotopes in the areas of intensive fallout, from actual radiation injuries and from a future in which large populations will suffer abnormal increases in a very wide range of cancers, may make the effects in Poland, Scandinavia and northern Europe seem 'trivial'. But a dismissive approach to international health effects will undermine international safety standards, wreck transfrontier contamination agreements and deceive the public. The damage could be far greater and more long-lasting than anything arising from prudent overstatement.

Time and again during the days following the Chernobyl accident, the nuclear experts and government spokesmen put down the genuine concern of the public to lack of knowledge, stupidity, fear of the unknown. It is true that many of those who rang the government hotline or wrote to their MPs were genuinely ignorant, or may have wanted to remain so to avoid thinking about that particular subject. But it is highly arrogant to describe all those who expressed concern as ignorant. Many people today have educated themselves quite thoroughly about the hazards of nuclear power.

The official attitude was perfectly typified in a gushing profile in the *Observer* of 4 May by Carmel Fitzsimmons. The subject was Nigel Dodd, a scientific officer at the NRPB. After detailing his jolly family life with his kids and his cats and his pretty house, he was quoted making a number of reassuring statements. Speaking of the return of the British students from the Soviet Union, he said: 'People know so little about radiation and really all they want is reassurance. Everyone at Heathrow wanted good news – it's like hearing your car has passed its MOT.'

This, said the interviewer, was the 'pleasant calm' of the scientist who knows his field. What about nuclear energy as a threat then? 'Some people do have fears,' said Mr Dodd, 'but they tend to be educated enough to appreciate that the powers-that-be who laid down the safety regulations and radiation levels knew what they were doing.'

This is a breathtakingly complacent attitude in view of the constant lowering of safety thresholds that we have seen over the years.

So let us look yet again at these safety levels. First, it cannot be emphasised sufficiently that the 'natural background radiation', which we are constantly told everything is measured against, is a broad and extremely imprecise term which includes both truly natural radiation – for instance, from granite – and man-made radioactivity from nuclear tests in the atmosphere and emissions from nuclear installations. Persistent nuclear emissions become, in these terms, 'background radiation', with the implication that all of it is quite natural. Radiation from man-made sources can, therefore, creep slowly and relentlessly upward and still be described as apparently natural background radiation.

As I have already pointed out in the Glossary, the new

measurements of grays, becquerels and sieverts are not as precise as would first appear, as so many different considerations have to be taken into account. What all this adds up to is that safety standards in this country could be wrong by a factor of between two and ten.

On 12 May 1986, the BBC series *Panorama* blew the whistle on the whole question of safety in an edition called 'How Safe is "Safe"?' In Britain, the current 'safe' dose for a member of the public is considered to be 0.5 millisieverts (5 rems in the old measurements) per year. However, this was the very maximum level considered 'safe' by the International Commission on Radiological Protection (ICRP) in its recommendations of May 1985, and they strongly recommended that all countries adopt a safety threshold of only 0.1 millisieverts. In West Germany, the threshold is 0.30 millisieverts in a year, and in the US it is 0.25 millisieverts. A British ICRP expert, when asked why the British level had been set so high, at 0.5 millisieverts (without any Parliamentary discussion), said he thought the higher limit had been accepted 'through inertia, then left because it was convenient'.

However, it seems that all previous calculations may be wrong. *Panorama* revealed that scientists are currently working on a report re-assessing the effect of the Hiroshima bomb on its victims. (Current measurements are still based on data from the radiation effects at Hiroshima.) Contrary to some recent reports, the experts discovered that, in fact, the rate of cancer among survivors is still actually increasing abnormally some 40 years on. Basically, it appears that, by the 1980s, world experts had decided that they had got their sums wrong, with the result that they had had a distorted view of how radiation had affected those concerned. The report has yet to be published, but it will say that radiation is twice as harmful as had been realised up to now.

Dr Edward Radford, a former US government adviser on radiation, said: 'The risk is higher than authorities have hitherto been willing to admit.' This was partly because the Hiroshima study only used cancer *deaths*, not all cancer *cases*. He feels that the 'safe' threshold level should be lowered by a factor of at least ten. Those working on the new report reached this figure by considering all radiation-induced cancers (not just cancer deaths); adding the 'background' radiation; taking into account the fact that some people seem to be more vulnerable to cancer than others (this was not done when the first Hiroshima calculations were made); and then adding on the extra radiation experienced by those living near nuclear installations, or fishing in water into which radioactivity is discharged. In fact, the current figure may be out by a factor of about twelve.

'The scientists have not only been wrong, they have been seen to be wrong,' said reporter Fred Emery. Which leads one to ask where that leaves the complacent Nigel Dodd of the NRPB.

Panorama invited the Environment Minister William Waldegrave, Employment Minister Kenneth Clarke and Health Minister Barney Hayhoe to appear on the programme, as the responsibility for setting the 0.5 millisievert level seems to have been passed from one to the other. They were first asked to appear before the Chernobyl disaster. Then, Waldegrave refused, saying it was the responsibility of other departments, and Clarke said, no, it was a scientific matter on which he could not comment. At first, Hayhoe agreed to appear, then changed his mind, saying it was essentially a scientific matter for the NRPB and that it was necessary to keep the NRPB 'at arm's length as I believe it is inappropriate to discuss or defend the Board's scientific judgement.' True to our traditions of openness and lack of secrecy, all three still refused even after Chernobyl.

So who decides exactly what is a calculated risk and who is to be put at risk? If the scientists have now got it wrong, as seems clear, where does that leave those who will suffer as a result of the disaster at Chernobyl? So much for those 'educated' people who appreciate the experts who knew what they were doing when they set the safety levels . . .

We cannot know now nor will we ever know how many people will die prematurely as a result of the Chernobyl disaster. But we can be sure that there will be quite a lot of them, and even if it is only one, it will be one too many.

Implications

Other than those who have died or are sick and dying, the major casualty of the Chernobyl disaster is the nuclear industry, and that particularly applies in Britain. As all the opinion polls show, no longer do the majority of people believe the anodyne and complacent statements of government and nuclear 'experts' on the safety of nuclear power. From television 'vox pops' to the letters that have poured into newspapers, the people have stated in no uncertain terms their distrust, cynicism and dislike of the nuclear industry and its supposed certainties.

Its most fervent admirers both in government and in the industry itself have now admitted openly that they have an enormous task on their hands if they are to 'win back public confidence' – if that is ever possible. There must, they say, be 'more openness', 'less secrecy' and, most of all, 'better presentation', so that people are not afraid of nuclear power through ignorance.

For the first time, a blinding light has been shone on our own nuclear industry, and many people do not like what they see. They wonder about the safety of our ageing Magnox reactors, and look with concern at the fact that necessary inspections of these are falling behind and that what is found will not be made public. They look at the reports of bad workmanship and poor supervision which dogged the construction of Chernobyl, and then they remember the criticism of the building of the AGRs. A huge majority do not want a PWR here at any price. A US government study, revealed at the time of Chernobyl, showed that, between 1969 and 1979 alone, there had been 169 accidents in PWRs which could have led to a meltdown.

The Soviets, said a number of Western experts in the immediate aftermath of the disaster, were at fault for building their nuclear station so near centres of population. Ours are far nearer – imagine the effect of an accident at Hinkley, Berkeley or Oldbury with a strong westerly or south-westerly wind (our prevailing wind).

It can now be seen, with crystal clarity, that Britain is totally unprepared to deal with the result of someone else's accident, let alone one of its own.

As to an accident here, we have already looked in some detail at the unrealistic plans made for such an emergency, but it is worth just glancing at them again in the light of Chernobyl.

To begin with, we were informed, there was hardly any chance of a serious accident in this country 'owing to the superior design of our reactors'. However, if there was one, think of the evacuation plans revealed at the Sizewell inquiry, when inhabitants living within *one-and-a-half miles* of the nuclear plant would be moved. One-and-a-half miles? The Russians had to clear people from a radius of 19 miles around the plant and that was criticised over here for being insufficient. (In the US, the statutory distance is 10 miles, and in Sweden, it is between 25 and 50, depending on the severity of the accident.)

Then the operational support centre would open – some 7 miles from the accident – and the police, as we have been told, would then walk around knocking on doors handing out potassium iodate tablets. When they had finished that, they would be clearing people off any nearby beaches.

After Chernobyl, 9400 bpl was recorded in rainwater in Scotland and 225 bpl in milk – and that is a long, long way from Chernobyl. Milk was banned 400 miles away in Poland and 800 miles away in Sweden, yet British plans say that there would be no additional risk to drinking milk produced more than 25 miles from an accident! Restrictions on British vegetables would only apply within a radius of *five miles* of the reactor . . .

On 11 May 1986, an *Observer* article provided the only entertainment of an otherwise black fortnight. Journalists discovered, on ringing the Ministry of Agriculture, that what the Ministry considered to be priority supplies for any operational support centre included headed notepaper, kettles and crockery for use outside normal office hours. The CEGB keeps, for such emergencies, a stock of 500 pairs of wellington boots.

As we have already seen, an accident at Sizewell would require the transport of casualties to Ipswich (which would also be in the path of any radioactive plume if the winds were blowing from the east), although hospital doctors in that medium-sized town say they could only deal with four or five victims at any one time and envisaged stretcher cases being stacked up outside.

As to evacuation proper, well, taking that much-criticised Russian radius of 19 miles and applying it to areas around such reactors as Berkeley, Oldbury and Hartlepool, what do we see? According to Dr Stan Openshaw, a Newcastle University geographer and the author of a recently published book, *Nuclear Power – Siting and Safety*, there are almost 1 million local inhabitants involved in each case. Where would they go? 'If you tried to evacuate people from the area, you would also generate incredible panic and jam the roads within minutes. You just could not get people out.'

We can forget the one-in-a-million chance and the plane crashing on the football pitch. The Russians have had two serious nuclear accidents in 500 years of accumulated reactor-operating experience. The United States has had two – Three-Mile Island in Pennsylvania and Fermi in Detroit – in 900 equivalent years. Britain's Windscale accident happened after 600 years of reactor operation. Anthony Tucker, writing in the *Guardian* (7 May 1986), said, 'With about 300 nuclear power reactors worldwide, an accident appears likely every seven years.' In fact, just seven years had elapsed between the accidents at Three-Mile Island and Chernobyl. Who will be next?

Another major casualty of Chernobyl has been the truth. The Soviet Union concealed what had happened for as long as possible; the Americans hyped it up; and the British floundered along as usual. Aware that there is now a great deal of opposition to nuclear power, we have been promised that things will now be different here.

The first sign of this was the revival of the 1976 ruling which said that *all* accidents had to be reported to the relevant minister and then made public. In 1979, when the Thatcher administration took over, the nuclear industry was told that it only had to report 'major' accidents. There has since been much dispute over what constitutes a major accident.

However, that is both the first and – at the time of writing –

the only sign of a change of attitude by the powers-that-be. When the CEGB gave a press conference to explain what had happened at Hinkley B on 29 November 1985, they refused to make public the report on the accident. This was, said a CEGB spokesman on Television South West on 14 May 1986, because employees might otherwise not feel able to give evidence in the event of a future mishap. On 15 May, I took part in a BBC Radio programme in which various statements were made by a 'spokesman' for UKAEA, including that there could be no fire at a Magnox reactor as the graphite is cooled by carbon dioxide (so what about Windscale in 1957?), that there was no release of radioactivity at the Hinkley accident of 25 October 1985 (when the Energy Secretary had had to admit there had been) and, finally, that a Chernobyl-type accident could not happen here. So much for better presentation and openness.

If there is a serious gas explosion, people can die or be injured as a result, but it is a local problem and, sad as it is for those involved, it affects no one else. The same applies to an accident at an oil terminal.

A pit accident is a tragedy – and I write as a miner's daughter – and those who work in the mine can suffer long-term disease, which shortens life, as my own father knows. But children living 30 miles from the pithead do not also suffer from pneumoconiosis.

Nuclear power is different; no other form of energy poses such a threat. Next time you are told that there is no chance of a major accident happening here, remember that that is what *Soviet Life* told the people of Chernobyl just two months before it did. Think, too, of all those who have died and will die as a result of Chernobyl, as a result of 'the safest form of energy known to man'.

Appendix 1

On 24 February 1986, Friends of the Earth placed the following advertisement in the *Guardian*:

SELLAFIELD
'Our record would stand up to scrutiny'
BNFL, 20th February 1986

HERE IS THE BNFL RECORD

21 October 1950	Abnormal X-ray exposure
October 1952	Plutonium ingestion
1952	Plutonium ingestion
4 January 1953	Plutonium contamination of hands in R&D facility
16 June 1953	Alpha contamination of road inside separation area
18 June 1953	Beta & gamma facial contamination
7 July 1953	Instrument trough spillage, reprocessing plant
10 July 1953	Plutonium contaminated wound
16 October 1953	Spillage of uranyl nitrate
2 November 1953	Crane failure, reprocessing plant
30 November 1953	Spillage, R&D laboratory
23 May 1954	Fume emitted in plutonium residue recovery operation
15 September 1954	Beta & gamma contaminated wound, R&D laboratory
16 November 1954	Liquor spillage in R&D laboratory
28 March 1955	Abnormal plutonium discharge to effluent treatment
16 August 1955	Personal alpha contamination, plutonium recovery
15 November 1955	Alpha-contaminated wound

293

2 November 1956	Personal beta contamination, storage facility
14 January 1957	Fire in metal recovery lab
March 1957	Contaminated separation area roads
8 October 1957	Major fire in the reactor
13 June 1958	Abnormal film exposure, R&D laboratory
21 June 1958	Incident in plutonium finishing plant
20 July 1958	Abnormal exposure of instrument mechanic
23 October 1958	Personal alpha contamination in plutonium finishing plant
October 1958	Apparent criticality clearance contravention
27 January 1959	Liquor spillage in storage facility
6 February 1959	Personal contamination
27 August 1959	Accidental withdrawal of fuel element into operating area of Windscale pond
27 January 1960	Fire at effluent treatment plant
30 March 1960	Plutonium spillage, R&D laboratory
25 May 1960	Personal contamination, R&D laboratory
June 1960	Abnormal film doses, plutonium finishing plant
24 June 1960	Plutonium contamination, R&D laboratory
December 1960	Abnormal waste exposure, R&D laboratory
1961/62	Failure of plutonium evaporators, reprocessing plant
1 April 1961	Whole-body exposure greater than 3 rems
31 August 1961	Explosion in fume hood (perchloric acid) in R&D lab
16 October 1961	Fire in Drigg trench
January 1962	Abnormal exposure
23 May 1962	Floor contamination in R&D laboratory
November 1962	Abnormal exposure
24 September 1963	Plutonium contamination in R&D laboratory
28 July 1964	Glove-box pressurisation, R&D laboratory
2 December 1964	Fire in Drigg trench
3 December 1964	Glove-box explosion in R&D laboratory

5 March 1965	Over-exposure in Magnox ponds
17 May 1965	Personal alpha contamination, R&D laboratory
25 January 1966	Personal alpha contamination, R&D laboratory
January 1966	Over-exposure, chargehand fitter
Jan/Feb 1966	Over-exposure, shift foreman
12 February 1966	Over-exposure, fitter
1 April 1966	Over-exposure, rigger
October 1967	Apparent loss of small quantity of plutonium
7 November 1967	Plutonium wound, plutonium recovery plant
29 November 1967	Fire in Drigg trench
December 1967	Over-exposure F/M, in Magnox pond
18 March 1968	Plutonium wound in R&D laboratory
23 July 1968	Personal contamination, Magnox ponds
29 August 1968	Plutonium wound in R&D laboratory
30 August 1968	Plutonium wound in R&D laboratory
September 1968	Leakage of activity to Seaburn sewer in excess of authorisation
3 October 1968	Spillage in reprocessing plant
23 October 1968	Spillage in reprocessing plant
28 October 1968	Spillage in reprocessing plant
4 January 1969	Apparent reinfringement of criticality clearance, plutonium recovery
17 February 1969	Alpha-contaminated wound, R&D laboratory
	Fire in R&D laboratory
18 February 1969	Liquor spillage in R&D laboratory
March 1969	Spillage in storage facility
13 March 1969	Plutonium liquor spill in R&D laboratory
25 March 1969	High film dose, reprocessing plant
9 May 1969	High beta & gamma hand dose, reprocessing plant
19 June 1969	Plutonium release, reprocessing plant
9 July 1969	FP liquor spillage, head-end plant
10 October 1969	Abnormal exposure, uranium purification
7 November 1969	Spillage, plutonium finishing
8 February 1970	Plutonium-contaminated wound, plutonium finishing
28 May 1970	Personal alpha contamination, decontamination plant

June 1970	Apparent over-exposure of 4 persons, storage facility
July 1970	Over-exposure of transport driver
24 August 1970	Criticality accident in plutonium recovery
22 September 1970	Release of plutonium in R&D laboratory
7 December 1970	Radiation over-exposure, HA liquor storage
17 December 1970	Release of plutonium in R&D laboratory
December 1970	Radiation over-exposure of HP monitor
6 March 1971	Personal contamination, R&D laboratory
19 March 1971	Fire in plutonium finishing plant
30 June 1971	Plutonium-contamination wound, plutonium finishing plant
16 July 1971	Fission product contamination of fitter, storage facility
18 August 1971	Apparent contravention of criticality certificate, reprocessing plant
28 August 1971	Fume off (butex/nitric acid reaction), storage facility
5 September 1971	Electrical supply failure, plutonium finishing plant
October 1971	Radiation over-exposure of F/M, head-end plant
18 October 1971	Personal beta & gamma contamination, HA liquor storage
25 October 1971	Plutonium exposure, plutonium finishing plant
3 November 1971	Radiation over-exposure of hands, Magnox ponds
29 March 1972	Plutonium-exposure wound, plutonium recovery plant
15 May 1972	Abnormal shoe contamination
May 1972	Abnormal extremity dose, Magnox ponds
December 1972	Iodine-131 discharge, reprocessing plant
11 April 1972	Criticality clearance infringement, plutonium finishing plant
May 1973	High film dose, reprocessing plant
2 July 1973	High beta & gamma head dose, reprocessing plant
12 July 1973	Personal beta & gamma contamination in Magnox ponds
September 1973	High film dose process worker in reprocessing plant

26 September 1973	Blow-back incident in head-end plant; 35 workers contaminated
7 December 1973	Loss of electrical power in R&D laboratory
4 January 1974	Personal beta contamination in reprocessing plant
30 January 1974	Personal contamination in R&D laboratory
January 1974	High film dose, process worker in oxide ponds
9 April 1974	Loss of Windscale suit exhaust filters
10 April 1974	Loss of Windscale suit exhaust filters
22 May 1974	Apparent infringement of criticality clearance, plutonium finishing plant
29 May 1974	Personal plutonium contamination in plutonium finishing plant
27 June 1974	Glove-box incident in R&D laboratory
3 July 1974	Beta- & gamma-contaminated overall
2 September 1974	Personal alpha contamination in R&D labs
26 September 1974	Beta- & gamma-contaminated sock in change room
27 September 1974	Arrival at Windscale of a contaminated CEGB flask from Berkeley
December 1974	High film dose, Magnox ponds
1 February 1975	Personal plutonium contamination, R&D labs
7 February 1975	Personal contamination, plutonium finishing plant
17 February 1975	Irradiated metal in inactive waste tip
15 April 1975	Spillage of plutonium liquor in R&D labs
14 May 1975	Leakage of activity to River Calder Abnormal overall contamination, Magnox ponds
May 1975	Radiation over-exposure of C/H process worker
4 June 1975	Spillage of HA liquor in shielded cell, R&D labs
10 June 1975	Spillage from flask on Leven Fisher, Barrow
July 1975	High film dose, process worker, plutonium finishing plant
	High film dose, C/H plutonium finishing plant

23 September 1975	Personal alpha contamination, active laundry
September 1975	Abnormal film exposure
	Abnormal film exposure, Magnox ponds
	Quarterly whole-body dose, greater than 3 rems, Magnox ponds
6 October 1975	Contaminated pliers on inactive waste incinerator tip
10 October 1975	Contaminated clothing, fitter in oxide ponds
14 October 1975	Contaminated clothing, process worker in Magnox ponds
7 December 1975	Spillage of Magnox pond water
14 December 1975	Crane left in controlled area unmonitored
11 January 1976	Primary separation plant dissolver pressurisation
21 January 1976	Cooling-coil leakage, high-active storage tank
13 February 1976	Abnormal coverall contamination
26 February 1976	Abnormal trouser contamination
1 March 1976	Abnormal coverall contamination
3 March 1976	Abnormal film dose
13 March 1976	Abnormal lab coat contamination
26 March 1976	Abnormal coverall contamination
March 1976	Abnormal film dose
7 April 1976	Abnormal coverall contamination
7 May 1976	Abnormal coverall contamination
14 May 1976	Abnormal coverall contamination
22 May 1976	Spillage in 1st floor corridor in uranium-purification plant
4 June 1976	Spillage in ground-floor corridor in uranium-purification plant
14 June 1976	Abnormal lab coat contamination
	Spillage in uranium-purification plant drain tank
17 July 1976	Spillage in uranium-purification plant lift well
20 July 1976	Personal contamination of laundry worker
July 1976	Spillage, sample bulge, primary separation plant
10 August 1976	Spillage, scrubber circuit, primary separation plant

17 August 1976	Personal alpha contamination, R&D laboratory
2 September 1976	Abnormal film dose
	Personal contamination, plutonium recovery plant
14 September 1976	Radiation over-exposure, uranium-purification plant
10 October 1976	Seepage from silo containing high-activity waste
14 October 1976	Contamination of basic trousers worn by process chargehand
24 October 1976	Release of airborne activity in primary separation plant
1 November 1976	Apparent criticality clearance contravention in Magnox ponds
2 November 1976	Personal contamination event requiring therapeutic intervention
3 December 1976	Personal contamination: person involved had to return home with skin contamination in excess of DWL
9 December 1976	Skin exposure in excess of statutory quarterly limit
14 December 1976	Defect in cladding of fuel element in reactor in containment building
15 December 1976	Tritium discovered on the beach near Windscale
22 December 1976	Mononitrotoluene emissions at Drigg site
12 January 1977	Three process workers externally contaminated with plutonium
15 January 1977	Process worker exposed to higher than normal air concentration of plutonium
20 January 1977	Process worker found to have plutonium contamination in finger wound
27 March 1977	500–600 sq. yards of grass contaminated with ruthenium-106
26 April 1977	Three workers contaminated with plutonium
28 April 1977	Laboratory worker heavily contaminated with plutonium due to pressure rise in a chemical reaction in laboratory
12 May 1977	Traces of xenon-133 gas found in AGR; building evacuated
22 May 1977	BNFL inactive waste tip found to be contaminated

14 June 1977	Worker received three times permitted annual skin dose
22 June 1977	Two workers contaminated with plutonium
6 July 1977	Leak of radioactivity from a sample point in the primary separation plant
9 July 1977	Spillage of plutonium-contaminated liquor in finishing plant
13 July 1977	Crane driver contaminated with radioactivity
21 July 1977	Worker in Magnox de-canning plant received in excess of permitted annual skin dose
28 August 1977	Process shift manager received in excess of permitted quarterly skin dose
25 September 1977	Worker received three times permitted annual skin dose
2 October 1977	Pond process worker exposed to radioactivity in excess of permitted annual skin dose
4 November 1977	Pond process worker contaminated
12 November 1977	Process worker in Magnox de-canning plant received in excess of permitted quarterly skin dose
18 November 1977	Spillage of radioactive liquor in highly active liquor storage plant
11 December 1977	Two process workers contaminated with plutonium
13 December 1977	Process worker in plutonium finishing plant exposed to airborne plutonium
15 December 1977	Two maintenance workers received in excess of permitted whole-body dose
3 March 1978	Fitter in Magnox de-canning plant received in excess of permitted quarterly skin dose
30 March 1978	Radioactivity detected in soil samples taken beside low-active liquid waste tank
25 April 1978	H/P monitor's hair contaminated after contact with Magnox fuel flask
12 May 1978	Fitter in primary separation plant received five to six times permitted annual skin dose
13 May 1978	Process worker found to have plutonium contamination in hand wound

3/4 June 1978	Contaminated wood from Calder Hall burnt on works tip
5 June 1978	Rigger contaminated in Magnox fuel storage plant
18 June 1978	In a plant handling mixed plutonium/uranium oxides, mass limits exceeded due to an *under-estimate* of the residual material left in plant from a previous operation
20 June 1978	Fitter in medium-active evaporation plant contaminated
14/17 July 1978	Radioactive contamination found on grass outside the controlled area of the Windscale site
25 July 1978	Process worker in Magnox storage plant found to have exceeded permitted quarterly skin dose
29 July 1978	300 litres of low-active effluent overflowed into roadway adjacent to primary separation plant
31 August 1978	Worker in plutonium plant contaminated Process foreman in Magnox storage plant contaminated
8 September 1978	Rail wagon carrying empty irradiated oxide fuel flask derailed on Windscale rail link
9 October 1978	Process worker found to have plutonium contamination in thumb wound
14 October 1978	H/P monitor found to have received 1½ times permitted annual skin dose
25 October 1978	Fitter in plutonium-purification plant contaminated
31 October 1978	Abnormally high concentration of hydrogen gas detected rising from a silo in which Magnox cladding removed from irradiated fuel elements is stored
7 December 1978	During routine washout operation on a highly active evaporator, contaminated liquid leaked from a valve
18 December 1978	Release of radioactivity into air from workshops in primary separation plant
20 January 1979	H/P monitor received 1½ times permitted annual dose

31 January 1979	Spillage in Magnox fuel storage plant
4 February 1979	Fire in old separation plant
16 February 1979	Contamination on grass inside perimeter fence
6 March 1979	Process worker received twice annual permitted skin dose
12 April 1979	'Administrative oversight' led to BNFL reporting that, in December 1978, shift manager in Magnox de-canning plant exceeded annual permitted whole-body dose
5 May 1979	Worker received in excess of annual permitted extremity dose
23 May 1979	Worker contaminated with plutonium in finishing plant
11 July 1979	Leak from low-level pipe
12 July 1979	Worker found to have plutonium-contaminated wound
16 July 1979	Fire in Magnox de-canning plant
24 July 1979	Criticality clearance exceeded
31 July 1979	Worker in plutonium-purification plant found to have contaminated wound
3 August 1979	Criticality clearance exceeded Laboratory worker found to have contaminated wound
29 August 1979	Worker contaminated in reprocessing plant
5 September 1979	Worker contaminated in plutonium-purification plant
11 September 1979	Release of airborne plutonium from effluent treatment plant
5 October 1979	Worker contaminated in effluent treatment plant
9 November 1979	Over-exposure in R&D laboratory
18 November 1979	Worker contaminated in Magnox plant
17 December 1979	Worker contaminated with plutonium in effluent treatment plant
9 January 1980	Worker contaminated in plutonium recovery plant
12 January 1980	Over-exposure of radiographer
30 January 1980	Radioactivity found in bore holes in fuel storage pond Worker contaminated in chemical separation plant

14 February 1980	Worker contaminated in plutonium recovery plant
23 February 1980	Worker contaminated in chemical separation plant
6 May 1980	Over-exposure in reprocessing plant
19 August 1980	Worker contaminated in plutonium plant
30 August 1980	Over-exposure in Magnox plant
15 September 1980	Worker contaminated in plutonium recovery plant
16 September 1980	Worker contaminated in plutonium recovery plant
4 November 1980	Worker contaminated in plutonium plant
15 December 1980	Worker contaminated in plutonium plant
30 December 1980	Over-exposure in plutonium finishing plant
26 March 1981	Worker contaminated in plutonium plant
27 March 1981	Worker found to have plutonium-contaminated wound in plutonium recovery plant
16 April 1981	Over-exposure in Magnox plant
11 June 1981	Over-exposure in separation plant
18 June 1981	Over-exposure in Magnox plant
6 July 1981	Over-exposure in Magnox plant, three times the annual limit
17 September 1981	Worker found to have plutonium-contaminated wound in plutonium fabrication plant
21 September 1981	Worker contaminated with plutonium in laboratory
22 September 1981	Worker contaminated with plutonium in laboratory
4–23 October 1981	**Release of radioactive iodine into the atmosphere**
15 November 1981	Worker found to have plutonium-contaminated wound in plutonium recovery plant
19 November 1981	Worker contaminated in plutonium plant
30 December 1981	Over-exposure in chemical separation plant
19 March 1982	Fire at Drigg dump
	Over-exposure at Magnox plant

At this time, the criteria for reporting accidents and incidents were changed by the government, which meant that BNFL are no longer obliged to report every incident

303

1 November 1983	Over-exposure at Magnox plant
11 November 1983	Release of approximately 4500 curies of radioactive effluent into Irish Sea
27 June 1984	Over-exposure of process worker
27 January 1986	Release of 440 kilograms of uranium nitrate into Irish Sea
5 February 1986	15 workers contaminated with plutonium nitrate; one received total annual dose
18 February 1986	Leak of 250 gallons of radioactive waste from Pond 5; two workers contaminated

Appendix 2

On 12 March 1986 the House of Commons Select Committee on the Environment published its *First Report on Radioactive Waste*. The following is a very brief summary of its most important findings. The writing of this book had been mainly completed before the Report was published.

The report's two most startling conclusions were (1), that reprocessing nuclear waste at Sellafield does not even make economic sense; and (2) that if it is not too late, the new THORP reprocessing plant at Sellafield should be abandoned as there is little point in taking in nuclear waste from other countries when we cannot, apparently, cope with our own.

The Report first summarised the different types of waste and where they came from, and went on to say that Committee members had visited waste-disposal sites in the USA, Sweden, France, West Germany and Canada, and that we lagged well behind all of them in almost every respect.

The Committee paid special attention to Britain's only large land burial site for low-level wastes – the giant pit at Drigg near Sellafield, which they found wanting. While being assured it was safe as they looked down at the apparently random heaps of drums, boxes, etc., they were confidently told by Dr Lewis Roberts, chairman of NIREX, that the trenches were open so that water could percolate through them, 'then run out at the bottom and the monitoring is of what contamination, if any, it has picked up on the way. The water flow is towards a large volume of water . . . where the dilution [is] immediately enormous.'

The Committee found this profoundly unsatisfactory. At a low-level waste disposal site in France, at Centre de la Manche near Cherbourg, all waste was carefully categorised in labelled containers in a fully engineered facility. The trenches, says the report,

> are concrete and clay-lined, covered and segregated by more concrete and eventually capped with concrete and clay. Special channels, which we walked along, run underneath all the trenches with special collection and monitoring points to check the very

small amounts of run-off or drainage water which might permeate the covering layers.

At Drigg, individual packages of nuclear waste from various sources, which are not within the definition of low-level waste (LLW), can be disposed of, and allowed amount of radioactivity is measured on a daily basis and not on the activity of individual packages or unit volumes. Given the large volumes of scarcely contaminated materials which are not even considered waste, 'the overall daily limit could well admit packages well above the LLW limit.' This was acknowledged by Dr Feates.

The NRPB told the Commons Committee that 'assessments show that the risks to people from the two sites are very low.' However, this did not reassure the Committee, owing to what members described as 'the haphazard approach of what goes into Drigg'. Committee members were surprised that there was no systematic on-site check of what goes into the trenches and that once a nuclear facility has decided something is suitable for the dump, 'then the disposal operator accepts it as such, without check.' It appeared that separating it was all too much trouble.

In France, however, the drums at the Centre de la Manche store were all properly labelled in terms of alpha and beta/gamma content. At the now abandoned West Valley facility in the United States, they were shown equipment which could produce a precise isotope analysis of every drum of waste.

The unsatisfactory nature of waste disposal at Drigg meant that there were no proper checks on sources or on the daily amount of radioactivity, and

the current practice had the double disadvantage of adding unnecessarily to the volume of waste and of letting through dangerous long-lived and toxic radio-nuclides. If the monitoring of the stream did one day reveal too high a level of radioactivity in the water issuing from Drigg it is difficult to know what BNFL would do about it. With nothing labelled, nothing recorded, pinpointing the offending waste would be virtually impossible.

The Committee recommended that, if Drigg continued to be used, only truly short-lived waste should be disposed of there and some radio-nuclides should be prohibited. All wastes should be properly sorted before arrival and then compacted or incinerated where they lend themselves to be so treated. All waste should be put into appropriately labelled containers and monitored on arrival to ensure they contain only what the new authorisation allows.

However, the Committee said, 'We conclude that Drigg is not an acceptable model for any future disposal site.'

The Committee then examined methods used elsewhere for the storage of waste including deep land facilities in such places as deep salt mines (as in West Germany), and research into deep ocean emplacement and under-seabed tunnels and caverns.

Finally, it concluded:

The poor state of research in the UK means that it is impossible at this stage for us to recommend any disposal option with total confidence. However, we make two specific recommendations here:

(1) Near-surface disposal facilities are only acceptable for short-lived, low-level wastes, and must be fully engineered on a complete containment basis.

(2) Considerably greater emphasis must be given in research, development and policy to seabed options, especially to the use of the tunnels under the seabed and from land.

Next, the Committee turned its attention to radioactive discharges, and to Sellafield.

The UK discharges more radioactivity into the sea than any other nation. As the Ministry of Agriculture confirmed to us, Sellafield is the largest recorded source of radioactive discharge in the world. The anxiety and controversy which this arouses in the UK is well known. It also creates anxiety in other nations. We found, for example, that the Swedes could identify radioactive traces in fish off their coast being largely attributable to Sellafield, greater even than contamination from adjacent Swedish nuclear power stations. Similar experiences were reported to us by the Isle of Man government. That the UK, with a comparatively small nuclear industry, should be so dramatically out of step is a cause for concern.

The Committee then looked into the different processes at Sellafield, leading them next to 'pathways to man'. High concentrations of radioactivity had been found in edible fish and shellfish in the vicinity of Sellafield, the dominant radio-nuclides being caesium-137 and ruthenium-106.

The Sellafield method of piping its effluent into the sea to dilute and disperse it was shown to work 'only very imperfectly'. Radio-nuclides returned to the shore and entered the food chain in a variety of ways. Substances were concentrated in plants eaten by sheep and cattle and built up in the animals' kidneys. In fact, researchers are now finding very much higher than average concentrations in the organs of animals in the Sellafield region. In one case they found 'remarkably high concentrations in the liver and kidney of a grazing animal and they were getting very near to the acceptable limits of ingestion.'

The Committee noted that there is still no proof that low-level radiation emissions from nuclear plants are a hazard to health but 'we also note that, throughout its history, the nuclear industry's discharges have been continually revised downwards as more knowledge about health effects becomes available . . .'

The Committee found the management of the nuclear industry and Sellafield in particular to be remote, self-confident, yet unaccountable. Con Allday of BNFL told the Committee that 'nuclear power used to be a glamour industry and it no longer is.' However, the Committee were not impressed:

> Sellafield is our primary interest here. Not only is it not glamorous, it has become a byword for the dirty end of the industry in the nuclear world. The international colleagues of Sellafield's scientists and engineers appeared to be embarrassed. They did not want to criticise it too openly, but very soon in conversation we realised that it was bad publicity for the industry.

Sellafield suffered, in part, from being the first in the civil reprocessing business. The impression it conveys, says the Committee, 'is one of error and misjudgement. Against this background, it must be difficult for the industry to be believed by the public.' Nor is it as accountable as it should be. The duty to justify the need for reprocessing has been neglected by governments because it has fallen into a gap between two departments.

Finally, the committee concluded that reprocessing spent fuel from Britain's Magnox power stations was simply not economically viable: 'Other countries have concluded that commercial gains do not outweigh the risks.' Insufficient work has been done on alternative ways of dry-storing Magnox fuel rods. In addition, there were many contradictions in the evidence given to the Committee. For example, they were told that if a ship carrying nuclear waste in a special flask had an accident 'the flask would remain intact for many hundreds of years at the bottom of the sea.' The Committee found this 'slightly puzzling. We have been constantly told that long-term storage and disposal of spent Magnox fuel is not feasible.'

Most important of all, uranium is now so cheap that it would be far more economical for Britain to buy it in from abroad for

its nuclear needs than to reprocess it from spent Magnox fuels
rods.

The Committee then turned its attention to the thermal oxide
reprocessing plant (THORP) under construction at Sellafield and
designed to take in the world's nuclear waste for reprocessing. It
was obvious from their conclusions that, ideally, the MPs would like
THORP to be abandoned. The reason for continuing with it
appears to be financial, and the government is portrayed as 'trapped
by decisions taken by their predecessors'. The Committee felt that
the whole operation should be reassessed and figures should be
published to show what would need to be paid in penalty clauses
if THORP were to be abandoned; and there should also be an
investigation into the problems of unemployment that might be
created.

Officials of the nuclear industry stressed to the Committee that
THORP would be a great moneyspinner, but the Committee
pointed out that, while two-thirds of the cost of reprocessing at
THORP will be paid by foreign customers, one-third

is paid for by the home generating boards and, ultimately, by the
domestic and industrial electricity consumers. Thus benefits of
foreign earnings are somewhat diminished by the disbenefits of
UK electricity price increases quite apart from all the waste
management problems which are created.

On top of this, the Committee did not think, from the evidence they
had received, that the current commercial advantages that reprocessing holds for BNFL are assured. In part this is because of a price
increase of 30 per cent that has been levied on overseas customers
nearing the end of their contracts, some of whom are now thinking
very hard indeed about whether to renew them.

The Committee investigated the Nuclear Industry Radioactive
Waste Executive (NIREX), noting that while they had been meeting NIREX had become a limited company and the government had
acquired a 'special share' in the new company and a veto over its
activities if necessary. The Committee found NIREX secretive, to
say the least, and stated that it must be made more accountable and
thereafter be *seen* to be accountable.

The Committee looked briefly at methods of transporting waste,
preferring rail to all others, and concluded that there was no case
whatsoever for transporting it by air – which is what is proposed for
the Dounreay reprocessing plant.

As to contact with the public the Committee felt that the industry
should review its whole approach and be more open and forthright.

The public should be involved in decision-taking at local and national level. It should embrace the concept of the 'Rolls-Royce' (i.e. the best) solutions to convince the public in actions as well as words and should adopt a presumption that all technical papers should be made available to the public, apart from those concerned with defence.

The Department of the Environment should give serious consideration to compensating those who live near nuclear dumps; there should be strong and widely representative local liaison committees for all future waste-disposal sites with power to influence decisions. The Committee found that only Britain shrouded its nuclear industry in such secrecy. In the USA, facilities were open to the public for inspection; managers admitted the 'terrible mess' one site at West Valley had been at one time; they frankly discussed the problems connected with storing waste, saying that it was still

> a big headache. We don't know yet. But we're learning a great deal from the other stages and we're testing out our ideas all the time. We've got plenty of time and we just want to make sure we get it right in the end.

The Committee found this reassuring and candid presentation amazing. The difference between this approach and that of BNFL was remarkable. The USA knew it had a problem which needed to be dealt with and they were going to make it a public concern, not by rushing something through and hiding it away in secrecy but 'by deliberately opening up the operation as a demonstration project and sparing no expense'. Work in Sweden was also 'marked by a similar openness and a realisation that the public must be taken along, not fought against.'

Notes

Chapter 1: The Alchemists
p. 18 'Unlike pressurised-water reactors, . . .' Reproduced from *The PWR Decision. How Not to Buy a Nuclear Reactor*, London, Friends of the Earth, 1983

Chapter 2: 'The Waste Remains and Kills . . .'
p. 39: Incidents at Hanford Reservation and West Valley: information in this section has been taken from: Walter C. Patterson, *Nuclear Power*, London, Penguin, 1st ed. 1976, 2nd ed. 1983; Rosalie Bertell, *No Immediate Danger*, London, Women's Press, 1985; briefing papers from the Union of Concerned Scientists.
p. 43: Accident at Chelyabinsk: Alan Roberts and Zhores Medvedev, *Hazards of Nuclear Power*, London, Spokesman Books, 1977; Zhores Medvedev, 'Two Decades of Dissidence', *New Scientist*, 4 November 1976.
p. 49: Living with death: account by Sylvia Collier, *Observer*, 10 March 1985; information from Glen Alcalay, consultant to US National Committee for Radiation Victims, and from the Union of Concerned Scientists.

Chapter 3: The Impossible Accident
p. 69: The Idaho Falls accident: Rosalie Bertell, *No Immediate Danger*, London, Women's Press, 1985; Walter C. Patterson, *Nuclear Power*, London, Penguin, 2nd ed. 1983; Robert D. Pollard (ed.), *The Nugget File*, Cambridge, Mass., Union of Concerned Scientists, 1979.
p. 71: The Detroit accident: Patterson, *op. cit.*; Bertell, *op. cit.*
p. 76: 'It was later revealed': Daniel F. Ford, *Thirty Minutes to Meltdown*, New York, Viking Press, 1982.
p. 77: 'Unit 1 was supposed': *Ibid.*
p. 78: 'On 19 October 1977': Presidential Commission findings, November 1979.
p. 79: 'On 12 May 1978': *Ibid.*
p. 80: 'Given what we have found out': *New Scientist*, 8 November 1979.
p. 84: 'There have been charges': Presidential Commission, *op. cit.*
p. 85: 'being unable to provide': *Ibid.*
——: 'We heard the word': *Ibid.*
p. 86: 'bathing in a radiation level': *New Scientist*, 19 April 1979.
——: 'the team sent to inspect': *Guardian*, 7 March 1980.
p. 87: 'hampered by the fact': *Ibid.*
p. 88: 'The first television inspection': *Guardian*, 23 July 1982.
——: 'On 14 April 1983': *Guardian*, 15 April 1983.

Chapter 4: Britain Without a Nugget File

p. 97: 'Wylfa on Anglesey': Walter G. Patterson, *Nuclear Power*, London, Penguin, 2nd ed. 1983.

——: 'Bradwell's two Magnox reactors': *Guardian*, 8 January 1981.

——: 'the two reactors at Dungeness A': *Ibid*.

p. 98: 'When one of the reactors': *Guardian*, 24 February 1984.

——: 'Dungeness A had other problems': Patterson, *op. cit*.

p. 99: 'In November 1979, a report': report published in *New Statesman*, 7 December 1979.

p. 101: Dungeness: *Ibid*.; Patterson, *op. cit*.; *Daily Telegraph*, 1982.

p. 103: 'described by an expert': John Large of Large Associates to author; repeated in *Guardian*, 30 November 1985.

——: 'Arthur Hawkins': Patterson, *op. cit*.

——: 'An ominous rattling noise': *Ibid*.

p. 104: 'In June 1977': *Ibid*.

——: 'On 25 October 1985': press information given to author and to Television South West, 29 October 1985.

p. 105: 'Following questions in the House of Commons': written answer to Parliamentary question.

——: 'the most serious nuclear accident': this story was researched by the author at the time for various publications, including *New Statesman*, *Labour Weekly* and *Western Morning News*.

p. 108: Hunterston: Patterson, *op. cit*.; Peter Bunyard, *Nuclear Britain*, London, New English Library, 1981.

p. 109: Wylfa: *Guardian* and *Daily Telegraph*, both 17 June 1985.

p. 110: Trawsfynydd: documents shown to author.

p. 112: Sizewell: *Daily Telegraph*, 17 January 1986; statement to author.

——: 'its engineers had controlled': information shown to author.

p. 115: 'The inquest finally took place': *Scotsman*, 17 February 1984.

p. 120: 'a substantial increase': *Guardian* and other newspapers, 3 February 1986; information shown to author.

Chapter 5: Windscale: Nuclear Dustbin to the World

p. 125: 'Dunster told those attending': Peter Pringle and James Spigelman, *Nuclear Barons*, London, Sphere, 1983.

p. 126: '194 incidents': Peter Bunyard, *Nuclear Britain*, London, New English Library, 1981.

——: 'the Health and Safety Executive published a major report': Health and Safety Executive, *Windscale: The Management of Safety*, London, HMSO, February 1981.

p. 132: 'The accident of 8 October 1957': Walter C. Patterson, *Nuclear Power*, London, Penguin, 2nd ed. 1983; *New Scientist*, 14 October and 18 November 1982.

p. 136: 'The accident at the head-end plant': Patterson, *op. cit*.; *Guardian*, 13 February 1975.

p. 138: 'Silo leaks': Health and Safety Executive, *op. cit*.

p. 139: Spillage of 29 July 1978: Bunyard, *op. cit*.

Notes

——: Fire of 4 February 1979: Health and Safety Executive, *op. cit*.

p. 140: The B701 leak: *Ibid*.

p. 126: 'a major report': *Ibid*.

p. 128: 'Traces of caesium-137': *The Impact of Nuclear Waste Disposal on the Marine Environment*, PERG Report RR-8, March 1982.

——: 'In a paper': Peter Taylor, *The Control of Radioactive Discharges from Nuclear Fuel Reprocessing Plants: The Best Available Technology*, paper prepared for the Paris Commission on behalf of Greenpeace, Dublin, March 1984.

p. 129: The contamination of the Cumbrian beaches: reports from Greenpeace and from journals and newspapers, including: *New Scientist*, 22 and 29 December 1983; *Observer*, *Sunday Telegraph* and *Sunday Times*, all 11 December 1983; *Guardian*, 8 December 1983. Also, National Radiological Protection Board, *An Analysis and Radiological Assessment of Survey Results and Samples from the Beaches Around Sellafield*, RM101, December 1983, and *A Further Assessment of Survey Results from the Beaches Around Sellafield*, RM102, February 1984.

p. 129: 'Confirmation of the Drigg hotspot': *Guardian*, 14 November 1983; Judith Cook, *The Price of Freedom*, London, New English Library, 1985.

——: 'John Taylor': *New Statesman*, 22 July 1983.

p. 131: 'after a very low-key trial': information from Greenpeace.

p. 141: Fire in the de-canning plant: *Ibid*.

——: Spill of 11 September 1979: *Ibid*.

p. 146: 'The first statement': BNFL replies to inquiries published in the media, 24 January 1986.

p. 148: 'The first statement from BNFL': *London Standard*, 5 February 1986; *Guardian* and *Daily Telegraph*, 6 February 1986; response to author, 6 February 1986.

——: 'Jim Coote': *Guardian*, 7 February 1986.

p. 150: 'the disappearance': *Mail on Sunday*, 2 February 1986; *Guardian* 3 February 1986; conversation with Greenpeace, 3 February 1986.

p. 151: 'confidential report leak': *Guardian*, 11 February 1986.

Chapter 6: More Problems

p. 156: 'It is clear': Peter Bunyard, *Nuclear Britain*, London, New English Library, 1981.

——:'During one four-week period': *Ibid*.

p. 157: 'a report by an American engineer': *Daily Telegraph*, 22 July 1982.

p. 159: 'The French unions revealed': Bunyard, *op. cit*.

p. 160: 'The group took samples': information from Miwako Ogilo, chairperson of Fukui Citizens Council, in article by Anye Finkle in British Society for Social Responsibility in Science (eds), *Science for People*, vol. 40/41, autumn, 1978; article by Chikja No Koe, June 1981, a précis of which appeared in *The Ecologist*.

p. 161: 'The Mihama No. 1 site': *Ibid*.

p. 163: 'the nuclear-powered cargo ship *Mutsu*': Walter C. Patterson, *Nuclear Power*, London, Penguin, 2nd ed. 1983.

p. 164: 'the first major reactor accident': Rosalie Bertell, *No Immediate*

Danger, London, Women's Press, 1985; Patterson, *op. cit.*; and a variety of other sources.

Chapter 7: The Broad Street Pump

p. 168: 'In 1979, Dr Richard Bates': *Environmental Health Perspectives*.

p. 170: 'Harry Daghlian': Peter Goodchild, *'Shatterer of Worlds': J. Robert Oppenheimer*, London, BBC Publications, 1980.

p. 171: 'The circumstances clearly': *The Times*, 6 August 1982.

——: 'In January 1984': Carl J. Johnson, 'Cancer incidence in an area of radioactive fallout downwind from the Nevada test site', *Journal of the American Medical Association*, 25 January 1984.

——: 'there was a rapid increase': Rosalie Bertell, *No Immediate Danger*, London, Women's Press, 1985; author's discussions with Glen Alcalay, consultant to US National Committee for Radiation Victims.

p. 173: 'Ted Lombard': Bertell, *op. cit.*

p. 174: 'Joe Harding': Nicholas Hildyard, *Cover Up*, London, New English Library, 1981.

——: 'Dr Thomas Mancuso': Bertell, *op. cit.*; Peter Bunyard, *Nuclear Britain*, London, New English Library, 1981; briefing papers from Union of Concerned Scientists.

p. 178: 'Dr Gerald Drake': Bertell, *op. cit.*

——: 'she analysed death rates': *Ibid*.

p. 182: 'discharges from Windscale': *Conference Proceedings*, vol. 18, pp. 390–9.

p. 183: 'deliberate discharge': *Daily Telegraph*, 8 March 1985.

——: 'researchers working': *Ibid*.

——: 'The first report': National Radiological Protection Board, *An Assessment of the Radiological Impact of the Windscale Reactor Fire, October 1957*, NRPB R135, November 1982.

——: 'The re-assessment': addendum to NRPB R135, September 1983.

——: 'Professor Joseph Rotblat': *Guardian*, 21 September 1983.

p. 184: 'some 30 more unfortunate souls': Peter Taylor, *An Investigation into the Incidence of Cancer in the Areas Affected by Discharges from the Nuclear Fuel Reprocessing Plant at Windscale, Cumbria*, Political Ecology Research Group, February 1983.

p. 187: 'revealed a different picture': James Cutler, 'Checking the figures', *New Statesman*, 18 January 1985.

——: 'The Black Report also omitted': *Ibid*.

——: 'All the statistics used by Black': *Ibid*.

p. 188: 'Four of the wards': *Ibid*.

——: 'assumed that the blood cells': James Cutler, 'Close to the bone', *New Statesman*, 1 February 1985.

p. 190: 'doctors working on the west coast of Scotland': *Observer*, 13 November 1983.

p. 195: 'Dr Michael Busy': *Guardian*, 7 October 1982.

p. 197: 'a lengthy paper appeared': *British Medical Journal*, 16 August 1985.

p. 198: 'The point was made': 'Why Shouldn't We Be Scared When They Won't Tell Us The Truth?' Anthony Tucker, *Guardian*, 1 March 1986.

Chapter 8: The Plane Crash on the Football Ground

p. 203: 'John Dunster': *World in Action*, Granada Television, broadcast 4 August 1980.

p. 204: 'first part of an interview': *Ibid.*

p. 205: 'they had assigned': Peter Pringle and James Spigelman, *Nuclear Barons*, London, Sphere, 1983.

——: 'unusually frank and stringent criticism': US Nuclear Regulatory Commission: memo from V. Gossik, Executive Director, 18 January 1979; and press statement, 19 July 1979, Ref. 79/19.

p. 209: 'the results of which and the data behind them': Francis Nectoux and William Cannell, *Accidents Will Happen*, London, Earth Resources Research/Friends of the Earth, 1984.

p. 211: 'US Nuclear Regulatory Commission said': NRC press statement, *op. cit.*

p. 213: 'one from the NRPB': *Advice for General Practitioners in the Event of a Nuclear Emergency*, DHSS and NRPB Annex, B., HC(85) 24, Supplement to HC(77) 1, July 1985.

——: 'the second from the DHSS': *Health Service Arrangements for Dealing with Major Accidents*, DHSS Circular HC(85) 24, Supplement to HC(77) 1, July 1985.

Chapter 10: Too Dear at Any Price

p. 231: 'Back in 1970': Peter Bunyard, *Nuclear Britain*, London, New English Library, 1981.

——: 'According to Peter Bunyard': *Ibid.*

——: 'The Flowers Report': Royal Commission on Environmental Pollution (chaired by Sir Brian Flowers), *Nuclear Power and the Environment* [The Flowers Report], London HMSO, 1976.

p. 234: 'In a speech': Hilary Bacon and John Valentine, *Power Corrupts*, London, Pluto Press, 1981.

p. 235: Didier Anger: Bunyard, *op. cit.*

p. 236: Dr Gordon Macleod: *Ibid.*

p. 237: Karen Silkwood: Richard Rashke, *The Killing of Karen Silkwood*, London, Sphere, 1983; 'Did the Nuclear Industry Kill This Girl?', *The Ecologist*, November 1979.

p. 242: Hilda Murrell: Judith Cook, *Who Killed Hilda Murrell?*, London, New English Library, 1985.

p. 247: *Rainbow Warrior*: Information from Greenpeace, and reports in the *Guardian*, *Daily Telegraph*, etc., 11 July 1985 and subsequent days in July, plus 16, 17, 18 August and 19, 20, 21, 23, 24 September 1985.

Chapter 11: The End of an Era

p. 252: 'an accident in Spain': Reuters tapes.

p. 253: 'Dr Eduardo Rodriguez Farre': *Ibid.*

Selected Bibliography

Nuclear energy

There are a considerable number of books available on nuclear energy (which is a good thing). The following are particularly useful.

BACON, HILARY and VALENTINE, JOHN, *Power Corrupts*, London, Pluto Press, 1981.

BERTELL, ROSALIE, *No Immediate Danger: Prognosis for a Radioactive Earth*, London, Women's Press, 1985.

BUNYARD, PETER, *Nuclear Britain*, London, New English Library, 1981.

CANNELL, WILLIAM and CHUDLEIGH, RENÉE, *How Not to Buy a Nuclear Reactor*, London, Friends of the Earth, 1983.

COYNE, P. and GEORGE, M., *The Politics of Nuclear Power*, London, Pluto Press, 1978.

DURIE, S. and EDWARDS, R., *Fuelling the Nuclear Arms Race*, London, Pluto Press, 1982.

FORD, DANIEL F., *Three-Mile Island: 30 Minutes to Meltdown*, New York, Viking Press, 1982.

INCE, MARTIN, *Sizewell: What Happened at the Inquiry*, London, Pluto Press, 1984.

OPENSHAW, STANLEY, *Nuclear Power – Siting and Safety*, London, Routledge, Kegan Paul, 1986.

PATTERSON, WALTER C., *Nuclear Power*, London, Penguin, 1st ed. 1976, 2nd ed. 1983.

——, *The Plutonium Business*, London, Paladin, 1984.

PRINGLE, PETER and SPIGELMAN, JAMES, *Nuclear Barons*, London, Sphere, 1983.

ROBERTS, ALAN and MEDVEDEV, ZHORES, *Hazards of Nuclear Power*, London, Spokesman Books, 1977.

SWEET, COLIN, *The Price of Nuclear Power*, London, Heinemann, 1983.

Nuclear morality

GOODCHILD, PETER, *'Shatterer of Worlds': J. Robert Oppenheimer*, London, BBC Publications, 1980.

JUNGK, DR ROBERT, *Brighter than a Thousand Suns*, London, Gollancz, 1959.

Associated topics

COOK, JUDITH, *Who Killed Hilda Murrell?*, London, New English Library, 1985.

HILDYARD, NICHOLAS, *Cover Up*, London, New English Library, 1981.

RASHKE, RICHARD, *The Killing of Karen Silkwood*, London, Sphere, 1983.

Reports and papers

Advice for General Practitioners in the Event of a Nuclear Emergency, DHSS and NRPB Annex B., HC(85) 24, Supplement to HC(77) 1, July 1985.

BRITISH SOCIETY FOR SOCIAL RESPONSIBILITY IN SCIENCE (eds), *Science for People*, vol. 40/41, autumn 1978.

CHUDLEIGH, RENÉE and CANNELL, WILLIAM, *The Gravedigger's Dilemma*, London, Friends of the Earth, 1984.

COMMITTEE FOR THE STUDY OF THE ECONOMICS OF NUCLEAR ELECTRICITY (chaired by Sir Kelvin Spencer), 'The True Cost of Nuclear Energy', *Ecologist*, 1981.

FRASER, PATRICIA *et al.*, 'Collection and validation data in the United Kingdom Atomic Energy Authority Mortality Study', *British Medical Journal*, 17 August 1985.

HEALTH AND SAFETY EXECUTIVE, *The Contamination of the Beach Incident at British Nuclear Fuels at Sellafield*, London, HMSO, 1983.

——, *Windscale: The Management of Safety*, London, HMSO, February 1981.

Health Service Arrangements for Dealing with Major Accidents, DHSS Circular HC(85) 24, Supplement to HC(77) 1, July 1985.

HOUSE OF COMMONS SELECT COMMITTEE ON THE ENVIRONMENT, *First Report on Radioactive Waste, 1985–1986*, London, HMSO, 1986.

The Impact of Nuclear Waste Disposal on the Marine Environment, PERG Report RR-8, March 1982.

JOHNSON, DR CARL J., 'Cancer incidence in an area of radioactive fallout downwind from the Nevada test site', *Journal of the American Medical Association*, 25 January 1984.

KENDALL, HENRY (ed.), *The Risks of Nuclear Power Reactors: A Review of the NRC Reactor Safety Study WASH-1400* [The

Rasmussen Report], Cambridge, Mass., Union of Concerned Scientists, 1977.

NATIONAL RADIOLOGICAL PROTECTION BOARD, *An Analysis and Radiological Assessment of Survey Results and Samples from the Beaches Around Sellafield*, RM101, December 1983.

——, *An Assessment of the Radiological Impact of the Windscale Reactor Fire, October 1957*, NRPB R135, November 1982.

——, *An Assessment of the Radiological Protection Aspects of Shallow Land Burial of Radioactive Waste*, HMSO and NRPB, 1984.

——, *A Further Assessment of Survey Results from the Beaches Around Sellafield*, RM102, February 1984.

——, *Natural Radiation and Radioactive Waste Disposal*, 1/84.

——, *Radio-nuclides in House Dust*, R181, April 1985.

——, *Small Doses of Radiation to Members of the Public*, R175, April 1985.

NECTOUX, FRANCIS and CANNELL, WILLIAM, *Accidents Will Happen: An Inquiry into the Social and Economic Consequences of a Nuclear Accident at Sizewell B*, London, Earth Resources Research/Friends of the Earth, 1984.

NUCLEAR REGULATORY COMMISSION, *Nuclear Regulatory Commission Policy Statement on the Reactor Safety Study and Review by the Lewis Panel*, Washington D.C., NRC, January 1979.

POLLARD, ROBERT D. (ed.), *The Nugget File*, Cambridge, Mass., Union of Concerned Scientists, 1979.

ROYAL COMMISSION ON ENVIRONMENTAL POLLUTION (chaired by Sir Brian Flowers), *Nuclear Power and the Environment* [The Flowers Report], London, HMSO, 1976.

SHEEHAN, DR PATRICIA M. and HILLARY, DR IRENE B., 'An unusual cluster of babies born with Down's syndrome to former pupils of an Irish boarding school', *British Medical Journal*, 12 November 1983.

TAYLOR, PETER, *The Control of Radioactive Discharges from Nuclear Fuel Reprocessing Plants: The Best Available Technology*, paper prepared for the Paris Commission on behalf of Greenpeace, Dublin, March 1984.

UNION OF CONCERNED SCIENTISTS, *Disposal of Radioactive Waste* (briefing paper), Cambridge, Mass., 1984.

——, *Energy Strategies*, Cambridge, Mass., November 1983.

——, *Nuclear Power Economics* (briefing paper), Cambridge, Mass., 1983.

Waste Not? Want Not?, London, Channel 4 Television, 5 December 1985.

The Windscale File, London, Greenpeace, 1983.

Index

Brezhnev, Leonid, 263
British Electricity Authority, 219
British Medical Journal, 191,
    192–3, 197
British Nuclear Fuels Ltd.
    (BNFL), 1, 2, 30, 33, 35, 95,
    118, 119, 124–32 *passim*, 135,
    137, 138, 142–55 *passim*, 179,
    181, 182, 183, 185, 186, 189,
    190, 219–20, 221, 228, 257–60
    passim, 268, 293, 303, 308,
    309, 310
British Rail, 30, 33, 34, 35, 217
British Steel, 217
Brookhaven National Laboratory,
    83
Brown, Michael, 37
Brown's Ferry, Alabama, 68
Buker, Dr Gerald, 238
Bull, David, 56
Bunyard, Peter, 116, 231
Bureau of Mines, 238
Burghfield, Berks, 254, 255, 256
Burke, Michael, 185
Busy, Dr Michael, 195
Byrnes, John, 69, 70

caesium, 23, 24–5, 30, 39, 46, 47,
    128, 256, 265, 278, 307
Calder Hall, Cumbria, 97, 125,
    152, 220, 254
Caldicott, Dr Helen, 22–7
Callaway, Missouri, 224–5
Cam, Glos., 196
Campaign for Nuclear
    Disarmament, 227, 233
Canada
  nuclear power programme,
    164–7
  and waste-disposal sites, 305
Canadian Deuterium Uranium
    (CANDU) reactors, 164
cancer
  bone, 3, 51, 136, 169, 177, 180,
    181, 191, 284
  brain, 187
  breast, 52, 285
  and cell division, 25

  genital, 197–8
  intestinal, 284
  legal settlements, 130, 171, 181
  liver, 284
  lung, 22, 26, 30, 51, 55, 138, 238,
    284
  lymphatic, 187, 256, 284
  pancreas, 115, 177, 284
  prostate, 197
  rectum, 284
  skin, 51
  stomach, 115, 174, 181, 185, 195,
    284
  studies, 40, 51–2, 53, 55, 135,
    171, 175–9, 181–8 *passim*,
    190–91, 194, 195–7, 256–7
  testicular, 197
  throat, 167
  thyroid, 25, 84, 135, 193, 197,
    284, 285
  see also leukaemia; lymphoma;
    sarcoma, osteogenic
Cannell, William, 209
Canonsburg, Pennsylvania, 49–57
Cap de la Hague, 128, 155–9
    passim, 223
Capenhurst, 128, 219
carbon-14, 106
carbon dioxide, 98, 102, 105, 111,
    112, 133–4
Carter, Jimmy, 84, 87
cells, and radiation, 25, 26, 188–9
Census Office, 185
Central Electricity Generating
    Board (CEGB), 2, 29, 30, 34,
    35, 36, 98, 100–112 *passim*,
    194, 195, 196, 207, 217,
    219–29 *passim*, 260, 264, 272,
    275, 276, 284, 290, 292
Central Intelligence Agency
    (CIA), 44–5
Central Protection Service Against
    Radioactivity, 281
Centre de la Manche, nr
    Cherbourg, 305–6
CFTD (French union), 156
Challenger space shuttle, 3
Channel 4 television, 246, 254, 257

Index

325

RMBK (light-water pressurised-tube graphite-moderated reactor), 263
Roberts, Dr Lewis, 305
Roberts, T. D., 119
Rocky Flats, Colorado, 65–6
Roentgen, W. K., 169
Ross, Stephen, 197
Rostow, Dimitri, 231
Rosyth, Fife, 251, 254, 256
Rotblat, Professor Joseph, 183–4
Rovinsky, 47
Rowntree Trust, 223
Royal Commission on Environmental Pollution Report, 59–60, 185
Royal Commission on Nuclear Energy, 30
Royal Ordnance Factory, Burghfield, Berks, 254, 255
Ruchill Hospital, Glasgow, 191
Runton, Geoffrey, 187
ruthenium, 30, 142, 145, 307
Ryder, Eddie, 275

safety standards, 41, 62–4, 66, 67–8, 73, 76, 77–8, 93, 94, 100, 111, 114, 116, 119, 120, 126, 127, 137–8, 139–40, 149, 156, 166, 195, 212, 238, 239, 240, 286–8
Sagan, Leonard, 175
St Bartholomew's Hospital, 280
San Clemente, California, 63–4
Sanders, Dr Barkov, 176
Sanders, Jacqueline, 171
sarcoma, osteogenic, 25, 26
Savannah, NSS, 163
Savannah Nuclear Station, Texas, 66–7
Savours, Dale Campbell, 145
Saxmundham, Suffolk, 213
Schilling, Dr C. J., 195
Schull, Professor William, 175
Scientific Institute, Barcelona, 253
Scorpion, USS, 252

Scotland, and Chernobyl, 277, 279, 290
Scottish Health Service, 191
Scottish Health Service Common Services Agency, 120
Scottish Office, 280
'scram', 21, 73
sea dumping, 28, 57–9, 128, 142–7, 152, 156, 184, 212, 221, 255, 307
Sea Wolf (nuclear submarine), 59
Seascale, Cumbria, 131, 142, 184–90 *passim*, 193
Sellafield plant, Cumbria, 1, 2, 28, 29, 30, 44, 95, 97, 103, 119, 121, 122, 124–56 *passim*, 161, 178, 179–86 *passim*, 189–93 *passim*, 195, 199, 207, 211, 220, 227, 228, 229, 233–4, 235, 254, 259, 274, 285, 292, 293–304, 305, 307–8, 309
Semenov, B. A., 261
Semple, Ken, 129
Sheeham, Dr Patricia, 191
Sheffield, Illinois, 42
Shropshire Peace Alliance, 245
Silkwood, Karen, 3, 93, 235, 237, 239–42
Sizewell, Suffolk, 4, 16, 18, 20, 33, 34, 75, 95, 98, 104, 107, 112, 186, 194, 195, 203, 207–10 *passim*, 212, 213, 224, 225, 227, 228, 233, 243, 245, 246, 290
Smith, Peter, 246
Smolensk, 262
Snow, Dr John, 168
sodium, 113, 116, 159
South of Scotland Electricity Board (SSEB), 35, 109, 216, 229
Southern California Edison Company, 63
Soviet Academy of Sciences, 46
Soviet Life, 261, 292
Spanish Nuclear Energy Board, 253
Special Branch, 233
Special Constables Act, 233

World in Action (TV series), 121,
  122, 204, 206, 207
Wylfa, Anglesey, 97, 109–10
Wynne, Brian, 122, 123

xenon-133 gas, 83

Yorkshire Television, 130, 131,
  184, 185, 186, 251, 254, 256,
  257
Young, Hugo, 274, 275

Zewe, William, 79, 80
Zion Nuclear Power Station,
  Illinois, 79
zirconium, 20, 125–6